THE
LIVING AMERICAN
HOUSE

THE LIVING AMERICAN HOUSE

The 350-Year Story of a
Home—an Ecological History

GEORGE ORDISH

⁓

Illustrated by Clarke Hutton

William Morrow & Company, Inc.
New York   1981

Library of Congress Cataloging in Publication Data

Ordish, George.
    The living American house.

    Bibliography: p.
    Includes index.
    1. Ecology—Massachusetts—Duxbury.   2. Human
ecology—Massachusetts—Duxbury.   3. Bartons House,
Mass.   4. Barton family.   5. Household pests—Massa-
chusetts—Duxbury.   I. Title.
QH105.M4O72   591.5′268   80-24265
ISBN 0-688-00356-7

Printed in the United States of America

First Edition

1 2 3 4 5 6 7 8 9 10

BOOK DESIGN BY BERNARD SCHLEIFER

To my grandson Guy Shipton

PREFACE

MANY people have helped in the preparation of this book and I am very grateful to them. First, there are a number of authors, both living and dead, of books and papers to whom I give my thanks. (See note below.)

Secondly, I have had much help from many libraries and learned bodies, particularly the New York Historical Society, the New York Natural History Museum (where Mrs. Jane Safer kindly arranged a series of important interviews for me), the New York Public Library, the Smithsonian Institution (Washington, D.C.), the Plymouth Plantation (Massachusetts), the Duxbury (Massachusetts) Historical Society, The Natural History Museum (London), The American Museum in Britain (Claverton), and the Information Section of the United States Embassy, London. Mr. David John, of Rentokil, New York, was good enough to supply some valuable information, as have also a large number of individuals almost too numerous to mention, who helped in field trips and many other ways. I would, however, particularly like to thank Messrs. G. E. Bevan and Dino Gregory (St. Albans, England), Jack and Linda Grobstein and Mr. Kyrill Schabert (Long Island), Dr. John T. Schlebecker (Washington, D.C.), Mrs. Dorothy Wentworth (Duxbury, Massachusetts), and Virginia and Willis Wing (Kennett Square, Pennsylvania). My two daughters—Mrs. Jennifer Leopold (New York) and Mrs. Meliora Dockery (Rye, New York)—have been most helpful.

Finally, I would like to thank my wife for many useful suggestions and for her careful reading of the manuscript.

—GEORGE ORDISH

NOTE: Bracketed numbers in the text refer to publications listed in the Bibliography at the end of the book. Thus, on page 22, ". . . rates easily above whey [65]" will refer the reader to item 65 in the Bibliography, Wood, Wm. *New England Prospects.*

CONTENTS

LIST OF ILLUSTRATIONS

FIGURES

The reader must not expect in this work merely the private uninteresting history of a single person. He may expect whatever curious particulars can with any propriety be connected with it. Nor must the general disquisitions and the incidental narratives of the present work be ever considered as actually digressionary in their natures, and as merely useful in their notices. They are all united with the rest, and form proper parts of the whole.

—J. WHITAKER, *History of Manchester* (1771–1775)

The Lord hath been pleased to turn all the wigwams, huts and hovels the English dwelt in at their first coming, into fair, and well-built houses, well-furnished many of them.

—E. JOHNSON, *Historie of New England* (1652)

Here is a very fine house! It stands on dry land.
The owner is rich, and a very fine man.
May he still keep increasing in honor and fame.
The house it stands square, and in a fair view
Of a river, fine meadows and neighbours a few.
The timber is square, and is well put together;
May God bless the owner, forever and ever!

—*Lines especially written for an old-time house-raising ceremony.*

FAMILY TREE

THE HISTORY OF BARTONS

DATE	THE PEOPLE	THE HOUSE
1633–1679	John Barton III m. 1633 Susannah Palmer b. 1608, d. 1679 b. 1614, d. 1681	1632 House started, "cellar" only 1633 Bedroom, with cellar beneath, kitchen and loft added
1680–1681	Thomas Humility Experience Susannah John IV b. 1633 b. 1634 (a daughter) d. 1681 d. 1635 m. Patience Hathaway, 1652	1635 Hurricane destroys thatch, replaced by shingles 1639 Lean-to extension started and destroyed by earthquake 1640 Extension rebuilt 1680 Glass quarrels replace oiled cloth in windows
1682–1723	Experience Barton Susannah 5 other children (a son) b. 1656 b. 1654 d. 1723 m. 1674 Abigail Gifford	1682 East ell added, 2 new fireplaces, inside privy, porch to main door; ivy planted on east wall
1724–1738	Desire of Prudence Fear of the Lord Alice the Lord b. 1676 no issue no issue b. 1675 d. 1738 d. 1675 (injudicious bundling)	1730–31 West wing added for hired help, and second story replaces loft of original building 1735 Well dug in corner of kitchen
1739–1754	Jethro Barton m. 1716 Bashuah Simmons b. 1696 b. 1697 d. 1754	1752 Gutters fitted, thus keeping footings much drier
1755–1759	John Barton V Caleb Tryphena Jethro b. 1717 b. 1720 b. 1722 b. 1730 d. 1720 d. 1720 d. 1783 d. 1731 m. 1740 Theophilus Chilton no issue	1758 Hand water pump installed in kitchen
1760–1787	Tenancy of Elkanah Hoag (to 1782)	At first structure neglected and crowded with people; empty (except for a year, E. Hopkins using it as a hideout), and attic window blown in

DATE	THE PEOPLE	THE HOUSE

1788–1831	House sold in 1788 to a Boston merchant
	Stephen Deane m. 1790 Beulah Howland
	b. 1765 b. 1764
	d. 1831
		1788 House repaired
		1790 Ceilings added to many rooms
		        Old fireplace bricked in and
		        cast-iron stove fitted
		        New main chimney

1832–1860	Stephen Deane II Mary 3 other children
	b. 1791 b. 1793
	d. 1860 d. 1856
	
	m. 1838 Alice Baker
	     b. 1813, d. 1889
		1792 Plague of crickets
		1856 Primitive fly-screens installed
		1860 Coal-burning stove in
		        cellar (an early form
		        of central heating)

1861–1905	Theophilus Deane Beulah Jane Emily
	b. 1840
	killed in action 1864 m. 1861 Sophrinia Frost
	                       b. 1840
	                       d. 1905
		1862 Bathroom, toilet, and
		        septic tank drainage installed
		1891 Large cooking stove
		        (coal and wood) in kitchen

1906–1942	Stephen Deane III Theophilus II
	b. 1862, d. 1942 b. 1863
	                    d. 1910
	m. 1885 Janet Snow
		1906 Gas lighting installed;
		        public piped water supply
		        Bathrooms added
		1920 Central heating installed
		1921 Wired for electricity,
		        own generator
		1923 House rewired and connected

1943–1963	Edward Deane Victoria 2 other daughters
	b. 1887 b. 1888 no issue
	killed in action d. 1963
	1917, no issue
	           m. 1910 John Barton VI
	          ("a distant cousin")
		to public supply. Old fireplace
		        uncovered and used again
		1938 Chimney pots fitted when
		        hurricane damage repaired
		1951 Northwest corner of roof falls
		        in (wood-borer damage);
		        bats enter roof space

1964–1980	John Barton VII Janet James
	b. 1913 b. 1915 b. 1918
	                   d. 1962
	m. 1935 Caroline Costa
		1952 Woodwork in whole
		        house treated with DDT
		1961 Roof insulation undertaken and
		        double windows installed

	Edward Barton Desirée Phoebe b. 1938 b. 1939 b. 1941 m. 1958 Angela Fontana	

	Angela Barton II Edward Deane
	b. 1960 b. 1962 b. 1965
	m. 1979 Nathan Comstock
		1978 House converted to a
		        restaurant. New stair-
		        cases added; some
		        partitions removed;
		        new kitchens, food
		        storage and preparation
		        rooms added. New
		        rest rooms and toilets
		        put in

	Edward Barton Comstock Angela b. 1980 . . . . twins . . . . b. 1980	1979 Solar heater installed on roof

1

～

BUILDING AND
POPULATING THE HOUSE

THE IMMORTAL STORY of Don Quixote starts with the words "In a part of La Mancha, the name of which I do not care to remember, lived a knight . . ." Similarly the author of this book does not care to recall the place in Massachusetts where Bartons, the house in question, is situated. It was built by the immigrant settler and farmer of that name.

John Barton III was the grandson of the John Barton who built the house Bartons End in Kent, England, in 1555, an account of which has been given elsewhere [40]. John Barton III was born in 1608; he was the last of seven children and at the time of his birth had two older brothers and one sister alive.

The Bartons were prosperous farmers devoted to the Protestant cause, and some of them were much worried by the powers of the bishops in the reformed (Episcopalian) church which, it was felt, could easily become as oppressive as the Roman Catholic establishment. A few members of the Barton family had emigrated to the Netherlands, where they prospered as craftsmen and were able to worship as dissenters from the Episcopalian persuasion. As it happened, the year of young John Barton's birth saw a treaty of mutual defense signed between England and the Netherlands and there was considerable commerce and friendship between the two countries.

Young John was a bright, healthy lad and profited from his education at the village school and from his visits to his relatives in England and the Netherlands. In the latter place the "oppression" by the bishops of the reformed church was much discussed. That it was "driving men to dissent" was frequently asserted. Moreover, said Uncle Thomas Standish, Leyden was no place to bring up an English child. The Netherlands were friendly enough but the English boys and girls were becoming Dutch men and women. Why, that very day his grandson Paul had mocked his English pronunciation of 's Gravenhage. That was one of the penalties of bringing up children abroad: they spoke the language so much better than one did oneself.

Naturally the refugees' thoughts turned to the New World and the reported wonders of Virginia—the old Queen's splendid new colony—where one could shape one's own life, yet remain a loyal Englishman.

Young John worked on the family farm in Kent and wanted to be a farmer, but as the youngest of his family, he realized he was not likely to inherit enough from his father to enable him to pursue that calling. He had a friend, Experience Mitchell, a year younger than himself, with whom he used to consort in Leyden.

Experience, aged fourteen, emigrated to America in the ship *Anne* in 1623, and over the next few years wrote to young John about life in the New World and the opportunities it offered; especially attractive were the land grants for merely seven years' labor, and religious freedom—there were no bishops to contend with. Experience had not yet noticed that the local pastors had become even more powerful than the bishops.

Alas for freedom! Soon books were being publicly burned in New England (one of the first being Wm. Pinchon's *Meritorious Price of Redemption,* on Oct. 16, 1650), even as they were in Europe.

As is well known, the *Mayflower* company missed Virginia and settled in Plymouth, where they were joined by the settlers from successive ships—the *Anne* being the third. By 1627 the Plantation had thriven to such an extent that they had been able to buy out the original London shareholders and make land grants on yet easier terms. Much of their success was due to their "secret weapon"—measles and smallpox—which had decimated the Indian tribes, leaving the countryside comparatively empty, but much more was due to the newcomers' knowledge, determination, and skill.

Undoubtedly it was the almost free land that appealed to

young John Barton more than the freedom from episcopal con-
trol. Experience Mitchell had also told him of others of the
Barton name in the colony, including the "wicked" Marma-
duke Barton, who had left the employment of his patron,
Francis Weston, and probably joined the renegade Thomas
Morton at Liberty Hall.*

In 1630 John Barton III joined in the rush to settle in the
Massachusetts Bay area and emigrated to Plymouth. Experience Mitchell had by then moved from Plymouth to Duxbury,
where he had married a Miss Cook. John stayed two years
with his newly married friend, learned about the New World,
and then, aged twenty-four, took up land to the north of Duxbury. He built a lean-to shack; a year later he married Susannah
Palmer and started to build the house, known then and ever
since as "Bartons." It began as a very modest structure and
has been added to repeatedly—and all of the additions have
had an effect on the life within it.

The tasks facing the settlers were immense, for not only
did they have to clear the new land of trees and bush, then
establish and fence their farms, but they also had to build their
houses, which meant providing the raw materials for them.
Timber was the main component, and wooden frames of immense beams were assembled as they would have been in
England or the Netherlands.

As the settlers poured into Massachusetts Bay, they were
first billeted on established families and then given land in the
new extensions constantly being made. The land mostly had
been "purchased" from the Indians, sometimes in a rather
rough and ready fashion.

The new areas were always adjacent to old settled areas, to
reduce the risk of attack by Indians or rival colonizers, such as
the French. Plots were of about twenty acres, although the
original contract had spoken of grants of one hundred acres,
and the parcels were distributed by the drawing of lots. The
settlers also had rights of pasturage on the common lands and
were bound by certain conditions: for instance, no house might
be more than half a mile from a meetinghouse. The early com-

---

* Marmaduke Barton was a ne'er-do-well who was subsequently before the
courts for misbehavior, in Essex in 1638 and Boston in 1642. He was condemned to be branded and sold as a slave.

munal system, in which the land was held and worked in common, had not succeeded, though its Marxian appeal (". . . to each according to his need, from each according to his ability") had much in common with the Puritan ethic. The young men refused to work for the old, and the wives objected to their husbands' working for other women. By the time John Barton took up land, private ownership had been adopted but with no right of succession. However, reversion to the state on the death of the owner was never enforced.

John and Susannah Barton were fortunate in securing Lot 8, one which contained a few once-cleared acres now reverting to bush and on their way to the vegetational climax of forest. These bushy acres had been part of an Indian settlement, abandoned when a mysterious disease had almost destroyed the whole of the Wampanoag tribe. In that area the forest was of oak, hickory, chestnut, and elm; pines were comparatively rare in those days, though they abound now.

The first problem was where to site their house. A guiding factor then in England was water—a good well was essential for a house or farmyard—so that professional water diviners, or dowsers, were frequently employed. One of the things that surprised and delighted the early settlers was the abundance of "fair water." In their experience water was usually so contaminated that everyone drank beer, and William Wood (1634) said that though, as a drink, the New England water was not better than the best beer, it was "certainly better than the worst and rates easily above whey [65]." The Reverend Francis Higginson in 1629 found the very air itself delightful. "A sup of New England's Aire is better than a whole draft of old England's Ale . . . it is of a most healing nature to all such as are of a Cold, Melancholy, Flegmatick, Reumatick temper of Body [24]." Alas! In spite of these advantages the reverend gentleman died, after only a year in the country, of tuberculosis.

The profession of dowser was an easy one in New England, for water would be found anywhere one cared to dig, and springs of splendid water poured out from all sorts of places. Appreciation of the waters of northeastern America persisted for some time. George Washington wrote of the water at Roslyn, "The spring waters there are as good as the small beer here." While obviously it would be easier for the Bartons to build their house on the bushland rather than in the forest itself, they also had to consider the fact that crops had to be planted as soon as possible if they were to survive.

John Barton was one of the new generation of farmers; he believed in trying new methods and new crops. He even read books on the subject and had brought with him from England two of the textbooks of that day. One was Herebach's *The Whole Art and Trade of Husbandry . . . Enlarged by Barnaby Googe Esquire* [22] and the other was Gervase Markham's *The English Husbandman* [35]. Barnaby Googe loved farming, and the book was a great solace to John Barton amidst the hard work and difficulties of his new life. "Husbandry," wrote Googe, "is cousin-germane to wisdom. . . . A great number of emperors have sprung from the plow. And to let others goe, it is knowne that the Emperors Galerius and Maximus, came both from poore Heardmen to the Imperiall Dignitie." Another passage was of help in the matter of the building of the house. Googe quoted the advice of Cato the Censor, born in Tusculum, 234 B.C., who "would have a man long in the determination to build, but to plant and sow out of hand." But the winters in New England were much harder than they were in Tusculum, all said and done, so they must have a house, but a simple one. As trees for the house would have to be cut in any case, they chose a site on the edge of the forest where it joined the bushland; thus they would not be using land that soon could be sown with crops.

Not everything advocated by Googe's improved Herebach would have turned out to be possible in either old or New England—the cultivation of olives, for instance—but some advice was very sound, then and still to this day: for instance, the incorporation of clover in pasture and the value of the master's foot in manuring and improving land.

The settlers (they were not called Pilgrims until about 1720) helped each other, and John's friend Experience Mitchell supplied a most valuable service: he sent him a carpenter, Mr. Zaccheus Hussey, who lived in one of the two temporary buildings they had put up, one a "cellar" and the other an Indian hut. A cellar was a pit dug out on a slope to about five feet on the upward side and lined with stone or timber studding (upright planks or beams). The upward side was topped with short studding of about two feet; and similar treatment, but with longer planking, was given to the sides and downward side, which contained a small window of oiled canvas and a door.

A difficulty in making these cellars was that there was no chalk in the area from which lime could be prepared to use in the mortar for the walls. Without a mortared wall the cellar would be very damp. The only nearby source material for lime was the numerous clamshells, which were eagerly collected. Not only were the clams good food but the shells could be burned and used for mortar and for limewashing walls. John Barton had been collecting shells for a year or more and was also lucky in that he found an abandoned Indian midden heap consisting almost entirely of shells. Burned with great care, they provided enough lime mortar for the walls and floor of their cellar, thus keeping it comparatively dry. The roof was of rafters and battens covered with a thatch of reeds and water grass. There was no fireplace or chimney and cooking was done outside in all weathers.

The Indian hut was made of withies bent over to give a semicircular roof, and thatched with reeds and grass. Boughs and reeds were woven among the uprights to make the sides. It was by no means the traditional wigwam of the Wild West.

So much effort, and precious lime, had been put into making the cellar that John decided it had better be incorporated into his house, and so eventually his house was built over and around their first refuge.

During the winter of 1633–34 John and Zaccheus felled trees, trimmed off the branches, selecting some to make angle pieces either for the house or the shipwrights. Fish being so plentiful in their bay, there was a tremendous demand for ships' timbers of all sorts. When the local ship builder wanted a particular angle piece for his vessel, he would walk through the woods looking for a tree having a branch of the right size and at the desired angle and then have that tree felled. John Barton had an eye for this sort of material. He made quite a collection of angled spars and sold many of them to the shipyards, saving the builders a lot of time searching in the forest, and providing John with money for his house-building activities.

The two men also built a sawpit where Mr. Hussey's prize possession—a two-handled crosscut saw some ten feet long—could be used to fashion the beams for the framework of the house.

In January and February the felled trunks were hauled out of the forest along the frozen tracks, the slippery surface making the journey to the sawpit much easier. Oxen were hired from neighbors and the men themselves came along to help. "Keep her moving" was the cry, as once the initial inertia of the heavy log had been overcome, one wanted to avoid having the log bog down and all the trouble of starting it again.

A rough plan of the house had been made (see Figure 1); it was to be of one and a half stories and to consist of two rooms. The house was then marked out on the ground with cords over the snow, and from this and the plan it was possible to calculate what summer beams, bearers, and rafters would be needed. The main framework required three large summer beams, one supporting the bedroom floor and the others the ceilings of the kitchen and bedroom. The summer beam supporting the bedroom floor, which was also the cellar ceiling, was trimmed only on three sides: the bark was left on the underside, as appearance was not of much importance in the cellar and the labor of cutting a plain surface was saved. Labor was their scarcest commodity. The floor bearers in the cellar ceiling (the bedroom floor) mostly had the bark left on them too, a fact which had a bearing on the life in the house.

Stone, clay, and mortar were needed for the fireplace, which was massive and built of stone to the shoulder. The chimney was of wattle covered with clay. The roof was of reed thatch. To save timber, only the floor of the bedroom over the cellar was to be of timber; the kitchen, which was also the living room, was to have a dirt floor.

In February another heavy task was started: sawing the beams out of the trunks of oak trees. Every day, as soon as it was light, the big saw had to be sharpened; then John and

Zaccheus set to, taking it in turns to be the under sawyer, a most unpleasant position. In spite of the cold, Zaccheus insisted that John strip to the waist before starting work, quoting the old sawyers' adage: "Strip whilst you're cold and live to grow old." Susannah provided enormous meals to keep these mighty men at work and full of energy.

The main food was that which had served the Indians so well; the settlers called it hominy, a word derived from the Indian language. It was powdered Indian corn boiled to a thick paste and taken with goat's or cow's milk. Corn—Indian corn—was one of the miracles of the New World because of what we now call the seed ratio. In England in the seventeenth century, if a farmer sowed a bushel of seed wheat he would harvest some six or seven bushels of grain—a ratio of 1:6. In America a sown bushel of the new corn would give twenty to fifty bushels at harvest, a much improved ratio and one usually obtained for less effort. Moreover, the Indian practice, which the settlers at first followed, was to destroy the forest trees by ringbarking and later burning them. The roots and stumps were not taken out. The corn was planted amid the ash on little mounds, and beans were sown among them. The indigenous American beans (string beans) climbed up the cornstalks and supplied the food proteins the corn lacked. The corn was fertilized by burying a few fish in each hillock, another device taught to the settlers by the Indians.

Corn hominy and samp (corn porridge and much the same thing as hominy) were greatly used, which meant that corn was continually being pounded in wooden mortars. This, it was said, made so much noise that in foggy weather ships off the coast knew in which direction the land lay.

The Indians also showed the settlers how to grow and use squashes, which were plants unknown in Europe. The new arrivals adopted the easier part of the Narragansett Indian word—*asquutasquash*—for what became an important food. At first the colonists did not like the pumpkin, but nevertheless it was much eaten. Almost anything edible was eaten. Edward Johnson, in his *Wonder Working Providence* (1654) referred to "The times when old Pompion was king [29]." A "colonial poet" wrote:

We have pumpkins at morning and pumpkins at noon.
If it were not for pumpkins we should be undone [16].

They were dried for winter use and made into pumpkin bread, half pumpkin and half corn.

The settlers got a certain amount of meat from occasionally shooting deer and wild birds, such as the heath hen and the turkey, the former bird being much commoner and used for the first Thanksgiving dinner. Alas, it is now extinct. Pigs, cattle, and goats were quickly introduced and added to the meat supply.

John, Susannah, Zaccheus, and Experience Mitchell had many discussions about the house. The young couple intended it to grow into a fine farmstead; consequently it was of importance to decide which way it was to face and to leave room for expansion. Susannah quoted her mother, who maintained that a house should face east, with the length of the house running north and south. The reasons for that were several: first, the easterly face meant that the rising sun would shine into the bedrooms and get people up early, while the westerly setting sun shining into the kitchen and workrooms would mean that work could continue much longer. The south wall should be blank; having no windows facing south ensured that furnishings and curtains would not be faded by the bright light. However, in spite of her mother's advice, Susannah rather wanted the house to face south because there was a splendid view down to a creek and the open sea. She could see herself standing at the open door and watching the ships come into the creek with essential supplies for the colony and letters and news from home. John also favored this aspect for two—even three—reasons. He too admired the view, but the house should face south mainly because the New England winters were so much colder than at home, and they could do with the aid of the winter sun. Moreover, being an educated man and having sailed the Atlantic and noted how the captain daily made observations of the height of the sun and thus calculated the latitude, he pointed out that as they stood they were at latitude 42°N whereas in Kent, England, they had been at 51½°N. This meant that the winter sun, when it shone, would be nearly ten degrees higher in the sky than at home and would warm the house that much more, and though the summers would be hotter than in England, the summer sun would be so high that it would beat on the roof more than on the walls and windows of the house. The thatch would thus protect the house from excessive heating. Zaccheus did not quite follow the argument, but pointed out that the lie of the land favored a southern exposure, and thus it was arranged.

By early April enough beams had been sawn, and Zaccheus ceased to be a sawyer and became a skilled carpenter. First he measured and cut the three summer beams, leaving it to John to trim with an axe the lower edges of the two that would be exposed. The cellar summer, it will be recalled, was to be left untrimmed. Next the uprights were cut and the mortise and tenon joints were made to connect with the summers; the tongue of the joint was on the upright, as this gave greater strength to the structure. The mortises were held with wooden pegs, and the holes in the tongues offset a little inward, so that they tightened as the peg was driven in. Zaccheus had made an interesting discovery—in spite of the adage, he found that a square peg in a round hole was a much better arrangement, as it lasted longer and was more secure. After the joints had been made they were marked with successive Roman numbers, because these numbers could be cut with a chisel, and they served to identify each individual joint. The pegs were then knocked out, and whenever the weather was fine the men carried the beams out to the site and assembled the structure flat on the ground. Here it was that the numbering proved to be of such value: there could be no doubt as to which two, or even three, timbers were to be joined.

The work put into sawing the timbers and making the joints was enormous, and as a consequence the frame was the most valuable part of a house. Wattle and daub for the filling could be found anywhere, and if one wanted to move, one knocked out the filling, threw off the thatch (or collected the roofing shingles), drove the pegs out of the framing, and took one's house to the new location. For instance, Governor Winthrop in 1630 had a house built at Charleston, and when he transferred to Boston he took the house down and moved it there.

There was no time to season the wood, but as large timbers were used that was not of much importance. The framework groaned a little as it dried and the cool of night followed the heat of day.

Stone was now collected and moved to the site mostly by wheelbarrow, mortar was mixed, and the large fireplace was formed up to a height of about ten feet. A bread oven was built at the side of the fireplace. The four sides of the framework of the house, now flat on the ground, were moved into position around the giant fireplace, and shallow trenches were dug, filled with stone and rubble. Under the doorstep John put a shilling and a little bag containing corn, wheat, rye, and beans, "for luck," as he said, which Susannah thought a very superstitious practice. After that the rest of the framework was quickly assembled. The rafters of the roof were steep-pitched, as they needed to be for thatch and also because it made more room in the loft. About noon on Thursday, the twentieth of April, 1634, John nailed a flag to the last rafter placed, to celebrate the completion of the framework. The assembled neighbors cheered and enjoyed a feast of beer, cornbread, pork, and heath hens.

During the spring and summer the rest of the house was completed. Its two windows were of oiled canvas, which could be closed by a sliding shutter inside; the chimney had been completed with wattle, heavily covered with puddled clay, the spaces between the framing being filled with wattle daubed with a mixture of clay, hay, hair from slaughtered animals, and cow dung. A start was made to cover the exterior with weather-boards, which were obtained by splitting trunks lengthwise with a wedge and beetle, a much more rapid—though cruder—process than sawing them. The inside walls, of the clay-hair-hay-dung mixture, were smoothed and limewashed to improve the lighting inside, though the neighbors thought this such an extravagant use of a scarce commodity that Susannah gave away a lot of the shell midden they had found.

The first house was dark because it had very small windows; the door was usually left open to provide more light, which meant that all sorts of animals could enter. Hens and pigs were just a nuisance, but rattlesnakes were dangerous and wolves at that time were much feared. In fact, a wolf would be most unlikely to enter a house in spite of the evidence provided by Little Red Riding Hood!

The disadvantages of New England, as seen by William Wood (1634), were ". . . rattlesnakes, mosquitoes, gnats, greenheads and lazy men [65]." As to rattlesnakes, at any rate in the house, these were overcome by a device of John Barton's —the split, stable, or snake door. The door was divided horizontally so that the bottom half could be kept shut, keeping out all but flying animals, and the top left open whenever the weather was good enough. As to greenheads ("young, immature or untrained intellects [44]") neither the Bartons nor any of the early or mid settlers can have suffered greatly from these defects, as may be seen by their achievements. Perhaps the men were lazier than the women. Listen to an abstract from the diary of a young girl, Abigail Foote of Colchester, Connecticut. A day's work was:

> Fixed gown for Prude—Mend Mother's Riding Hood—Spun short thread—Fix'd two gowns for Welsh's girls—Carded tow—Spun linen—Worked on Cheese-basket—Hatched flax with Hannah, we did 51 lbs apiece—Pleated and ironed—Read a sermon of Dodridges—Spooled a piece—Milked the cows—Spun linen, did 50 knots—Made a broom of Guinea wheat straw—Spun thread to whiten—Set a red dye—Had two scholars from Mrs. Taylor's—I carded two pounds of whole wool and felt Nationaly—Spun harness twine—scoured the pewter [16].

A pity there was not a clay soil; she might have made some bricks in her spare time.

Working physically very hard, the early New England settlers were at the same time an educated band and prized learning for themselves and their children; the early establishment of Harvard University (1636) shows that. The community from its start believed in education for women too. Many of them spoke Latin and Greek, were skilled in arithmetic, and were studying the Indian languages in their efforts to help those people. However, this equality could be pushed too far. In 1645 Governor Hopkins, of Hartford, Connecticut, brought his wife to Boston where, unfortunately, she had a collapse. It seems she had received a call to preach, which then—as now—annoyed a considerable body of the established clergy. She wrote books too. John Winthrop, in that year, commented that the

> loss of her understanding and reason, [was] by occasion of her giving herself wholly to reading and writing, and [she] had written many books. . . . For if she had attended her household affairs and such things as belong to women and not gone out of her way and calling to meddle in such things as are proper for men, whose minds are stronger . . . [etc.], she had kept her wits, and might have improved them usefully in the place God had set her [63].

Naturally they were virtuous. A century later a strange anomaly arose: New England women were not supposed to read plays, play cards, or converse about whist, quadrille, or operas. They talked about history, geography, and mathematics, and presumably their children and houses. Many still spoke Latin and Greek. In conversation with them a man could not mention a garter, leg, or knee: the anomaly was that he might ask the lady to bundle with him [18]. (See p. 60 for a comment on this strange custom.)

At night, light came from the hearth, the burning of splinters of pitch pine—a process shown to them by the Indians— and candles. As animal fat, particularly tallow, was scarce and in demand for cooking, leather dressing, and soap, candles were also made from the wax myrtle bush (*Myrica cerifera*). Its brown berries were picked in the fall and thrown into boiling water. The wax rose to the top, looking like green tallow; the pot was allowed to cool, the wax collected, and eventually made into "dips." The wax had a higher melting point than tallow so the candles did not melt in summer, nor did they smoke so readily as tallow candles, and on being extinguished they gave off an agreeable smell. The candleberry bush was quite a pleasant discovery for the early settlers. It gave them the blessing of a good light at night, though of course it also attracted insects.

The best candles were made from beeswax and the European bee was introduced by the early settlers as much for its wax as its honey. Permission was needed to keep bees and at

first only six licenses to do so were granted in the Massachusetts Bay area, but as the insects' utility became so obvious,
the restrictions were soon forgotten. *Apis mellifera* took to
America very well: in addition to the settlers' hives, the bee
set up colonies in the wild, in hollow trees, holes and burrows
in the faces of cliffs and banks, and in cavities in all sorts of
buildings, church roofs and steeples being favorite spots.

Numerous additions were made to the house by the succession of people who lived in it. In the summer of 1716, the year
Jethro Barton, John and Susannah's great-great-grandson married, a colony of bees started to form in the interior of the
southwest wall of the house, which was the original wall of
the first structure. There was a considerable space between
the timber cladding and the interior plaster where the wattle
and daub filling had rotted away. By 1719 the bees' nest was
quite big, with a constant stream of bees, in summer, going in
and out. A furious buzzing was heard when the west wall
heated in the summer afternoon. It was the bees "fanning"
with their wings to try and reduce the temperature. After baby
John V had been stung in July 1719, Jethro decided to get rid
of the nuisance.

Smoke was blown into the cavity; smoke makes the bees
gorge themselves on honey, and they are then less inclined to
sting. The boarding was then torn away and large lumps of
comb were discovered. The queen was found among her at-
tendants—though at that time there were still many who
regarded the ruler of the hive as the king—and all were transferred to an empty skep. Three bucketfuls of honey and comb
were obtained and only three people stung. Jethro was a
skilled bee-handler.

The honeybees were not only a direct asset to the colonists,
they also provided certain indirect advantages of which the
settlers were quite unaware. The bees increased crops by ensuring better pollination and thus more seed per plant. Jethro's
find provided polish for his floors and furniture and made
some grand candles.

A disadvantage of the old candle was that it needed constant trimming. As the candle had a straight stringlike wick,
unless the charred wick was cut away every half hour or so,
the candle would smoke and eventually go out. The plaited

wick of the modern candle was invented in France by Jean-Jacques Cambacères, who patented it in 1825. The plaited wick, as it burns, turns into the flame and consumes itself. The candle needs no trimming, a luxury the seventeenth and eighteenth centuries did not know.

On their new farm the Bartons lived a happy and complete life; it was an extremely hard one, but unremitting toil was what they expected. While on the whole they dominated all the life in the house, there was much of which they were not aware and a great deal of which they were only vaguely conscious. With some of it, such as rats and mice, they were constantly at war, and to others, such as butterflies and spiders, they were indifferent. Life is a cycle of birth, growth, reproduction, and death. The pattern of living in the house may be said to be a series of circles, slowly moving, expanding, changing, declining, and merging with that of the human beings the dominant factors, so that the history of the house is a figure resulting from the intermovement of the various circles of the life forms in the house.

As time went on, over the 350 years from the house's construction to the present day, some new circles were brought into the pattern, such as those of the cockroach and bat; and others, such as the bedbug, were taken out of it completely or, as in the case of wood borers, almost completely. In the following chapters I give some account of these circles and how they waxed and waned.

We cannot really say fundamentally what life is. What we do know is that living forms consist of cells, which can use food and combine it with oxygen to produce growth, movement, and the reproduction of their own kind. Animal life may be a highly specialized collection of cells, such as a man, or just one cell, such as an amoeba. The cell itself consists of two parts contained within a membrane (the cytoplasm), and within this the nucleus. The nucleus of a cell is the important part and carries the threadlike pairs of chromosomes. Any one species of animal always has the same chromosome pattern in all its cells: for instance, man has forty-eight pairs and the cat has nineteen. The chromosomes contain the genes, which are all different but are arranged in a characteristic pattern in the chromosome, and it is the genes that will determine the nature of the offspring, cell, or zygote, resulting from the sexual fusion of a male and female cell. It is the genes that have controlled all the inherited characteristics of any animal. The living cell, if supplied with food, oxygen, and the correct environment, will grow by means of cell division.

It is a mysterious and wonderful thing that a complex animal like a man grows from only one cell, and by the division of this cell, and the division of the cells resulting from the first division, and so on, the process controlled solely by the genes and the supply of food. The cells divide and become specialized. Some become bone, some flesh, some hair, some brain, and so forth. How very remarkable it is that this cell by dividing should produce a man and not, say, an oak tree, or equally that the one cell in an acorn (the zygote) should divide and divide and divide and produce another oak tree and not a man. How rarely it happens that something goes wrong and the human zygote produces an abnormality, a hunchback or a dwarf. The success of the zygote is a commonplace, we are used to it, and it would be a strange world if it did not occur, but nevertheless it is extraordinary to realize that a man has arisen from one cell and become a collection of millions of cells, and that at present this is happening some 247,000 times a day, which is approximately the world's daily human conception rate.

When animals reproduce themselves by sexual means the gene pattern can be greatly varied, as half come from the male and half from the female. This means that the children can either resemble or differ from their parents to quite a considerable extent. The range of possibilities varies greatly between species and even within species; thus, a species of animal is said to be heterozygous where the gene composition of the germ cell nucleus is very mixed and homozygous where it is not. Ants are very homozygous: man and dogs are probably the most heterozygous species, but in certain cases the mixed character of the genes can be much reduced. For instance, the ancient pharaohs and Incas were pure lines, very homozygous because brother usually married sister for the very purpose of keeping pure the royal, god-descended line. Similarly the Elizabethan ruling classes tended to be much more heterozygous than the inbred peasantry. However we must not exaggerate this too much, because, firstly, successive waves of conquest had left a very heterozygous stock from which to start and, secondly, there seems little doubt that the squire and his sons injected their bloodstream into those of the local peasantry from time to time; occasionally a squire may have been almost literally the father of the village, or at least a good proportion of it, a condition which would again tend to induce inbreeding and increase the homozygous makeup of the community.

In addition to the wide variation made possible by the recombination of the genes in sexual reproduction, there is also the possibility of mutation. A gene may suddenly change and give rise to some variation in the offspring. The reasons for the change are obscure. It may be induced by radioactivity or by certain chemicals, but once produced, the change persists and continues to manifest itself in the succession.

It is characteristic of all forms of life that they have the urge to reproduce themselves and to the greatest possible extent. The lower the form of life the more offspring are produced, so that if there were no checks on the survival of a species it would rapidly cover the entire globe: the highest forms of animal life are the slowest breeders. Charles Darwin gives the example of the elephant:

> The elephant is reckoned the slowest breeder of all known animals, and I have taken some pains to estimate its probable minimum rate of natural increase; it will be safest to assume that it begins breeding when thirty years old, and goes on breeding till ninety years old, bringing forth six young in the interval, and surviving till one hundred years old: if this be so, after a period of from 740 to 750 years there would be nearly nineteen million elephants alive, descended from the first pair [12].

If the population of such slow breeders as elephants can grow at this rate, think what the population of mice would become when a female will have about six litters a year, were there no checks to their expansion.

The fact that more progeny are produced than can survive led Darwin to propound his theory of natural selection and the survival of the fittest. It is obvious that as food is scarce those progeny which are best adapted to obtaining it are most likely to get it and thus to survive, and however heterozygous an animal may be, some of its offspring will resemble it. Consequently any favorable combination of genes will tend to be passed on to all subsequent generations. This also applies to all favorable mutations: these again will tend to appear in the offspring and if advantageous to the race, will persist in it. There is constant competition among all animals, both within a species and between species, for the scarce resources of the environment, and that is why few animals have time for any activity—such as play—other than food-gathering and reproduction.

The same immutable laws may be said to have applied to the Bartons as well. They survived and prospered, firstly because man was a successful animal and dominated the other animals of the environment, and secondly, they survived in the competition among their own species, among men, because they were adaptable and could use their intelligence to take advantage of the conditions they found present.

The success of the settlers was phenomenal.

So much downright work was perhaps never wrought on the earth's surface in the same space of time as during the first forty years after the settlement. But mere work is unpicturesque and void of sentiment.

—J. R. Lowell [34]

Their chief resource was wresting land from the wilderness and from the Indians, which land they turned into profitable farms. The stock and machinery for these new lands—that is, the capital—were obtained by profitable trading. Exports of fur (mostly beaver), fish, and timber paid for imports of essential goods, such as tools, nails, cloth, and glass, and even for such luxuries as books and paper. Schools were an early priority, and to facilitate studies fees were often accepted in kind —a bushel or so of corn, dried fish, or furs.

In the animal world the checks on the indiscriminate reproduction of the species are the lack of food, oxygen, and a suitable environment, and also the attacks of enemies such as parasites, predators, and diseases, and it is these factors that controlled the volume of life in John Barton's house through the 350 years of its existence.

The house was built to provide a suitable environment for John and Susannah Barton; to it they brought their food and they obtained their oxygen as a free gift from the atmosphere outside. They and their human successors differed from almost all the other animals in the house, in that Susannah and John's object in life was not solely the production of offspring, but also the worship of God, the embellishment of life by the arts, by enjoyment and social intercourse. Susannah gave birth to a child every year, which was about as near to maximum production as possible, but this annual event, which was a commonplace for that age, cannot be considered as the only object of their existence, as it can be of the brute creation.

The farm produced corn, wheat, oats, and barley and meat in the form of pigs, cattle, goats, and chickens. A few horses were also bred. The surplus produce was sold to buy iron from Europe and sugar from Barbados. The early New England settlers would have nothing to do with slaves from that island or from Africa. At first they knew milk only in the spring and summer flushes and they made much of it into butter and cheese.

A minor, though important, product was the earth from the stables, because it absorbed the urine from the animals, and the salt potassium nitrate formed in it. This earth was in great demand, not as a fertilizer for the fields, as might be imagined, but as a source of saltpeter for the manufacture of gunpowder. There would not have been enough of it to make much difference to the fields but such earths were the only way to obtain the essential ingredient so much needed for shooting and defense against Indians, some of whom were resenting the incursions of the white men. The civic authorities could demand that the niter earth be surrendered to them for the purposes of preparing powder. Charcoal was burnt in the woods and sulphur imported. The Bartons sometimes prepared their own gunpowder, but it was unreliable stuff, and after 1661, when a batch in preparation caught fire and blew up, they abandoned the practice.

The food needed by all the animals in the house was of four main types—carbohydrate, protein, the mineral supplements, and vitamins—and of course water which, though hardly a food, is yet the medium by which the cell works. The most important and the most difficult to obtain is the protein.

Proteins are a class of organic chemicals whose essential feature is a content of some 15 percent of that almost inert gas nitrogen, and it is again a curious matter that this very shy chemical, nitrogen, should be so essential to life. The very life substance itself, the cell nucleus, contains protein and must accumulate more before the nucleus can divide and cause the animal to grow; hence nitrogen is one of the factors limiting the expansion of animal populations. Although the atmosphere in which animals live is four-fifths nitrogen, they are unable to use it in this form (except for a group of bacteria found in association with leguminous plants, which can) but must obtain it already combined with other substances—usually as protein in plants or other animals. Nitrogen, however, can be made to combine with other gases, such as oxygen, if submitted to great pressure or if passed through an electric spark. This happens in a flash of lightning, and a modicum of combined nitrogen falls with the rain in a thunderstorm and enriches the earth. This dull, lifeless chemical—nitrogen—which is so essential to life, is possibly so because of its very dullness. When it combines with other chemicals it is only held in a loose bond by them, so that, for instance, a substance like potassium nitrate—a chemical containing potassium, nitrogen, and oxygen (KNO_3)—can be absorbed by the roots of a plant and easily broken up by the chlorophyll and sunlight in the leaf because the nitrogen is held so loosely by the atomic attractions within the potassium nitrate molecule. It is for the same reason that nitrates are used in explosives: The molecule is easily broken up and releases oxygen to feed the explosion. Moreover, the nitrates are readily soluble in water, which enables them easily to move into the plant.

"All flesh is grass," and no animals are able to live in the last analysis except by eating plants; even a carnivore such as a lion lives by eating animals that live by eating plants. It is only plants that are able to take simple salts in the soil and combine them with oxygen and carbon from the air to form protein and carbohydrate. They do this by means of the action of sunlight on the chlorophyll in the leaf: a process known as photosynthesis.

Even the plants cannot use the nitrogen of the air but must obtain it in the combined form from the soil, and the soil has three ways of obtaining it: (1) from rainwater, (2) from the decay of organic matter in the soil such as feces and plant and animal remains, and (3) by the action of certain bacteria (Pseudomonads) which live in the nodules of the leguminous plants and do have the power of directly using atmospheric nitrogen.

Living things are characterized not only by living but also by ceasing to live—by dying—usually by falling victim to some other form of life, for this is true whether they are killed young as food for another animal, or become enfeebled by old age and fall victim to some disease. It is of course possible for an animal's organs to be so weakened that it just fades away, but usually there is some life-form in the neighborhood which, taking advantage of this enfeebled condition, profits itself by feeding on and killing the weakened individual. The reverse process then starts and the complex chemical compounds of the body break down to the simple elements from which they arose, though here again there may be a chain of life-forms involved. Of course the living body is also taking in complex compounds as food, using some and breaking the rest down into simpler ones all the time, the simpler products being disposed of in the expelled breath and excrement of different kinds.

In the pattern of life the process of decay is indeed as important as the synthesis of the compounds itself—a fact recognized by the sculpture of Germaine Richier, which usually suggests the breaking up of her subjects into their elementals.

Life is a flow of certain chemical atoms to a constantly rearranged pattern. Some millions of tons of nitrogen, carbon, oxygen, hydrogen, phosphorus, potash, and other elements are constantly being assembled by the life process and made into complex compounds and then being broken down again, often to the basic elements themselves.

The Buddhists and Theosophists believe that the soul is reincarnated time after time in animals and men. In the latter case, human pride tends to lead one to think of oneself in a former incarnation as an important individual, women preferring to have been Cleopatra or the Queen of Sheba rather than a laundry slave, and men such heroes as Alexander or Julius Caesar.

It is difficult to know about our souls, but our bodies are constantly using elements that have been used before. Ants after feeding on sugar or nectar regurgitate a drop, hold it in their mouths and pass it to another ant. If you feed a few ants with a blue-dyed sugar solution, soon all the ants in the nest will be blue. This seems a rather revolting practice, but it is what we all do with our air. At the cinema, the cocktail party, boardroom, or lecture, we are constantly rebreathing other people's (so to speak) regurgitated air; every time you smell tobacco smoke at a gathering you are breathing air which has just been in someone else's lungs or mouth; moreover the process stretches backward in time. As Julius Caesar fell dead to the floor of Pompey's theater, he cried with his last breath, "*Et tu, Brute!*" and he expelled a few cubic centimeters of oxygen in doing this. Those same cubic centimenters of oxygen have been moving around in the world ever since, and one is quite likely to use some atoms of them oneself in the course of one's lifetime; for a man living to seventy will breathe some eight hundred tons of oxygen in the process.

On Tuesday, July 24, 1634, John and Susannah moved into their house; it was by no means completed because John had been able to give very little time to it. He had had to clear his bushland and get some crops planted. It was at this point that Susannah found she was three months pregnant.

But the two Bartons were not the first inhabitants of the house. The claim to this distinction belongs to the wood-boring insects that were actually present in some of the timber and wattle used in building the place, and to the spiders, which soon spun webs in the angles of the framework, even before it was pulled upright.

2

THE FIRST INHABITANTS— THE WOOD BORERS

I T IS A commonplace of entomology that the life of insects is so different from man's that although it is easy enough to describe, it is almost impossible for man to envisage and appreciate. Lewis Carroll makes this point amusingly in *Alice's Adventures in Wonderland*. In one of her frequently changing sizes, it will be recalled, Alice had a difficult conversation with a caterpillar. She remarked to it:

"... and being so many different sizes in a day is very confusing."

"It isn't," said the Caterpillar.

"Well, perhaps you haven't found it so yet," said Alice; "but when you have to turn into a chrysalis—you will some day you know—and then after that into a butterfly, I should think you'll feel it a little queer, won't you?"

"Not a bit," said the Caterpillar.

It is a form of life in which the animal is quite unaware of the reason for what is happening around it, of what has gone before, even in its own life cycle, or of what will occur later. At the same time insects may be aware of things of which we are not. For instance, bees can sense the plane of polarized light; some insects see, by means of ultraviolet light, things which are invisible to us; other insects can hear sounds beyond the range of the human ear; and most insects have a far more acute sense of smell than man. Moreover, many have the power of smelling by touch—the chemotactic sense—which assists them in finding food, mates, or suitable environments.

It is a life in which the response to any given stimulus is almost as automatic as pressing the starter of an automobile and where things are done to a pattern which, for want of a better name, we call instinct. It is a world where one might say there is little learning and much mechanism: that is, a mechanical response to the environment, not a reasoned one. It is a life with much waste in it, for few individuals survive from the thousands of eggs produced, in striking contrast to the many survivors of the few young produced by mammals, particularly man, other primates, and bats.

Although we can see that there is much waste, this is only from the point of view of any one particular species; from the contrasting point of view of life itself there is scarcely any loss, for the waste forms a basis for the nourishment of other forms of life. Insects feed on each other, spiders feed on insects, birds feed on both, cats and men both feed on birds, and so on. Elaborate food chains are established, all starting from the ability of the plant to make food and leading ultimately to the nourishment of the "higher animals," particularly man, who in the last analysis lives on the wastage of other forms of animal and vegetable life. Well may Genesis say of man, as the situation was then, and indeed is now, that he might ". . . have dominion over the fish of the sea, and over the fowl of the air, and over the cattle, and over all the earth, and over every creeping thing that creepeth upon the earth."

But, to return to insects: in their very different world, sometimes the response does not take place, as sometimes the engine may not start when we switch on the ignition. When confronted with an unusual situation—in fact a problem—an insect may well have no instinctive pattern to guide it. On the whole, insects are considerably inferior to mammals in solving problems, though most insects are able to learn to some extent and to profit from their learning; for instance, bees and wasps can find their way back to their nests over long distances by learning the way after successive explorations. Anything an insect does is done because it will be beneficial to the future of its species—it will add to the chances of survival of its offspring or itself; in general, insects are so prolific and the struggle for existence is so intense that there can be no time for any activity that does not bear on survival, because those kinds of insects (species or mutations of species) that do indulge in such inessential activities are most likely to become extinct and to have their places taken by others more survival-patterned. This is not a conscious activity on the part of the insects; it is merely the current conditions imposing a pattern of behavior on a species or extinguishing it.

With insects, out of the many thousands of young produced, only a few will survive to continue the race. This leads to the rapid adoption of characteristics favorable to the survival of the species, which characteristics then become instinctive and lead to the creation of new species, when the new characteristics become so different as to prevent breeding between the new and the old.

There are a few exceptions, when an insect's activities are not directly beneficial to the survival of the species, such as the autumn playtime of the worker wasps, in which they stop collecting nectar for the nest and indulge in an orgy of eating the food they collect, just before they die of cold or exposure. Such playtime is rare in the lower animals: in the case of the worker wasps it has no effect on the race because it takes place after the virgin queens have flown, which is perhaps why it can be permitted.

Also some kinds of insects are so successful that they appear to be able to spend a certain amount of time in play, or at any rate in nonproductive activities. The wood ants, for instance, waste time in this way, but possibly these games—such as mock battles and lounging around in the sun—are but training for more serious activities beneficial to the species [43].

The great antiquity of insects, their fecundity, and their quick life cycles compared to that of man mean that a pattern of life is rapidly fixed on a species, a pattern that will enable it to exploit existing conditions and, if these conditions alter, to change to meet these new circumstances. If any particular insects cannot do this, they disappear as a species—which is how the instinctive pattern arises.

It seems very wonderful that the hunting wasp will dig a burrow, find a caterpillar, paralyze it with a sting, drag it home, and lay its eggs on the paralyzed host, so that the wasp grubs will have food when they hatch, but if it did not have this pattern of behavior it would not exist as a species. That the female wasp can do all this for grubs it will never see and of which it is never conscious is indeed strange, but no stranger than that the human zygote grows into a human and the acorn zygote into an oak.

In spite of an apparent complexity in passing through a number of different stages and environments, such as egg, larva, pupa, and adult, perhaps crawling, then flying, an insect's life is a comparatively simple one. This is because nearly all its behavior is governed by the instinctive pattern set on it by generations of precedent—one might say that it is a real conservative. Nearly all the situations that arise can be dealt with automatically, for "problems" are comparatively rare and insects are not individually very clever at solving them, but in the main they may solve a problem because there are so many of them and some will have hit on the right answer by chance.

That is how new territories are acquired and why Bartons filled with life. But not all problems can be solved, for faced with the experience of a sheet of solid air, a fly does not know what to do, but continues to buzz up and down a window till exhausted, whereas men have escaped from the most extraordinary predicaments because their instincts did not bind them to a pattern of behavior.

Some of these points can be appreciated in describing the wood borers that went into Bartons.

The trees were felled in the forest that had been cleared to make part of the farm. The trimmed trunks lay from a few weeks to six months before they were hauled to the sawpit, and this gave the first wave of insects an opportunity to install themselves. When the trees were cut they contained a few tiny bluish-stained tunnels belonging to the pinhole borer beetles. The fertilized females of these insects had flown onto hardwood trees and started to bore tunnels, frequently with the help of the males, into the sapwood of the trees. After a considerable penetration they laid eggs in the tunnels and also introduced a special fungus around the eggs. As the eggs hatched, the fungus grew and the young larvae fed on it, thus returning along the route opened for them by their parents, although they had never seen them. The young grubs, who cannot live on wood alone, cooperate with the fungus so that the wood is partially digested for them, but the fungus will not grow unless the moisture content of the timber is high, and when the trees are felled they soon begin to dry out. A characteristic of the pinhole borer attack is that the galleries are straight, stained, and free of the dust that is usually found after other woodworm attack.

After the trees were cut, the fungus soon stopped growing and the larvae started to die, so that there were very few live pinhole beetles in the house by the time John and Susannah moved in, and there were no live ones left after they had been there a year.

However, the timber was not then free of borers, because as it lay in the forest, it was attacked by powder-post beetles. While the timber lay in the forest and the sawpit, the adult fertilized females of the dark *Lyctus* were flying around looking for suitable wood unprotected by bark in which to lay their eggs, testing the wood by tasting it. They were very particular in that they would only lay eggs on wide-pored hardwoods and only in the sapwood of such timbers. In the almost untouched forest the beetles did not thrive very well because they only had old fallen trees or branches in which to lay and these were few and far between. But in the Bartons' woodyard the sawn timber lay about awaiting use, which gave the females far better opportunities for finding the right places for egg-laying, and the sapwood of the New England oaks was ideal for this purpose.

The long, tapering, cylindrical egg was pushed by the female into a sapwood vessel, because the larvae will only thrive in sound timber having a high starch content, and the sapwood is the most recently formed wood of the tree, which is still living and contains this vital food. Each beetle can lay up to about fifty eggs, but not all of these necessarily hatch out to young larvae. Some of the eggs failed to hatch, some fell victim to other insects, some were dried up by the sun, and others were drowned by the rain.

When the egg hatches it is already in a wood pore of the timber, and as the young grub comes from the egg, it finds itself in a cell much bigger than itself, which means it cannot start its life of boring into the wood and feeding on its favorite food, the starch (though it must obtain some protein as well), because it is too small to get a grip on the walls of the cell pores and thus attack the wall. The larva first feeds on the remains of the yolk of the egg and such starch as it can find in the wood pore, and then when it is the same size as the pore, it starts boring down into the timber. As it forms its gallery, it leaves behind a fine powdery dust, and as it forges on, always in the sapwood, it grows in size. About a year is needed to complete the life cycle, so that by May the fully grown larva is approaching the surface of the timber, where it forms a cell and pupates, emerging in June as a fully grown *Lyctus* beetle. The beetles take to the wing, mate, and the females set about finding another piece of wood with wide pores and a suitable starch content in which to start the cycle over again.

Lyctus is essentially an insect of unseasoned sapwood, some of which was used in the house. A few sapwood joists contained living larvae, as eggs had been laid on them, but their numbers soon fell because sapwood is alive; the tissues transpire and use up the starch in the process. After about two years there was not enough starch present to make the wood sufficiently attractive to the egg-laying female beetles when they appeared in the summer months. These adults either escaped from the house and sought the forest or laid eggs on the log pile and kindling wood and were burnt in due course. By 1638 there were no more living *Lyctus* in the structure of the house, but they were brought in with the fuel and in the framing of extensions to the building.

Other inhabitants of the timbers were the horntails or sawflies. The ones attacking wood are large hymenopterous insects with yellow wings and yellow and black bands on the body, which is from 25 to 35 mm long. The adults fly around with a buzzing sound. The female is equipped with a long slender ovipositer, which often frightens people because it looks like a sting, but it is not. The ovipositer is remarkable in that the female can push this delicate tube through the bark and into the wood and there lay an egg. From the egg a grub hatches, spends two or three years feeding on the wood and boring a long gallery, and eventually pupates in a chamber near the surface, emerging as a winged adult. In the wild, horntails tend to attack weakened trees, but when the trees were in the yard awaiting sawing they presented a fine target,

HORNTAIL

and a number of eggs were pushed into the wood. This horntail has a symbiotic relationship with a white-rot fungus,
which can turn the wood first yellow and then soft and white.

Remarkable as the horntail's ovipositer is, what is yet more
strange is that there is a parasitic Ichneumon fly that can
detect the presence of horntail larvae in timber—how is not
really known. Perhaps the sound of the jaws boring through
the wood is heard or felt by the Ichneumon's sensitive feet.
This "fly" then also pushes its ovipositer through the wood and
lays an egg on or near the horntail grub, which it feeds on and
eventually kills.

Owing to the activities of the Ichneumons and the fact
that very substantial timbers were used, extremely little damage was caused to the house by the activities of any of the
borers already mentioned.

Other inhabitants of Bartons in its early days were the bark
beetles. As has already been mentioned, the undersides of the
cellar summer beam and bedroom floor joists were left un-
sawn, in order to save labor; many of them had the bark still
on them, and beneath many patches the elaborate pattern of
the bark-beetle galleries could be seen. Bark-beetle females

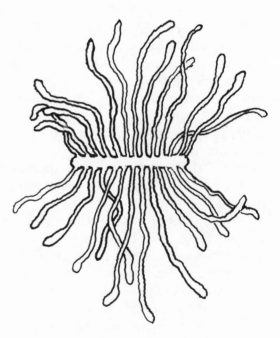

BARK BEETLE AND GALLERIES

bore a gallery straight into a tree through the bark, and when they reach the soft area between the bark and the wood proper (the cambium) they turn at right angles, feeding on the pulp as they go through this rich food zone. They construct a cell in which to deposit an egg, from which a grub emerges and starts making new galleries. There are many different species of bark beetles, each one making a different pattern of galleries. When the eggs hatch, the larvae start tunneling in the wood, further adding to the species' particular design. The feeding loosens the bark, which either falls or can be pulled away, and the beetle can be identified by the pattern disclosed.

If the bark beetles in a tree are numerous, they can in effect girdle the tree and kill it. At Bartons they did not do much damage; the two commonest species were the oak bark beetle in the main beams and the elm bark beetle in the rafters and floor joists, as elm was much used for these timbers. The elm beetle feeds on a fungus which unconsciously it introduces into the galleries, and when this fungus gets into a living elm the hyphae grow and can get into vital parts of the tree, such as the wood vessels, thus depriving it of water. The tree then dies. The disease is now, rather unfairly, known as the Dutch Elm Disease, not because it originated in the Netherlands and has been exported all round the world, but because the Dutch were the first people to do any proper scientific work on controlling this pest. International insults and innuendos in the naming of pests are all too common; examples are the Hessian fly (*Mayetiola destructor*) of wheat in America; the woolly apple aphid (*Eriosoma lanigerum*) of apple in Britain, called the American blight; and *Iridomyrmex humilis*, a pest of fruit trees in the tropics and subtropics, known as the Argentine ant everywhere except in Argentina, where it is called the Brazilian ant.

The wood in the house was exposed not only to beetles and horntails lurking in the forest but also to insects the settlers brought with them. For instance, John Barton had a prized wooden chest with a few worm holes in it caused by the furniture beetle (*Anobium punctatum*) and containing living larvae. In the early summer of 1634 adult beetles emerged from the chest, and after mating, the females sought suitable wood on

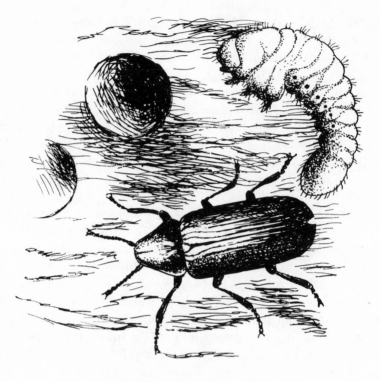

FURNITURE BEETLE

which to lay their eggs. But there was very little in the house that fitted in with their very specialized egg-laying and feeding requirements, so that they lived a somewhat precarious existence. They would only penetrate softwood some twenty years old, and hardwoods of sixty years or more, because the timber did not reach the right condition for the insect until after this period.

Once the right timber had been found by the adults, this particular race of beetles was able to thrive, as the larvae had adapted themselves to eating cellulose; they thus had an advantage over such other timber borers as *Lyctus*, who could not digest this difficult material.

The furniture beetle, or *Anobium*, is a small light-brown insect which varies in length from one tenth to one quarter of an inch. The freshly emerged insect is covered with a light, yellow down which becomes worn as it ages. The wing cases have a number of rows of pinspots on them (giving rise to the Latin specific name of *punctatum*; the generic name—*Anobium* —arises from its habit of shamming dead) running the length of the body. The head is curious in being shielded by a hard hood or lump on the insect's thorax, the middle segment of its body, which partly protects and conceals the head.

The furniture-beetle adults emerged from the pupal cases in June and lay quiet in their burrow for a few weeks in order that their newly formed parts might harden and take on their brown color. Some were males and some females, and when they were mature they ate their way out of the pupal chamber, leaving behind them the characteristic round exit hole, about one-sixteenth inch in diameter. Some of these new beetles mated almost at once, frequently with the female hiding in an old emergence hole and the male making contact with her from outside, and some of them flew off before mating. The primary duty and desire of the females was to find proper sites for their eggs.

As there was so little suitable wood in the house, some of the beetles just died; others escaped into the open and roamed quite far on the breeze. Most of them failed to find a fit site for their eggs and simply died from exhaustion, or were eaten by birds or other animals. At the edge of the wood was John's yard where the logs were being sawn. This could be imagined as a very paradise for *Anobium*, but in point of fact the insects did not find the wood very suitable, as most of it was too green to bring about the egg-laying reaction. However, some beetles were wafted into the woods where there were a number of fallen trees and branches fifteen or twenty years old. Some of the *Anobium* found this old wood and started to lay eggs in the cracks on the rough surface. These were deposited in groups of three or four; they were a dirty white in color and the shape of a lemon, and about a third of the surface at one end was pitted with little marks, while the rest was quite smooth. The eggs were often deformed a little as the females pushed them into the cracks, but such squeezing did the ovae no harm. The number of eggs laid by each female depended on the amount of food reserve with which it had started life and the amount of hunting it had had to do before it found a suitable site; between ten and forty eggs were laid by each of perhaps a dozen insects, so that the amount of infestation going into the forest at this moment was not great. However, it will be of interest to follow the typical life history of this wood borer, which is such a threat to furniture to this day. It finds some plywoods most attractive.

At the end of two weeks the eggs had started to hatch from the bottom and the young grubs immediately bored into the wood, their mothers having selected the sites most efficiently, as it would be very unusual for an *Anobium* to lay eggs where the grubs could not at once obtain food and shelter. The small, naked, unprotected grub is at its most vulnerable state at the moment of hatching: It could be attacked by hunting insects, or it could be dried up by exposure to sun or wind. So it can be seen that in the struggle for survival over the thousands of generations of *Anobium*, those females that were careful to lay their eggs near suitable food and those that laid eggs that hatched from the bottom were more likely to have offspring that survived. These offspring in turn were likely to have more descendants with these two characteristics, until in time this behavior became the pattern for the species—it has become instinctive for them to act in this manner. The larvae are so small that the hole they make in entering the wood cannot be seen with the naked eye, and the holes we do see are made by the adult insects coming out.

The larvae are grayish-white in color, with brown jaws, and are covered with fine hairs. Once safely inside the wood, they commence their long, uneventful existence of eating and growing in perpetual darkness, getting all they need from the wood itself—air, water, carbohydrates, protein, and vitamins. The hairs help the young larvae to get a grip on the walls of their tunnels and gnaw into the wood: gnaw, gnaw, gnaw, pause—gnaw, gnaw, gnaw, pause is the pattern which characterizes their life in the wood for from one to five years. The grubs tend to burrow along the grain of the wood—that would be up or down the tree were it standing in the forest—but sometimes they do move across the grain, either nearer to or farther from the center, till finally the wood is honeycombed with galleries and is completely rotten. The larvae move across the grain—from one ring to another of the wood—for various

reasons: to avoid another larva approaching in the same fiber
and to find places where the food is more to their taste—literally so. In particular, the grub must obtain a supply of protein in order to add to its own muscles, and thus continue
boring, and also to be a reserve for itself when it comes to
pupation and maturity, for a considerable stock of protein
must be incorporated in the next generation of eggs. Its carbohydrate is easily obtained from the wood itself, as has already
been explained, for this insect can digest cellulose directly;
nevertheless, sugar is an easier material to feed on, and the
grub grows more quickly where the wood contains a supply
of sugar, and always seeks out this material in its slow travels.

The grub also needs oxygen, which can only be obtained
from the air by diffusion through the wood and the galleries;
the siting of a gallery is a compromise between the ease of
obtaining oxygen and food, and of competition with other
grubs for these same items. It is obvious that a short gallery, or
a gallery near the surface, will more readily obtain oxygen
than will a long or deep penetration. In spite of being able to
digest cellulose, the grub eats far more wood than it needs for
its carbohydrate supply alone, because it wants other materials
as well (amino acids, proteins, and so on); consequently, a
great deal of waste is excreted behind the grub, and this fills
the passages through which it has passed. Anobium leaves a
fine granular powder, with little cylindrical pellets in it. This
dust, or frass, in the gallery means that oxygen diffusion down
the gallery is slow, and so is the dispersal of the carbon dioxide
generated as the grub breathes.

The action of burrowing calls for the use of a lot of energy,
as any miner will tell you, and consequently the grub, as it
bites forward, uses up the supply of oxygen in its immediate
neighborhood. For as the insect breathes, it burns up some of
the carbohydrate in its body and turns it to carbon dioxide and
water, in the same way that man or any other animal does.
Insects can usually tolerate a considerable volume of carbon
dioxide gas, but at some point the grub must wait for more
oxygen to seep in, either through the burrow or through the
wood itself. The life cycle of Anobium is much quicker in
the forest than in the house, perhaps because the oxygen is
changed more quickly in the former situation; the temperature

difference between night and day is greater out of doors than inside, which means a bigger expansion and contraction of the air in the galleries of the borers and a bigger exchange of the gases in them. Similarly, the wind blowing in the forest means more tiny variations of pressure outside the gallery, which again facilitates gas exchange.

On the other hand, the presence of the mass of frass in the gallery prevents the access of parasites, such as certain mites and other insects that might prey on the grub. Only at the last moment before emergence are the grubs likely to fall victims to parasites. There is a very delicate balance between success and failure, and by no means all the grubs that hatch and start their galleries into the wood are successful; some die of oxygen starvation, some from lack of protein, and some from poisoning.

This poisoning needs explaining: The only part of the wood that is living is the sapwood, and this transmits the water and salts extracted from the soil to all parts of the living tree. The heartwood of the tree is dead—it is frequently a different color —and it serves to support the tree and carry it ever upward so that the leaves can get the light and tower over other leaves in the eternal struggle for existence, which is just as intense among plants as among animals. Trees have waste products of their metabolism and they dispose of these to two places—the bark and the heartwood. Quinine and camphor are examples of tree waste of value to man, the products being found respectively in the bark and the heartwood. Some of these substances are of use to trees in preventing the attack of enemies. The oak excretes a certain amount of tannin into the heartwood, though most of it goes to the bark, and if some *Anobium* grubs get into a pocket of tannin and are not able to extricate themselves in time, they just wither away.

By the time John and Susannah moved into their house a new animal had established itself in America: the *Anobium* furniture beetle. It was one of the many such creatures brought in by the early settlers.

A certain number of beetle grubs were incorporated into the wattle brushwood used in the filling that formed the walls of the house, but few of them were able to emerge as adults, as the filling and limewashing deprived them of air. However, some adult beetles are very persistent and a few, near their full development inside the stems, did bore their way out through the plaster and escape to the wild. Among them were a few furniture beetles, some oak borers (*Scobia declivis* has been known to eat through the lead sheathing of telephone cables), and some longhorn beetles.

An ivory-marked longhorn emerged and laid eggs in the old carpenter's tool chest brought from England; more will be mentioned about this later on.

This then was the position when John and Susannah went to live in the house in July 1634. There were ambrosia beetles, or pinhole borers, both adults and larvae, boring in the new oak beams. As the green timber dried, the wood became unattractive for the beetle and was no more attacked, so that the house was free of pinhole borers by April 1665.

Next there were the powder-post beetles, or *Lyctus*. These were not very numerous, because they only attacked sapwood and not much of this went into the building of the house. The starch in the sapwood was soon used up and the wood became of no more use to the *Lyctus*. It was free of them by 1668.

The furniture, or *Anobium*, beetle was a different matter, for since it came in within the wattle and the old tool chest, the house was never again free from it. In fact, it might be said that Bartons belonged as much to the *Anobium* as to the humans who lived there.

3

~~

BARTONS

JOHN BARTON's sturdy cottage still stands, though it is now but the center of a considerable house, having been added to and altered over nearly 350 years of existence. During this period it was the scene of much biological activity.

The house supported a considerable collection of animals, nearly all of which depended to some extent on the humans, and we can best follow the ramifications of this life by studying a schedule of the people who owned or rented the house from 1633, the year it was started, till today, 1980. This is shown in tabular form on the endpapers of this book.

Five generations of Bartons lived in the house, starting with John Barton III, who came from England. On Saturday, August 15, 1635, a great hurricane struck the colony; it tore most of the thatch off the Bartons' roof, split the wattle-and-clay chimney, and the kitchen fire that burned all the year round set the remaining thatch alight. A burning roof was an event to which the settlers were accustomed at home; they had rakes and long-handled forks always at hand, ready for tearing off the thatch to prevent the loss of the whole house. Bartons lost its roof, but the frame and walls were saved, and their rough furniture. So vulnerable were the settlers' thatched roofs to fire that thatch was prohibited, for not only could the crude wattle-and-clay chimneys split in hot weather and the kitchen fire set the straw ablaze, but the thatch itself was liable to Indian attack.

After the hurricane, rain soaked the house, and John, Susannah, Thomas, and Humility sheltered beneath stretched blankets and their table. With no roof to the house they became particularly aware of what seemed to Susannah to be an ominous portent—an eclipse of the moon on Monday, August 17. John's Galilean explanation did not do much to calm her fears.

In the fall of 1635 John Barton replaced the roof with shingles, making his house safer and obeying the law. Shingles did not give such good protection against heat and cold. In those early days nails were imported and thus expensive; consequently they were used sparingly and small ones were preferred. For instance, one central nail per shingle was used instead of two, one at each top corner. The heat contrast between day and night in summer caused the nails to rise. John knocked them back in the late fall of 1636, but forgot to do so in 1637. Much to his surprise he found that to be advantageous: the nails protruding a half inch or so held the snow to the roof and kept the cottage much warmer. From that time on they never knocked the nails all the way home. Icicles hanging from the eaves of a roof, it was noted in a later age, are a sign of heat leaking from a house and "cost $5.00 per foot [53]."

The farm and family prospered, as did the colony itself; the fur trade and a strict code of conduct saw to that. Of this advance John Truslow Adams wrote:

> The Bible and the beaver were the two mainstays of the young colony. The former saved the morale and the latter paid its bills; and the rodent's share was a large one [66].

In the spring and early summer of 1639 John Barton started to expand his house, employing a recently arrived carpenter and a young boy. The plan was to add an extensive lean-to at the back, but neither man nor boy was experienced and the work was not well done. Consequently the severe earthquake tremors, lasting twenty days of June that year, shook many of the joints loose and the incipient structure fell, fortunately not hurting anyone. If the earthquake was looked upon by some as a punishment from the Lord, John Barton only regarded it as the penalty of not using skilled labor for a difficult task. He was able later to locate Zaccheus Hussey and persuade him to come, both by quoting the Bible to him (the

Biblical Zaccheus was the reformed tax collector and publican who gave liberally to the poor and with whom Jesus lodged [1])—"Today is salvation come to this house, forasmuch as he also is a son of Abraham"—and by paying him a substantial fee, £5 to be exact (about $11.50 at today's rate)! Zaccheus Hussey yielded to the combined God and Mammon approach and made a good job of the extension.

In 1664 a comet blazed in the sky for three months and came to be regarded as God's approval of the settlers' efforts and of forgiveness for such renegades as Thomas Morton, "the Lord of Misrule."

John Barton III died in 1679, shortly after the Indian War in New England had been concluded and the year New Hampshire broke away from Massachusetts. He was succeeded by his son Thomas, who greatly improved and extended the farm and house but made no additions to the latter. The oiled paper and cloth windows were replaced by glass "quarrels"—diamond-shaped pieces of glass two or three inches long, set in leaded strips to join them. They were imported and a great luxury, so much so that houses were often sold or let "without benefit of glass [15]." Even as late as 1805 young Noah Blake describes his prize possession, a glass window, which he took with him as he moved to different jobs.

Thomas Barton died in 1681 after running the farm on his own for only two years, though naturally he had helped his father. He was succeeded by his son Experience Barton, who added an ell to the east side of the house to accommodate his mother and siblings. The Bartons had now become so prosperous that the new wing was comparatively luxurious; it even incorporated a privy, a feature which attracted its own particular forms of life. The two first-floor rooms each had a fireplace, and there was a staircase leading up to the two bedrooms. The old part of the house had only a ladder to the loftlike attic.

The general prosperity of the area was slightly overshadowed by the extension of French influence and the organization of a French colonial empire, extending from Quebec to the mouth of the Mississippi, and running behind the New England settlements.

Experience Barton had four children, all girls. The first,

FIG. I. PLAN OF BARTONS HOUSE, c. 1920

with additions 6, 7, and 8 in 1979 when the building was converted to a restaurant.

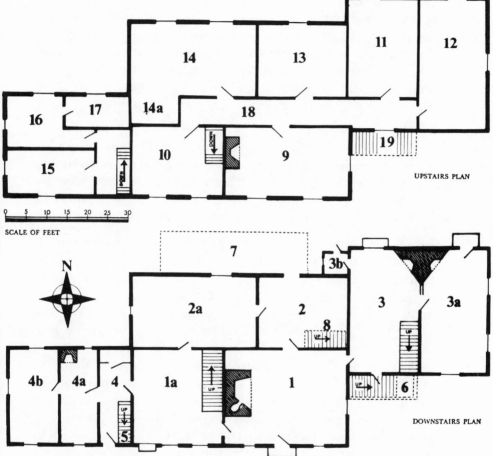

1. Original kitchen and living room, 1632; 1a. Original bedroom, cellar beneath; 2, 2a. Lean-to addition, 1639; 3, 3a. East wing added (3b indoor privy, a novelty at that time), 1682; 4. West wing, 1739; 5. Staircase to second story, 1740; 6 and 8. Staircases to upper restaurant, 1979; 7. Food preparation room and storage, 1979; 9. Main bedroom over old kitchen; 10–16. Bedrooms, 1905; In 1932 No. 13 became two bathrooms; 17. Closet, subsequently a bathroom, also 14a, 1910; 18. Corridor; 19. Access staircase built when house converted to a restaurant, 1979.

Present use:

1. Restaurant; 1a. Bar; 2, 2a. Kitchen; 3, 3a. (now one room) Restaurant with private rooms above; 4. Rest rooms; 5, 6, and 8. Staircase to upper rooms; 7. Food preparation and storage rooms

Desire of the Lord, died shortly after birth. The other girls as they reached maturity indulged in the curious custom, for that straitlaced age, of "bundling," much denounced by the clergy and vigorously defended by the worthy mothers and fathers of the period, who maintained that their daughters were far too pure to allow any sexual intercourse to take place during this practice and their sons far too noble to attempt it. However, in a later age Washington Irving, noting the phenomenal increase in the population, put it down in part to bundling (though much of the increase was due to immigration). He wrote:

> They multiplied to a degree which would seem incredible to any man unacquainted with the marvellous fecundity of this growing country. This amazing increase may, indeed, be partly ascribed to a singular custom prevalent among them, commonly known as *bundling* [26].

In New England no plank was put between the young, fully dressed couple as they were tucked into bed, and Prudence Barton became pregnant by a young man traveling through the neighborhood, who had been welcomed at the house. In spite of the prevalent custom that in such cases the man should marry the girl, Prudence refused to pursue him and she gave birth in 1696 to the illegitimate Jethro, who took his mother's name, Barton. Prudence inherited the farm in 1723, when her father, Experience, died (we may note in passing that Experience could be a name for either a man or woman). She was then forty-seven years old. Jethro had greatly helped his grandfather run the farm; he continued to manage it for his mother for the next fifteen years, until she died in 1738, aged sixty-two.

In 1716 Jethro, then twenty years old, married Bashuah Simmons and had four children: three boys, who all died young, and a girl, Tryphena, who lived to be sixty-two years old, married a wealthy sea captain, Theophilus Chilton, but had no children. The direct male line of Bartons, descended from Barton the settler of 1633, was now extinct.

In 1730 Jethro was extending the farm and needed space for his hired hands: no longer could they be pushed into odd sheds and outbuildings or accommodated on the kitchen floor, so he added the western wing—two stories high—consisting of a kitchen, a hallway with staircase, and two bedrooms above. An addition at this time was a well, sunk below the old cellar floor.

In 1760 Tryphena Chilton move to Boston in order to be near her husband's home port. The farm was let on a share-cropping basis to a tenant, Elkanah Hoag. The structure of the house was much neglected and the arrangement was not very satisfactory to Tryphena, especially during the Revolutionary War.

After the peace, in 1782, no more was heard of Elkanah and in 1784 the farm was sold away from the house. Tryphena died in 1783 and the properties descended to distant relatives who had moved westward. The house was left empty, or as good as empty, for four years: "as good as," because a strange recluse lived hidden in an attic there for over a year (see pp. 72–74). In 1788 Bartons was purchased as a speculation by a wealthy Boston merchant, Stephen Deane. However, the new owner came to love the property, its pleasant view and surroundings, and set about restoring and improving the house. Moreover, it was of wood, and it was well known that stone or brick houses were unhealthy, a prejudice much deplored by Thomas Jefferson [28]. Stephen thought it would be much safer to raise his family in a wooden house, and moved them in there. To celebrate his marriage to Beulah Howland in 1790, he put ceilings on the main rooms, thus enclosing the beams. A new cast-iron stove was fitted into the giant fireplace, which was bricked in. The wattle-and-daub chimney was replaced by brickwork. Stephen Deane died in 1831 and the house descended to his eldest son, Stephen II.

Among the drawbacks of a country house in those ages, and indeed today, too, were flies and mosquitoes. Stephen II took particular measures against them, installing primitive fly-screens of cheesecloth in 1856 and another essential to go with them—the spring-closing door. In 1860 a large coal-burning stove was put into the old cellar and vents made to the main first-floor rooms; it was an early form of central heating.

Stephen Deane II had married Alice Baker in 1838. When he died in 1860 he was succeeded by his son, Theophilus Deane, who fitted a water tank into the roof loft. The tank was filled by hand-pumping from the kitchen; a bathroom and toilet with drainage to a septic tank were also built. During his occupancy of the property he further improved the house and fitted wire fly-screens on removable wooden frames that could be put on in the spring and taken off in the fall.

During the Civil War, friends and relatives crowded into the "safe" area of New England and thus the human population of the house considerably increased.

Theophilus married Sophrinia Frost in 1861. The couple had two children, both boys. Theophilus joined the Union Army and was killed at Savannah in 1864. Sophrinia had a hard task bringing up her two fatherless boys. The elder, Stephen III, inherited the house when his mother died in 1905. In 1885 he had married Janet Snow. There were four children, of whom the eldest, Edward Deane, was killed in action in 1917 in France during the first World War. During this period piped water and town gas were laid on to the house. This not only made the place more convenient but kept it warmer in winter too. Several gas lamps burning in a room generate a lot of heat, fully equivalent to an old-fashioned gas stove in the house. Even in the late eighteenth century, a dozen candles burning in a room was not uncommon and supplied quite a lot of heat.

In 1910 Victoria Deane married a young man called John Barton, who claimed to be a descendant of the original builder of Bartons, though in fact his claim was not a strong one; there were many settlers with the name Barton in New England over the period of this history. So convinced of his ancestry was Victoria's husband that he called himself John Barton VI. Victoria and John VI had three children, John VII, Janet, and James.

In 1920 the house was supplied with a coal-fired boiler and central heating, which had a great effect on the life within it. In 1935 John VII married a woman of Italian descent, Caroline Costa, and had three children. Shortly after this marriage, mains electricity was fitted, as well as an oil-fired boiler and an improved central heating system.

Many farms were now being broken up and sold as building lots; in fact, the area was becoming a dormitory suburb of Boston. In 1978 the property was sold to a development company and turned into a fashionable restaurant, Bartons House, *cuisine française*, Manager Jules La Flèche.

In 1978 a solar water-heater was installed on part of the south-facing roof. Though done more for its publicity value than anything else, it bids fair to become a valuable addition for the future. In the meantime it helps salve the consciences of customers who have driven from Boston in order to enjoy the food and comfort of Bartons House.

Throughout the history of the house, unusual natural phenomena had an effect on the life in it: Some birds and mammals, particularly the humans, could become alarmed by earthquakes and eclipses. Prolonged darkness meant that daylight-feeding creatures could not forage, which could be a serious matter in cold weather. Migrating animals would have their carefully oriented rhythms upset by thirty-six hours or more of nightlike conditions.

The "dark days of terror," as they were called, were when heavy clouds blocked out as much daylight as an eclipse of the sun, or more, and lasted much longer. On at least three occasions these dark days occurred, disturbing some of the life in the house. On May 19, 1780, the skies scarcely got light at all and greatly worried the Hoags and the swallows (the latter were unable to go on building their nests). This happened just after the news had arrived of the fall of Charleston to the British, and speculation was rife as to whether these two events were in any way connected: perhaps the heavens themselves were mourning.

A second "dark day of terror" was on November 2, 1819, but Stephen and Beulah Deane were not so disturbed as the Hoags had been, because the cloud was more obvious and both Stephen and Beulah remembered the first one when they were children. But many birds were affected because they could not forage and got very hungry.

The great "yellow day of terror" was September 6, 1881, when a vast bank of fog rolled down from Newfoundland and kept everything dim and yellow all day long. It delighted the young and artistic Theophilus Deane, as it provided some interesting and much appreciated color changes in the house and landscape. His "Yellow Portrait of My Mother" was a success and is still hanging in the main dining room at Bartons House Restaurant. The migration patterns of many swallows and butterflies were upset by this thirty-six hours of dark yellowness and some following days of very little light.

4

~❧~

MORE WOOD BORERS

I N Chapter 2 an account was given of some of the wood
borers found at Bartons in the early days. Other insect
inhabitants of the forest, together with immigrants from England, also took advantage of the timber at the sawpit and in
the structure. Among them were the longhorn beetles. A
curious characteristic of these creatures is, as the name suggests, their long horns or antennae, which one would imagine
must increase the difficulty of emerging from the pupal cell.
On the other hand, long antennae mean the beetles have
more space for sensors: the antennae are important organs to
any insect and, with the eyes, supply it with most of its information about the outside world.

Longhorns are also called capricorn beetles, because of
the likeness of the antennae to a goat's horns.* The larvae
may live in the wood for many years, and it is only they that
tunnel, the adults being too encumbered by their appendages.

The adults are handsome creatures, visiting flowers and
feeding on pollen and nectar.

Eggs of the ivory-marked longhorn beetle, which in nature
is a wound parasite, were laid on oak logs, because to the
adult beetles these were equivalent to wounded trees. Similarly
the hickory borer laid eggs on hickory, and wood of both kinds
was used for additions to the house and in making furniture,
some of it containing eggs and young longhorn larvae.

On hatching, the grubs of the ivory-marked longhorn bored

---

* Beetles in the genus *Parandra* (of this same Cerambycidae family) are exceptional in having short antennae. They are known as "aberrant longhorns."

tunnels, winding at first between the bark and the wood, leaving the tunnels filled with wood dust. As they got older they cut down obliquely into the wood. Their legs being minimal, they pushed themselves forward with movements of the thorax and abdominal segments, as the powerful jaws mined the faces of the extending tunnels. Some of them stayed in the sapwood (the young wood) where there was more food, and some went into heartwood and even to the very pith in the center. The larvae did not feed on the wood itself but on carbohydrates and proteins contained in the cells. Even so, they broke down a certain amount of the cellulose in the timber. This enabled them to live in the heartwood, where the food value was low but there was no competition. In the heartwood oak, used for ceiling joists and a bed, and in some hickory used for furniture, a beetle grub lived for four years in the first case and for six in the second.

In 1639 young Thomas Barton, now six years old, was much intrigued by the tapping in the leg of a chair, and by much vigilance was able to watch the handsome hickory longhorn beetle emerge from its burrow.

Among the animals that reached New England from

DEATHWATCH BEETLE

Europe were the old house borer and the European death-watch beetle. This last insect is famous for the tapping noise the female beetle makes; it is a mating call to the male. The noise is often heard at night when all is still, as when a person is sitting by a sickbed or watching over a corpse. In the old days this noise was said to foretell a death in the family. The name deathwatch beetle has been applied to a number of insects, some of them not beetles, making eerie noises heard when all is quiet and mysterious (see p. 265).

The old house borer caused considerable damage to Bartons House in 1950. It is an insect that can attack any dry wood, especially pine, of which it seems to be particularly fond. Resinous wood appears to be the "answer" many trees have adopted to the attacks of borers and fungi: Many insects will not attack pinewood until the resin has faded away, which can be some twenty or forty years from felling. But the old house borer has managed so to condition its genes that the resin presents very little obstacle to its feeding on fresh-cut wood.

Some details of this creature may be of interest. These longhorns are dull to shining black in color, sometimes with a brownish tinge; they are from half an inch to one inch long, depending on how well the larvae have been feeding. Some specimens are hairy and others almost bare, but there are always two shining, distinctive bumps on the upper part of the thorax (the thorax is the middle portion of an insect, between the head and the abdomen). The grubs are long and narrow and broadest at the head end, hence the name flathead borer. They actually have six tiny legs, which may easily be overlooked. The burrows made by the larvae are large, broad and rather flat, and packed lightly with fine wood dust, sometimes formed into round or cylindrical pellets. The grubs may tunnel deeply into the wood, giving no external notice of their presence, though today one method of testing for them is to listen with a sensitive microphone for the noise of a multitude of mining jaws at work. Their rate of growth is much influenced by temperature and humidity, being fastest when both are relatively high. Under poor conditions they can spend five years or more unseen in the depths of the wood, reducing it to a mass of spongy galleries, a mass which will collapse when even slight pressure is applied. The larvae burrow deeply into the medium and, when mature, turn back toward the surface, stopping at a point just below it. Curiously enough, they do not construct a pupation chamber there but turn back again for an inch or so into the depths and there pupate. There is thus an exit passage from the pupation cell to near the surface for the adult, with its awkward longish antennae. It can move up this gallery relatively easily and gnaw through the final layer of wood or bark. The long exit passage is a device to protect grub, pupa, and adult from enemies, such as certain Ichneumon flies which can push an egg into a creature deep in a gallery. The emergence holes tend to be oval, and vary in size according to the size of the emerging adult beetle. The largest ones measure two fifths of an inch over the greater diameter.

The beetles emerge in May and then mate. In spite of their encumbrances (legs and antennae) the beetles are very determined to get out; after all, they have been preparing for this great event for years. At Bartons they were observed to have bored through sheet lead; plastics are child's play to them. In contrast to the grubs, the adults do not live more than one or two weeks.

The females lay some forty to three hundred eggs each, singly or in fan-shaped batches, in cracks, crevices, old emergence holes, and even on the surface of the wood. Though wood-living fungi may soften the wood and make conditions easier for the grubs, a fungus can be an enemy to the eggs; it can grow over a batch and stifle it. Not everything goes the old house beetle's way—fortunately for us, or we would not have a house left standing. On hatching, the tiny grubs may crawl over the surface for a little way before digging into the wood, another dangerous period for them.

In 1946 the pine rafters and battens holding the shingles in the roof of the west wing were in prime condition for the old house borer, and those insects were taking advantage of the feast spread before them. Even the shingles were being attacked and letting rain seep into the loft, just enough to keep the timbers damp but not enough to drip onto ceilings, stain them, and make its presence known. The moist timbers allowed the beetle to shorten its life cycle and increase alarmingly. In April 1951 the northwest corner of the roof fell in, scattering dust all over the place and drawing attention to the damage being done. Many of the rafters were just a spongy mass of wormholes.

The big brown bats immediately noticed the splendid new summer roost opened to them, but John Barton (John VII), after frantically trying to clear the structure of wormy wood, realized the task was too big for him and called in professional exterminators. He recalled the remarks of his supposed ancestor, John Barton III, who in his diary greatly regretted trying to build the lean-to addition to his house without proper advice.

The exterminators advised him to leave the bats alone for the time being—until the men could get to work—because the bats would eat a lot of the adult beetles as they emerged and reduce the risk of infecting the whole structure.

It soon became obvious that the entire house would have to be treated, as not only was the west wing a source of infection for the old house borer, but the experts also detected the presence of the European deathwatch beetle, the furniture beetle, and carpenter ants.

The treatment given was to spray all the wood in the house with DDT dissolved in a light oil, one a little heavier than kerosene. The time was fortunate for the Bartons because it was before the anti-DDT movement got under way, leading finally to a ban on its use. The treatment John's house received was both comparatively cheap and effective and seemed to do no harm to wildlife outside the house. The wildlife inside the house was busily destroying it, and these creatures were much harmed; such was the object of the exercise. But there was nothing very rare or beautiful destroyed, nor did the house represent an important environment for the few spiders and other arthropods sharing the place with him. John VII eventually came to the conclusion that the anti-DDT campaign was secretly supported by the pesticide manufacturers; otherwise it would not have been so successful. Making DDT was easy, very competitive, and thus unprofitable. A ban on it meant that more expensive and far more profitable substitutes had to be used instead [42].

The number of spiders and insects living in the house had

FIG. II.   POPULATION OF HUMANS AND WOOD BORERS.

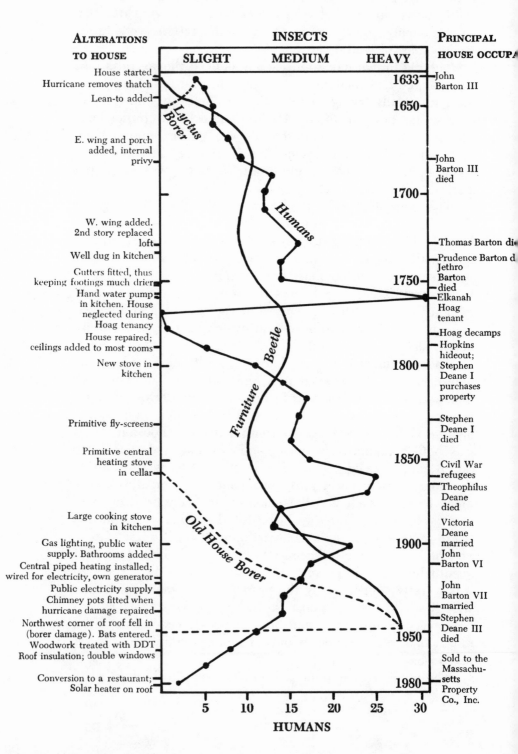

been much reduced by the installation of central heating, in a primitive way in 1860 and more effectively in 1920. The drying of the atmosphere made life more difficult for these creatures, even though an increase of temperature would have made things easier for the wood borers. The wholesale treatment with DDT extinguished all insects living on the surface of the wood and most of them in the wood that were anywhere near the surface. The oil, however, does not penetrate far into hardwoods, so that wood-boring grubs half an inch or so down in the timbers continued to live. But when they came to the surface to pupate, the insecticide got them. The timbers were guaranteed safe for twenty years.

The spiders coming into the house did not thrive because of the dryness, the DDT, and the fact that there were no insects breeding in the place. They could only live on insects that came in, as they did from time to time. Moreover, Caroline Barton always dusted the webs away. Life was hard for a spider at Bartons.

Finally, among the borers were the carpenter ants, the carpenter bees, and termites. The carpenter ants did not really live in the house but visited it to gather food and occasionally, as a trial or temporary nest, bored into untreated wood such as new furniture or timber used for extensions or repairs.

Carpenter bees were sometimes found in the house, particularly during the latter part of the eighteenth century. They were discovered at Bartons in rather a strange manner. A few years after the revolutionary victory, the farmers in Massachusetts fell upon lean times, mostly because of the confusion, lack of currency, distrust of paper money, and the losses and debts left by the conflict. The farmers were called upon to pay for nearly half of government needs by means of taxes levied on land and head counts, at a time when many of their traditional markets had been lost and prices of farm produce were falling. If they did not pay the taxes demanded, the courts distrained on them, taking cattle and crops in settlement. This led to Shays's Rebellion.

Daniel Shays, a veteran of Bunker Hill, led a march of farmers and others to Springfield, Massachusetts, in September 1786. Their objective was to prevent the court sitting and thus issuing distraint orders on farmers. In 1787, after numerous

CARPENTER BEE

raids, they were finally routed by the militia and Shays escaped to Vermont. He was tried in absentia and condemned to death, but was subsequently pardoned, on June 13, 1788.

Among the rebels was a middle-aged man, Edward J. Hopkins, who, after their defeat, became really frightened, escaped from arrest, and went into hiding. Walking eastward by night, and in terrible weather, to get as far away from the disaster as he could, he came by chance to Bartons, now empty. Almost at the end of his strength, he gained an entry to the house through the cellar and managed to cover his tracks so well that the instrusion was not noticed by the few people who went to or passed by the house. Still much frightened, he built himself a hideout in the attic of the east wing. He was still there more than a year later.

He only came out at night, when he collected what food he could, such as heath hens, passenger pigeons, squirrels ("a very fine dish," he was to say in later years), corn cobs, hickory nuts, and vegetables, which he cooked at night either deep in the woods or on a low fire in the Bartons kitchen, always removing the ash and concealing his presence. He found ink and paper in the house and he made pens from the quill feathers of various birds, passing the daylight hours in sleeping and recording details of the life found in the attic. He was a born naturalist.

In the spring and summer of that year (1787) he was much intrigued by the carpenter bees. They were large, hand-some, hairy creatures—like bumblebees—and with their strong jaws dug tunnels into the beams and rafters of the roof. The hardest wood did not seem to deter them, though he noticed that wood softened by rot gave them an easier start. The tunnels were lined with cut leaves and formed a succession of cells; in each one an egg was deposited. The mother bee also put in a supply of pollen and nectar on which the grub would feed when it hatched. The adult bees emerged from these galleries in due course and hibernated for the winter, as did Edward Hopkins, as much as he could.

He made himself a magnifying glass by carefully chipping away the bottom of a wine bottle; the lens greatly helped his studies, always carefully recorded. He noticed, for instance, the passenger mites that bees often carry on their legs and bodies. He also noted that the bees cut different shapes of leaf: Round disks formed the caps of the cells and a series of oval pieces served for the body of the structure. He recorded quite a number of other creatures, too, and gave them his own names and numbers, such as "Beetle 1, Beetle 2, Moth 1 . . ." There were quite a number of beetles coming out of the wood at that time.

Hopkins was extremely quiet and cautious and lived un-detected for more than a year in his hideout. He accumulated page after page of notes, and he was writing them one morn-ing in March 1788 when Stephen Deane and his agent, sur-veying his new property with an eye to making improvements, climbed into the attic and discovered his unbidden guest—a bearded, unkempt figure, not at all pleasant smelling, steadily writing away by the tiny attic window. Mr. Hopkins thought his last hour had come and Mr. Deane was none too pleased at finding a bum hidden in his new home. Or if not a bum, a spy with a pile of notes by his side. But what sort of spy? For Lord North or Captain Shays, or both? Or for the French, who were trying to cut off New England from the rest of the continent?

Explanations were then made, and Stephen Deane was so impressed with the volume of natural history notes, the strange story, and a feeling of sympathy for Daniel Shays and his men that he told Hopkins that there was no need for alarm, that Captain Shays had not yet been found and probably would be pardoned, that farmers' taxes had been alleviated, and that he would give Hopkins a job as gardener if he liked. "But you must get rid of those creatures destroying my house," he said. "No," said Mr. Hopkins, he could not do that; they had been his companions for so long (an unusual sentiment for that age), but he would block up all access points in the loft so that no more bees could get in.

Edward Hopkins took the job, his fears quieted, and he moved into the west wing, the hired-hands' quarters. His notes, alas, were never published.

5

LARGE AND
SMALL MAMMALS

THE BIOLOGICAL ACTIVITY of the mammals at Bartons was
dominated by the humans, some of whose social activities
were part of it, and were described in Chapter 3; indeed the
social and biological activities impinge on one another. A
certain social pattern among some of the hymenopterous insects has enabled a large environment to be occupied by vast
hordes of ants, bees, and wasps. The social pattern of a pride
of lions enables them to cooperate in obtaining their kills and
caring for the young, while social cooperation among man
has led him to dominate on earth, at any rate from soon after
his appearance until the present. There is no need to describe
the natural history of the more familiar mammals—man, the
cat, the dog—in such detail as I have described the less well
known insects, but we do want to think of these animals from
the point of view of numbers, descent, heredity, how and why
they got to the house, and why those that left it did so.

The mammals in Bartons were never completely driven out:
Though for some years from 1782 there were no humans
present—which meant that the place was also abandoned by
mice, cats, and dogs—yet the loft became inhabited by two
species of bats. Consequently mammals, as a class, have nearly
as long and uninterrupted a history there as the wood-boring
beetles.

It was natural that humans should dominate life in the
house, because they had built it for their own purposes. The
reason John Barton was able to build it in the first place was
that human technical ability took a big step forward during the

seventeenth century. A better understanding of the principles of agriculture led to better crops, which in their turn meant the release of more hands and brains for activities other than gathering or getting food. The number of mouths a man can feed by his efforts on the farm is constantly increasing. In the Stone Age the whole population was engaged in getting food by plant-gathering, agriculture, or hunting: It took the activity of one adult to feed a person and his or her young. Gradually skilled flint-workers set up what were in effect factories for making axes and arrowheads, which they traded for food. The principles of Adam Smith's *Wealth of Nations* were being applied: It was mutually advantageous to the axe maker and the axe user to exchange axes for food, and it is indeed surprising to discover over what long distances men would travel in neolithic times in order to get a well-made stone axe.

As time went on, the methods of agriculture, fishing, and hunting improved so that fewer and fewer people needed to be engaged in it. The husbandman (using the word to include all forms of food-winners) who could at first feed only himself became able to feed several people, which left a surplus of hands, and brains, to devote to other economic and social activities—to smelt metals, build houses, invent the wheel and money, appoint chieftains, kings, presidents, priests, to learn to write, to calculate, to paint and make music, but above all to develop nations, armies, governments, war, and in fact the modern world. In late medieval times about three quarters of the population was engaged in food-winning, which meant that the husbandman could feed about one and one-third persons, but by the time of the *Mayflower*, agriculture and industry had so improved that each husbandman was supporting perhaps four adult members of the population.

Today in the United States, 3.67 million farmers, land workers, and fishermen supply the whole country (203.21 million people) with practically all its food and export a considerable quantity as well (1970 census). Thus, on average here, one person is now raising food for more than fifty-five people. To begin with, the improvement in the ratio was due to the carving out of new farms from the forest and waste, to better management of the land, and to the new crop, Indian corn. Moreover, land was plentiful and the best could be chosen for the new settlements. For instance, many of the early settlers, such as John Alden, moved away from Plymouth to Duxbury because of the poor land at the former place. As time went on, other important factors in the agricultural advance were technical improvements (manures, machines, pest control, better seed, and so forth). The Bartons were particularly successful because they were not afraid to try new crops and methods. They started growing maize by the Indian method—and they continued to grow it on more modern lines when their neighbors were concentrating on European crops such as wheat, barley, and oats, which gave nothing like so good a return for the effort expended.

This trait persisted, and in the third American Barton generation, in 1718, Experience Barton started to grow potatoes from seed sent to him, oddly enough, from Ireland. For some strange reason the settlers as a whole did not take to that crop. A farmer at Hadley, Massachusetts, as late as 1763, had "a large crop of potatoes," eight bushels! A belief was prevalent that if a person ate potatoes every day he would not live more than seven years [15]. In the spring all potatoes left over were burnt, for if the cattle or horses ate them, it was thought they would die. Sir Walter Raleigh took potatoes (the *Solanum* species, that is; it was frequently confused with the sweet potato) and tobacco to Ireland, where both became popular crops. Coming from Ireland, they were distinguished from the sweet potato by the name Irish potatoes, and the fashionable way of cooking them was with butter, sugar, and grape juice; the paste was then mixed with mace, nutmeg, and pepper and covered with a frosting of sugar. Obviously they were trying to make them taste like sweet potatoes. The Solanums were suspect for a long time. King James blasted against tobacco from the first as much as do our doctors today. Tomatoes, the love apple, were not thought to be edible until about 1845, and they and potatoes were held "to induce lust" and thus not be suitable crops for the lower orders of society, though in New England that vice was not regarded as becoming to any stratum.

From the time Bartons was built to the present day the number of humans resident in the house has varied greatly—from zero to thirty-one. When John and Susannah moved in, in 1633, there were two of them. Children were born, some died and some throve; hired girls and men came and went, and parents, relations, and friends resided there for short and long periods, which caused the number of humans to fluctuate around the average of seven. This is shown by a table on page 70 given my census of humans in the house at ten-year intervals from 1635. The zero point was 1783 when the house was left empty after the defection of Elkanah Hoag. A considerable peak (eighteen) was reached in 1773 when Elkanah, in addition to having a large number of children, boarded various brothers, sisters, cousins, and hired hands helping him run the farm successfully. However, the maximum (thirty-one) was when Theophilus Deane had the place: During the later stages of the Civil War people crowded into the "safe" areas of Massachusetts, and Stephen took in many families of his friends and relations for the duration of hostilities.

The fertility of the humans in the house varied as much as did their numbers. It ran from zero—Tryphena Chilton (née Barton)—to fourteen—Elkanah Hoag and his wife in the late eighteenth century. Such numbers were by no means uncommon from the earliest days onward and were quite a factor in populating the countryside, though it must also be remembered that the infant death rate was high. For instance, three of Jethro Barton's four children died in infancy, as did two of Stephen Deane II's four.

Not only did the women bear many children but the length of the period of childbearing was also considerable—the spacing was not always that of maximum production. For instance, in Sandwich, Massachusetts, Daniel Wing married his first wife—Hannah Swift—in Tenth Month (December) 1641 (the year started in March and pagan names for the months were eschewed, e.g., Janus, Mars, Augustus). Over twenty-two years Hannah had nine children, dying in Eleventh Month (January) 1664, shortly after the birth of her last child. This is a typical case and by no means a record or in the least unusual. Moreover, there was a gap of five years between the Wings' first child (Hannah, 1642) and the second (Lydia, 1647) which the couple must have found most disturbing. Perhaps there was a series of miscarriages, but from Lydia onward all was well; four boys and four girls followed. After Hannah's death Daniel Wing married again and had three more children—Experience, Batcheldor, and Jashub [61].

John Barton, the so-called VII (born 1913), and his wife have had three children and eight grandchildren. Mr. Jules la Flèche and an assistant are the only people now living in the house.

These were the numbers that resided there. On special occasions such as parties, weddings, and funerals many more humans were found temporarily in the house. On June 5, 1716, when Jethro Barton married Bashuah Simmons, there was a great gathering of the two families, some friends and hired hands, amounting in all to seventy-four persons. Even this has been exceeded in modern times when the restaurant has been the site of a popular wedding reception or similar function. In June 1979, when Edward Barton's daughter Angela got married to Nathan Comstock, publisher, it was naturally decided to hold the party at Bartons House, the new management offering especially favorable terms in view of the advantageous publicity.

Present were 54 members of the Barton, Fontana, and Comstock families, 112 friends, and the restaurant staff (cooks, waiters, etc.) of 20, in all 186 people. But it is difficult to say if this total was ever actually all in the house at the time, as there was a large marquee in the garden. The party was a great success, as the somewhat diverse world of publishers, agents, and authors mixed with the Bostonian business one. A biologist might have been excused for thinking of these two strata as being populated by different species and wondering if they might prove to be intersterile; such concepts, if in fact they did occur, were disproved in time not only by Nathan and Angela Comstock's twins but also by a local literary woman there meeting and later marrying a Boston shipping magnate and producing a fine child.

The 186 humans is a small number compared with that of some of the mites and insects found in the house; even other mammals, such as mice and bats, exceeded that figure.

The house did not descend from father to child for very long: Some of the original gene pattern of John and Susannah, which was stamped on their children by the laws of heredity,

passed through five generations before the Barton genes, or
Barton blood as one would say in more familiar terms, disappeared through Jethro Barton's having no grandchildren.
However, if the claim of John Barton VII is correct (he was
born in 1913 and is still alive), the John Barton II genes were
revived in the house in 1910, to be lost again when the house
was sold to become a restaurant. John Barton II was born,
lived, and died in England. The Barton name might have been
lost to the house in 1723 had not Prudence Barton, through
injudicious bundling, produced a son. The boy took the Barton
name, but it only persisted for one more generation, as Jethro
(1696–1754) left no male heir.

Five generations from 1633 to 1731 meant that the original
settler Barton gene pattern had been halved five times, so
that John Barton V, his two brothers, Caleb and Jethro, and
sister, Tryphena (the only Barton of this generation who
outlived childhood), only carried $\frac{1}{32}$ of their genes from the
original builder of the house and another $\frac{1}{32}$ from his wife,
Susannah Palmer—which makes $\frac{1}{16}$ from the two of them, or
6¼ percent. However, as the generations extend one after the
other, lines of descent tend to mingle by intermarriage, though
the individuals may well be unaware of any relationship, and
thus some of the original genes will be brought back into the
family again.

Any discussion of the gene makeup of the humans depends
on the point from which we start—which in this case is the
first man and wife in the house—but of course these two
people were themselves the result of a complex descent stretch-
ing back thousands of generations.

Let us take the example of Susannah Palmer, who married
the original settler, John Barton III, in 1633. Susannah Palmer's
mother had been a Simmons and consequently Susannah's
genes were half Simmons ones. Susannah's mother, Patience
Simmons, was the sister of Bashuah Simmons's great-great-
grandfather, though when Bashuah married Jethro Barton
neither of them was aware of it. Bashuah naturally carried
some of the same genes that went into making Susannah
Palmer. If we calculate the proportion of the original John
and Susannah genes present in Tryphena Barton (born 1722),
we find they were slightly increased by this marriage of distant

relatives because Tryphena's mother, Bashuah Barton (née Simmons), carried some (¹⁄₆₄th) of the same genes as Susannah Palmer. That is, Tryphena had a ⁵⁄₆₄ quota of the original John III and Susannah genes instead of a ¹⁄₁₆ (⁴⁄₆₄) content that a completely unrelated descent would have given. It is these reassembled genes that tend to give a family face or a county or national pattern to a family or a community. The genes often seem to reassemble in blocks. How often when the new baby is presented to the assembled relations not only are such items as his mother's eyes and father's nose remarked upon but also Uncle Samuel's brow and Cousin Melissa's lips, and though Uncle Samuel may be on the father's side and Cousin Melissa on the mother's, yet, far back, they are likely to have had genes in common.

If a line of descent is traced back far enough, a certain intermarriage between lines must be uncovered, as will be found by a simple calculation.

A person has two parents, four grandparents, eight great-grandparents, and so on; a generation, at any rate in the settlers' times, may be taken as twenty years, so that from the building of the Bartons' primitive house till today some twenty generations have passed, which means that the present occupier of the house would be descended from over a million ancestors had no intermarriage taken place.*

This figure would be many times the population of seventeenth-century New England, even including the Indians, who were not very numerous at that time. In fact, as a person's ancestry goes back, the lines intermarry to a considerable extent and he finds himself descended from a much smaller number of seventeenth-century ancestors than the formula suggests.

What led the humans to abandon Bartons for five years? It was more a result of chance, the Revolutionary War, and changing social conditions than for any innate biological reason. After the victory, enthusiasm for the new nation, the possibilities of actually owning lands westward, and the advantages of quietly slipping away from his wealthy Boston landlady (Tryphena Chilton) led Elkanah Hoag to abandon

---

* $2^{20} = 1,048,576$

Bartons in the spring of 1782, taking most of the farm's portable assets with him. He salved his conscience with the thought that his rich landlady more than likely was a supporter of Lord North and his redcoats, for the rich never wanted any social change. Moreover, was he not Elkanah, named after one of David's mighty men? It was some time before Tryphena's agent realized that Hoag had gone. It hardly seemed worthwhile pursuing him, nor was the agent able to find a suitable new tenant. Sharecropping was not the sort of thing that fell in with the new republican spirit of equality and no kowtowing to the bosses.

In 1633, as winter's approach chilled and bared the ground, the native deer mice crept under the door, bead eyes staring, whiskers trembling, ready to scurry back at the first creak. At last in the sleeping darkness they found crumbs and grains of corn to nibble. This was a good place to live; it was even better than the Indian huts that once they had used so much as a winter refuge but which now were very scarce. John and Susannah were friendly with one of Massasoit's Indians, who in return for food and an axhead used to work for them from time to time. They were teaching him English and at

DEER MOUSE

the same time learning Indian words from him, and much of their early success was due to his help and advice.

The Indian's sense of smell was acute. He maintained that he could distinguish between a Frenchman, Spaniard, and Briton by the smell of the hands alone, and put to the test, he often seemed to be right [39]. The smell of deer spoor was an important factor in the Indians' tracking of those creatures. One day in October 1633, sniffing, he said "Jonihkais," and picking up the poker, drew the outline of a mouse on the earth floor, making a great flourish of its curly tail. Brought to their notice, the musky odor became evident to John and Susannah. "We must get a cat," said Susannah, but at that time she had a more important matter in hand—the birth of her first child—and the question of the cat was neglected until after that event. The European cat had reached America a little ahead of the *Mayflower*; they had landed in Maine from French fishing boats and had spread south from there in both half-wild and domesticated state, their utility and fascination making them much sought after.

After Susannah had recovered from the birth of baby Thomas, a female cat was acquired from Boston, but it was not so much the cat that drove the sweet-smelling deer mice out of Bartons. The European house mouse had also landed from the settlers' ships and was better adapted to commensal living with man. They did not fight the native deer mice, but succeeded in pretty nearly excluding them from Bartons by being just that little bit more efficient. It is man that gives his commensal—the house mouse—its advantage. In the wild the deer mice thrive to the exclusion of the introduced house mouse. The deer mice have an elaborate system of nesting burrows, with storage chambers and escape galleries, but if this wild habitat is much disturbed—for instance, by being plowed and harrowed for agriculture—and if such refuges for the house mouse are provided as houses, barns, and stacks, then the latter animal thrives at the expense of the former [4]. A place in which to live is the main critical factor in the introduced mouse's success, not a struggle for food.

This lesson was not unappreciated by Tantamous, the Indian. If the white man's mouse could drive out the native mouse, nuisance though it was, what might not the white man himself do? His friendship with the Bartons started to fall away.

A dog, a kind of mastiff, was secured at about the same time as the cat.

Needless to say, cats proliferated at Bartons, and though they shared the premises with the domestic dogs, they lived a life of a very different character, for the dog depends on man and in the main is subservient to him; the cat, on the other hand, does not appear to be beholden to man at all. One must be careful of attributing to these animals emotions and thought processes which are human; nevertheless, it is of interest to express the situation in these anthropomorphic terms and then to see how it can be explained in other terms. In return for its food and lodging, the dog appears to worship

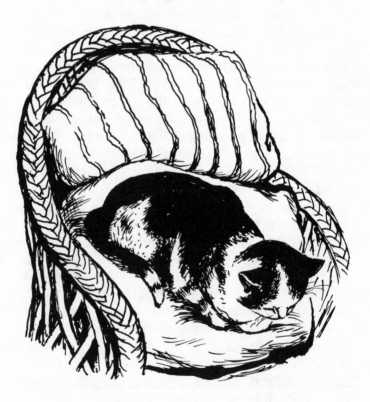

CAT

man and be ready and eager, on the whole, to obey him. In fact, between no other two kinds of animals is it possible for such firm, lifelong friendships to develop as between man and dog. Dogs have been known to defend the bodies of their dead masters; to starve rather than take food from strangers; and have displayed countless other forms of apparently disinterested activity for the benefit of man. In contrast, the cat does not seem to have any respect for his host and will only obey him if he feels like it. "I am not a friend and I am not a servant," says the cat in Kipling's *Just-So Stories*, for "He walked by himself, and all places were like to him."

Let us compare these two animals. In the first place, their natural history is very different. Cats are solitary, nocturnal carnivores; dogs are daylight creatures hunting in packs and have thus learned the advantages of cooperating with others. Both spring from a common ancestor, *Miacis*, which flourished some forty million years ago, in the Eocene geological period. The cats have not changed greatly since then, whereas the other branch that split off from *Miacis*—the *Cynodictis*—split again and became bears, wolves, dogs, and raccoons. A cat retains more innate fierceness than a dog; as it leads a solitary life it has had to develop and use more cunning in order to survive, whereas dogs, giving up an arboreal life, have lost the power to retract their claws and have developed instead a swiftness over the ground in order to run down their prey. Cats have retained the power to project and withdraw their claws under sheathlike pads, which enables them to climb trees and to jump and move with extreme quiet in order to stalk and surprise their victims. Both cats and dogs have flesh-tearing teeth, but dogs have long jaws for snapping at their food, while cats have short ones that enable them to seize and hold it.

The cats developed a wide-opening iris to the eye, which permits them to take advantage of dim light at night, but nevertheless the iris can rapidly be shut to a slit, so that the eye can also be used in daylight. The cat has enormously strong muscles for its size, adjusted to a skeleton framework that allows it to make the powerful, silent, killing spring common to the whole family from cat to lion. Cats walk on their toes, do not run like a dog, but trot or proceed in enormous bounds when they want to cover the ground at speed. This enables them to close with their prey at a great pace in the last dash, which is so important to success in this field. Their senses are acute. They have a particularly sensitive perception of moving objects, for it is a matter of importance in stalking game to be aware of the slightest movement of the quarry. The sight of dogs is not as good as that of cats and they are color-blind, but they are, like cats, sensitive to movement. In cats the sense of hearing is acute, except in blue-eyed white long-hairs, which are always deaf, apparently a case of a linkage of the recessive character (deafness) with this particular eye and coat color. Their sense of smell is well developed, though not employed for hunting to the same extent as is that of dogs. Cats appear to get pleasure from certain aromas, such as catnip and valerian, and may be said to have an addiction to them.

The wild cat has a wide range of food: It consumes all forms of rodents, birds, fish, frogs, certain insects and spiders, grass, and fruit; whereas the natural food of the dog is nearly always carnivorous, even carrion, with a certain amount of vegetable food obtained from the intestines of the herbivores killed. Alice's questions with regard to cats and bats can be answered by "yes" in both cases, provided a wide enough range is taken, for cats will readily eat a bat if they can catch one, and vampire bats will suck the blood of the puma if they get a chance.* Robins have developed a protection against cats in that they cause sickness when eaten; cats rarely eat a second robin, though some, not all, will continue to catch them.

It is sometimes thought strange that cats should be so fond of fish when they so dislike water; this dislike is more apparent than real, for all cats can swim and some do it regularly for pleasure.

Can we now explain the difference in the attitudes of cats and dogs toward man? Both relationships can be seen as associations for the mutual advantage of host and guest. Of the two associations, man/cat and man/dog, the latter is the older; in giving up his pack and attaching himself to man, the dog

* The questions—"Do cats eat bats?" and "Do bats eat cats?"—were asked by Alice as she fell down the rabbit hole. *Alice in Wonderland* by Lewis Carroll.

has become that much more dependent on man's favor. Dogs followed primitive men, cleaned up after their kills, and from this soon were being used by men, to the benefit of both groups.

Cats were a later addition to man's circle, probably attracted to it by his fire. They caught some vermin for him but were tolerated more for their elegance and totem value in religious ceremonies (they had a part in the oldest of the ancient Egyptian religions and also in pre-Inca Peru). They may also have had some value to primitive man as food and for their skins, just as dogs did.

The cat can quite easily revert to the wild state; it often does, though it does not then lead so easy a life. The dog, on the other hand, cannot, for in the first place he must form a pack to be really successful, and secondly, while man may merely dislike a wild cat's activities, every man's hand is against any dog that attempts a wild life, because it will do so much more harm (it will attack his sheep, for example). Worse still, the dog attempting to live wild was often thought to be rabid and much feared. The grown kitten escaping to the woods has a good chance of surviving; the young dog a poor one. However, neither the cat nor the dog sitting by the fire is conscious of this, so the differences in the instinctive pattern of behavior must arise from the different life patterns, aided no doubt by the fact that abandoned cats and some kittens have survived in the wild state and subsequently mated with tame domestic cats—which would strengthen the independent attitude of their descendants—whereas abandoned dogs and puppies have rarely, if ever, lived for long. The dog is more dependent on man than the cat. Lorenz has suggested that the dog has transferred to man the devotion and loyalty he once showed to the leader of the pack.

The Bartons, when they first took up residence, had to have cats not only in the house but in the farmyard as well, and soon the problem of numbers arose. The yard cats were always chased out of the house and lived a semi-wild life, being fed only with a little milk (and to begin with there was not much during the winter) and the birds and rodents they themselves could catch. The house cats had frequent litters and usually all but one or two of the numerous kittens would be drowned. A powerful selective factor was thus at work here, for the successive owners of the farm or their servants were constantly choosing one or two kittens to be kept out of a litter of some six or more. They tended to choose animals with an agreeable coat pattern or attractive features, whereas the more natural selection on the farm tended to develop the best hunters and the most vigorous and healthy specimens. Two separate races of cats did not arise, however, because the farm and the house cats continually cross-mated with each other, which did much to maintain the vigor of the domestic line, and possibly the elegance of the yard cats.

We are concerned only with those in the house; there always were some and there still are two at the restaurant, one a tom, a descendant of the long line of cats associated with the farm, and the other a neutered Siamese male, often found in the bar.

In 1693 Abigail Barton's "hired girl," Grace Hinson—a woman of about forty-five—who was very fond of cats, rescued an abandoned kitten from being chased by the dog, and the little creature became very attached to her and used to ride on her shoulder at times. Grace had once chased some boys who were stealing apples out of the garden, and the cat had sprung from the tree onto her shoulder. The boys denounced her as a witch, saying the cat was her familiar. At that time prosecutions and executions for witchcraft were numerous, and things might have gone badly for the poor woman had it not been for two things [3]. First, the excesses of the Salem trials had begun to alarm a considerable section of the population, and second, Abigail Barton spoke up for Grace with the local selectmen. At the risk of being denounced herself, Abigail said, "Has not the good and kindly parson George Burroughs been condemned as a witch? Yet at the foot of the gallows he made a letter-perfect recitation of the Lord's Prayer, a thing no witch could do." But Mr. Cotton Mather had hurried him away to execution. Now, people could hardly believe that God would permit Mr. Cotton Mather to err, yet he was human and could be mistaken. [66] Moreover, she continued, "If an accusation of witchcraft were to be a defense for apple-stealing, there wouldn't be a tree, aye, nor even a

pig nor a sheep safe in the whole country." Sheep stealing was
a crime that really moved people in those days.

As she warmed to her subject her husband, Experience,
began to get alarmed and intervened to point out that they
had always taken precautions against witches. For instance,
all the external doors of their house were witch doors (doors
with a Maltese cross in the lower panel) so that no witch
could come in that way. They had other ways of entering, said
a selectman; for instance, their specters could pass through
walls. Nor, said Experience Barton, would he permit superstitious practices in their house. He would not allow Prudence,
Fear, or Alice to look over their shoulders into a bowl of water
on Hallowe'en night to see the features of a future husband
(though one cannot help feeling that the girls did so just the
same).

"And what about these denunciations by interested parties?" broke in Abigail. They often took over the goods and
lands of condemned witches and she would like to know what
those two good-for-nothing girls at Andover, Ann Putnam, Jr.,
and Mary Walcott, got for their pains. Why, Mr. Dudley
Bradstreet, the Justice of the Peace, had had to stop taking
names after he had written down forty indicated by those two
crazed creatures, God help them, otherwise the whole county
would have had to be arrested. And, she continued, what
about the gentleman in Boston who when he was accused
said he would initiate a court action for one thousand pounds
damages from any one defaming his name? Let the selectmen
think of that new turn of events.

Experience Barton was by now getting really alarmed, but
the charge was dismissed, mostly because both the parson and
many of the selectmen had suffered depredations from the
same boys.

But the fervid belief in witchcraft took a long time to die
down. It was supported by most of the powerful in the land,
people who do not like their ideas opposed. As late as 1699
Robert Calef could get no local printer to publish his anti-
witch-trials pamphlet and had to send it to London, where it
was issued in 1700 [11].

Grace Hinson lived to a ripe old age and was always grateful for her mistress's spirited defense. Grace was a great help during the family disgrace—the birth of Abigail's illegitimate grandson, Jethro, in 1696. The shame, said Abigail, was killing her and in fact she did die shortly after this event, but not before Grace had shown her what a beautiful child the boy was, with her eyes and her father's nose, and had obtained her forgiveness for Prudence. The child could not fail to become an important man, and together they selected the name Jethro—the Priest of Midian and father-in-law of Moses. And Jethro would keep the Barton name alive too, said Grace. This child was a blessing, not a sin.

"Why," said Grace, "I think I should have a child myself."

"Oh Grace, Grace, do not jest on such a subject," said Abigail.

The hired girl, friend and almost part of the family, was an important asset in those days. Grace not only made her mistress's closing days peaceful but also helped the young mother, who seemed to take the whole affair very much in her stride—the stirring of the American spirit of independence. The same spirit had been shown by Abigail, Prudence's mother, when she was moved to defy authority in the matter of Grace's alleged witchcraft.

Cats, once often thought of as familiars, were an important factor in keeping down mice of all sorts; in Europe for many generations cats had preyed on mice and in the New World they continued their activities against their ancient food, as well as attacking a whole range of native creatures. Cats were particularly active in buildings. Their value was well recognized. When ceilings to rooms were made, to further the striving for elegance around 1717, it was soon found that these ceilings gave well-hidden protected runways and nesting sites for mice. They could be heard scurrying about in the spaces between the ceiling of the first-story rooms and the floors of the second story, where the cats could not penetrate. The answer was to cut cat holes at strategic points, so that the cats could follow the mice into their labyrinth. These runways frequently had patch doors at the entrances, each held by a nail, so that the run could be closed if necessary.

Soon after their establishment in the house, the Bartons acquired a mastiff bitch called Chase. The Indians had dogs

DOG

and naturally the introduced and native dogs interbred to a considerable extent, so that many different kinds and types of dogs came and went during the life of the house. In those early days nothing like so many different breeds were known, and the classification set down by John Caius (the founder of Caius College, Cambridge, England) in his book *De Canibus Britannicus* was still adhered to: "(i) Gentle, serving the game. (ii) homely, for sundrie necessarie uses, and (iii) currish, meete for many toyes [10]."

The early settlers were very frightened of wolves and bears, the fear of the latter being exemplified by the incident of "Soule's bear." In Duxbury, in the 1680s, a boy spread much alarm by saying he had seen a bear up a tree and everyone should be on the lookout for this new development in their habits. Young Soule was mistaken; the "bear" was only a squirrel's drey high in the branches, looking something like a bear. Many settlers thought the howling of wolves was the cry of lions, which many believed roamed the New World [17]. Couples or packs of dogs were of great help in keeping these animals at bay. Governor Bradford wrote of the utility of his "mastiff bitch and spaniels," the latter so called because it was thought the breed had originated in Spain [5].

In fact, bears caused much less damage than wolves and wildcats. For the first century of occupation bears in New England were very sociable, haunted the settlers' houses, and did very little harm. On the other hand, wolves and wildcats devoured sheep and goats and even children. Premiums were paid for destruction of these animals, the heads being nailed to doors. In 1635 the price for a wolf was 5 shillings, or about 50 cents at today's rate, a large sum for that period—one could buy a house for £25 ($50)—and yet two years later the premium was doubled, so destructive had the creatures become. Wildcats, or "foxes," were paid for at 1 shilling per head and that also was doubled in 1637 [6].

One cannot help wondering if it was not a lingering feeling of comradeship with the settlers' bears that led to the establishment of the present children's favorite, the teddy bear—joined, of course, with the appeal of Theodore Roosevelt.

The dog naturally brought into the house numerous other creatures associated with it, such as fleas, lice, flies, and worms (which I will discuss in subsequent chapters), but the greatest danger to humans from the dog was rabies—a terrible disease, almost abolished early in this century by the combined use of Pasteur's vaccine and the quarantine regulations. The hue and cry after a mad dog, or frequently one only suspected of madness, would cause panic throughout the countryside and particularly among parents, as children were easily bitten and poisoned by even a small quantity of the virus in the saliva. In spite of this, dogs were always welcome and encouraged: They kept down rats, leaving the mice to the cats, tolerated the household cats and chased off strange ones, and were admirable companions to most of the human inhabitants of the house.

At the present moment Jules La Flèche has an Afghan hound bitch with a litter of three puppies, all much admired by the customers of the restaurant and sought after in the strange world of prize dogs.

By the time Susannah lay in bed with the first American-

born Barton, a number of animals had established themselves
in the house. Spiders were making webs beneath the thatch
and in corners of the loft, feeding on the numerous insects
there, though the webs were always dusted away in the two
rooms on the ground floor. The woodworms were gnawing
patiently on. The carpenter ant had recognized the structure
as a source of food. The mice were the second kind of mammal
to enter the house: They are very "plastic" animals, for they
can very readily adapt themselves to varying conditions and
then be so altered as even to pass as different species. Their
plasticity is the reason that the European mouse has become
established throughout the world, usually being carried by
ships, though no doubt aircraft now spread them around as
well. At least two species of native deer mice entered Bartons,
but as has already been mentioned, they were soon replaced
by the imports from Europe.

The ancestors of the house mouse lived on the open steppes
of Russia, where they consumed the seeds of plants, so it is not
surprising that they attached themselves to man when he
became a farmer growing cereals; we describe them as commensals—feeding at the same table as ourselves—and, asso-
ciating with man, they have now spread all over the world.

In any country area there are usually two communities of
these house mice, the house-dwellers and the field-dwellers.
Though they belong to the same species of animal, these two
races do not usually have much to do with each other. There
is some basis in fact for the stories of the town mouse and the
country mouse, since there exist these two populations, each a
stranger to the other's environment. However, some of the
house mice go out into the fields in summer, where they continue to breed and seek to get back to the shelter of their
commensal in the fall. The other community of mice (the
same species at present, be it remembered) live and breed
wholly out of doors, where they construct burrows and nests
in hedge bottoms, banks, tree roots, and so forth. It is the house
mouse that is really harming the farmer both in his home and
in his fields and yards, not because the direct damage the
mouse does is dangerous—in the house the quantity of food
eaten is not great, though in a stack it can be serious—but
because mice spoil more food than they consume and can

carry serious parasites and diseases of man and animals. Mice will be attacked by fleas, which in turn can carry and transmit the plague to man.

Another danger from mice, which persists to this day, is trichinosis, a most distressing malady caused by a roundworm which passes from host to host when certain raw or insufficiently cooked flesh is eaten. Mice are not eaten by man either raw or cooked, but pigs sometimes kill and eat mice, and dead mice and rats were frequently thrown to pigs—perhaps they still are at times. The pigs become infected and then infect man in their turn. Pork, ham, and bacon have to be very thoroughly cooked to destroy the encysted trichinosis worms in their flesh. The Jewish and Muslim prohibition against the eating of pork obviously springs from the danger these worms present.

The original habitat of the mouse was the open plains, and its numbers under natural conditions were controlled by such predators as weasels, stoats, hawks, owls, and cats. In the wild state, mice lived in burrows and thickets, where they were reasonably safe from attack, but when they came out in the open to feed they were exposed to their predators. By contrast, in the house the mice may be under cover the whole time, or only exposed to one predator—the cat—for very short periods, so it is not surprising that the animal has adopted a very advantageous commensalism. It is no wonder that man has had to reply with traps and poison as well as cats.

Sometimes plagues of mice, squirrels, and lemmings arise, due to some change—possibly quite a small one—in the biological balance of a neighborhood. Such plagues occur at times when there is a lot of wasteland, for here, under the right conditions, a big population can build up, usually due to the abundance of some particular seed plant. Waves of animals then depart from these lands and invade the fields and houses of men. Their numbers are very impressive and spectacular, but probably these plagues do not cause as much harm to the farmer as the steady annual depredations of an ordinary mouse population in ricks, stores, and houses. The plagues of mice disappear seemingly as quickly as they have arisen and their vanishing does not seem to be due to any particular disease, parasite, or predator, though naturally all can be found during a mouse or squirrel plague. For instance, owls are much drawn to any such area but even so can have but little effect on the vast numbers present during a plague. Many mice are found infected with tuberculosis, but this again does not seem to be the reason for the reduction in numbers, as the disease does not shorten their lives to any appreciable extent.

There is a protozoan parasite, *Toxoplasma*, which attacks the brains of those small mammals, and while such a disease could decimate a population it has not actually ever been found to do so.

The population builds up because of favorable circumstances, not the least of which is a good supply of food. The increase in the growth of cereals brought about by the settlers considerably raised the mouse population. The young mice are sexually mature at three months old; the females can breed over a long season and carry their young for a period of surprising variation—from twelve to twenty-one days—and it would seem that an abundant food supply leads to a shortening of the period of gestation. Very soon after giving birth to a litter they come into heat again, so that soon another litter is on the way, to consist of some five or six blind, naked, pink young creatures who are ready to leave their mothers at less than three weeks of age. Obviously all the individuals of a fast-breeding species such as the mouse cannot survive or the world would soon be knee-deep in the creatures; for a population to be stable a certain "survival rate" must prevail, and it can be shown mathematically what this rate is.* To maintain a stable population—for instance a "normal" one, say, fifty pairs per acre—if the number of litters per three months is two, and the number of mice per litter is three, the survival rate of mice must be 40 percent.

Let us suppose a change occurs and the number of litters per quarter rises to four and the number of mice per litter to the same number, which is not a very big change; in these new circumstances the survival rate must be reduced to just over

* The survival rate to maintain stability can be expressed by the formula:

$$S = \frac{1}{\left(1 + \frac{r}{2}\right)^n}$$

where r = number of mice per litter and n = the number of litters per 3 months.

1 percent in order to maintain population equilibrium. This is a big difference from a rate of 40 percent, and when the change first occurs the rate is not likely to drop much, if at all; as a consequence the population numbers rocket upward and a plague occurs. The competition between individuals then reduces the survival rate; if this falls below 1 percent the population falls again. If, as is most likely, the mice per litter and the number of litters per three months also fall, then the collapse of the population is as rapid as its increase. It is comparatively small changes in the rates of breeding and survival that make these big differences in numbers. The same thing can be seen in the rise and fall of locust populations, and is based on the fundamental mathematical fact that a geometrical progression rises or falls in its later terms by big numbers. The mouse's life span is a year or eighteen months, and the sudden decline in population is accelerated by there being a considerable number of middle-aged individuals in the plague community who have a short life expectation, as well as a lower rate of breeding.

exponential

Over the years of Bartons' existence, plagues of squirrels were occasionally seen. In New England in precolonial and colonial times squirrels fed largely on acorns, and in a year when the acorns failed—usually following one in which they were abundant—swarms of desperate squirrels overran the countryside searching for food.

Lemmings are famous for their self-destructive activities when the population becomes too large, and the late James Thurber underlined a behavioral point in an amusing way [58]. A professor, walking on the cliffs in Norway, found himself in conversation with a lemming. (Unfortunately our author does not say what language—Norwegian or English—was used.) After talking for a while, the professor said he must go, but before leaving wanted to ask the lemming one question: Why did they gather together in vast crowds and rush down to the sea to drown themselves? The lemming replied that it was a strange question; he too wanted to ask the professor a question, which was why the humans did not do so? The philosophical pessimist can speculate that perhaps we have now started that process.

The house mouse is able to tolerate a wide range of temperatures provided it has food and shelter, though in general small mammals are less able to resist low temperature than big ones. The onset of the cold drives mice back to the house, but observations in recent years have shown that mice in refrigerated meat stores have remained perfectly healthy under conditions of seventeen degrees of frost. Under natural conditions mice would not survive at this temperature, as they would not have an unlimited supply of food, but these lived mostly on liver, which gave them plenty of protein and vitamins. E. M. O. Laurie found that they ate about one-third more food than did mice under more normal conditions, as is only to be expected. Mice need protection against excessive heat and long exposure to sunlight.

They do not need very much water—but though they can survive for a long time without it, they will not increase in weight or generally thrive unless they have some water, or at least moist food. In hot weather in such a place as a wheat rick, lack of water may be a serious handicap to mice and they will leave the place to seek it, but in normal weather they can get what little water they need by burrowing to the surface thatch or the windward side of the stack, where there will be water after rain or heavy dew.

When food is short, or lacks some necessary element such as a vitamin, the young in the nests frequently have their heads bitten off by the mothers, which suggests that this is a mechanism for adapting the size of the population to the available food supply. At Bartons the wheat stacks supported a far higher mouse population than the stacks of barley and oats, for wheat is a more satisfying food than the latter cereals. A diet of one cereal only is not ideal for a mouse, but mice increase in a stack because they are sheltered from their enemies and from extremes of climate. Here the numbers rise up to a certain point of infestation but do not pass it. As the stack ages it often collapses, due to the activities of the mice.

When the mice first entered Bartons they took about three weeks to become settled, during which time they made a very thorough investigation of the place and kept their feeding to a minimum. They rely very much on their knowledge of the neighborhood and do not like it when furniture or storerooms are rearranged; in fact, one of the ways of keeping down the depredations of these rodents is continually to rearrange their environment. The danger period for the mouse is when he moves from cover to food; he likes to be well acquainted with the routes and to use them at night when predators will not see him so well. But the mouse is a plastic animal, and if under any particular conditions the daytime is the safe period, he will adapt himself to searching and feeding in the light. The kitchen of the night watchman tends to be explored during the day.

Mice do not have very clear sight, nor are their eyes particularly well adapted to nocturnal life. Though they do not see shapes well, they are very sensitive to the intensity of light. They are very quick to notice movement, and either this or a change in light intensity immediately produces their attentive reaction, when the animal becomes alert and ready to run away if danger threatens. They react more at night and obviously prefer to be active then rather than during the day.

Their hearing is acute, especially for high notes. The squeaks in which they indulge are a language of a sort, in that this noise conveys information about danger or food supplies and seems most useful to them. They are frightened of loud noises and instantly seek safety in flight when one occurs.

Their sense of taste and smell is well developed: Smell is of great assistance to them in finding food, and they remember tastes sufficiently well to avoid, for a time at least, any food which has disagreed with them. This means that if a mouse has been made ill by a small quantity of poison bait, it will avoid that bait for several weeks until it has forgotten the experience.

The awareness or perception of their own movement—the kinesthetic sense—is very important in mice; they rely on it for finding their way in the dark and to escape from danger. A mouse likes to explore its neighborhood very thoroughly, and along all the various routes it learns the necessary sequence of muscular movements. It is as though it said to itself: "From the hole in the skirting board, twenty-eight paces to the door, turn right under the door, thirteen paces forward around the woodpile, twelve paces half-left, twelve up to the chair, then jump to the table, and food (the remains of the humans' supper) will be found." The mouse, of course, has no such actual thought in its head but it acts as if it had; it goes through this sequence of remembered muscular movements to produce this effect. This is a reason why the mouse at any one time ranges only over a strictly limited area. If it reaches a new zone, it has to learn this new field before it can feel at home.

When a new object appears in their particular environment the mice do not avoid it to the same extent that rats do, but rather explore it carefully so that the experience can be added to their kinesthetic memory. This sense is not absent in man but is not normally used by him, because other entities—mostly sight and memory—perform the function better and more easily. However, when a man loses his sight he greatly develops his kinesthetic sense and uses it continually to find his way about, a fact effectively illustrated by Bulwer-Lytton when Nydia, the blind slave girl, leads Glaucus and Ione to safety through the murk of ash-inundated Pompeii: "Her blindness rendered the scene familiar to her alone [8]."

The house mouse can get through a very small gap; a quarter of an inch can be quite sufficient. Mice have a keen sense of touch which enables them to appreciate small, narrow places where they can take cover when danger threatens. It is of great advantage to a mouse to have a small range, as this reduces the chances of its being attacked. They only wander far and wide when food is short, and at other times will keep their area of activity as low as is consistent with getting an adequate supply of food.

Mice must continually wear down their teeth by gnawing; if they are unable to do this, the incisors will become too long and they can no longer feed.

During the first hundred years of the house's existence, the mouse population at Bartons was nearly always high because the corn ricks and the barns provided a constant reservoir of population from which the depredations of cats and traps could continually be made good. In 1655 the rick yard was equipped with rat- and mouse-proof platforms, supported by the stone mushrooms which prevented the animals getting into the rick, or getting back into it once they had left it, as usually a few mice are built into a corn rick when the sheaves are piled in.

This greatly reduced the population of the house, but to this day they have never been completely eliminated in spite of the activities of cats, traps, poison, and owls.

A few mice in the house did comparatively little harm, and later the servants rather welcomed them as pets, but as they became numerous Susannah could not stand the sight of their droppings and the depredations they made on the food. Soon the cat and its descendants had considerably reduced the nuisance, though the house was never entirely free from mice again until the summers between 1782 and 1787 when it was uninhabited by man. As there was no food being dropped or left unprotected, there was no point in the mice remaining in the place during the summer, but with the fall they avidly sought shelter there against the severe cold. But in the absence of humans it was not an easy life. In many islands abandoned by man the house mice have become extinct; they could not live without their commensal.

At one time bats were another kind of mammal found in the house. They are the only members of this order (*Mammalia*) that have adapted themselves for true flight. Their wings are just fleshless skin stretched over a framework formed by their arms, hands, fingers, legs, and toes. Compared to the human anatomy their forearms have been elongated, as have also the bones of the fingers, except the first one. The leg, too, has been modified and turned around so that the foot faces backwards. The feet are relatively small and appear as the two little hands by which the majority of bats hang down when they are at rest. The chest and upper arms are provided with powerful muscles that flap the wings, enabling the creatures to fly, in which activity they show great skill.

Bats are a striking example of adaptation to a special way of life, the main characteristics of which are flight, hibernation, an insect and arachnid diet, and a low birthrate. Their flight is truly remarkable. They show the utmost agility and can swirl, turn, hover, and skim the surface of water with the greatest of ease. It has puzzled naturalists for a long time. How was it that, flying in the dusk or even in the dark, they could catch insects on the wing, avoid predators and objects ahead (such as stretched wires) with such skill? And however could the expression "as blind as a bat" have arisen? Perhaps because their eyes are so small and bright light confuses them.

As early as the eighteenth century the Italian zoologist Spallanzi discovered that bats did not find their way around by sight, for bats with their eyes covered still showed their remarkable agility in flight. In point of fact they use a form of echo-sounding comparable to radar, but by no means the same thing. Radar uses electrical impulses which, reflected back, enable the sender to calculate the distance and direction of an object ahead. The bat uses ultrasonic sound impulses, mostly inaudible to the human ear. The electrical signals move with the speed of light, whereas the same signals of the bat naturally go at the speed of sound, nearly 250 times slower. Nevertheless the bats use their fantastic powers with great effect.

The bats' hearing is far more sensitive, and is extended over a much wider range, than is ours, as is the case with many other animals as well. We can hear from sixteen vibrations to about forty thousand per second when we are young; there are few people over forty who can hear a bat. The bats use frequencies of from thirty thousand to seventy thousand vibrations per second. They send out a series of pulses at rates of about ten per second when at rest and up to thirty per second in flight. These signals are reflected back from objects in the creature's path, are received in its capacious ears, and tell it a great deal about the nature of the space ahead. When in flight, the greater the bat's need of information, the faster will the batches of signals sent follow each other.

Humans, too, can use echoes, but not to the same extent as bats. If you shout across a gap to a rock face you may get an echo back, and the time interval between the shout and its return gives an indication of the distance. In fact, if the time is accurately measured with an instrument, it will give an accurate figure. For instance, if the interval is one second, the distance of the echoing object is just over a mile. With sound traveling at 760 miles per hour, a signal will have gone $760 \times 1 \div 360$ in 1 second, which equal 2.1 miles for the double journey. The echo can also supply you with some information about the nature of the echoing face ahead. If it is clear and undistorted, the face must be smooth; if it is ragged, the surface is broken. If it comes back quickly, it must be near, and so on. A blind person fond of country walking can gather a lot of information by listening to echoes, but the bat has developed these powers to the full.

From the ultrasonic echoes received in two ears (thus a stereoscopic effect) the bat can tell how far away a thing is, its size, something of its nature, and how it is moving, which enables the animal to make a sudden turn to capture or avoid it as circumstances require. Of course, if you shout at your rock face and then repeat the shout before the echo has come back, you will probably drown the noise of the echo with your second shout. Children are often disappointed with echoes for this reason; they cannot contain their excitement. Big Guy's masterly shout is stifled by Martin's following too soon afterward, which in turn is spoilt by baby Timothy's, and a family quarrel develops!

Echoes, of course, have their place in literature. The original Greek nymph Echo faded away for love of Narcissus, who much preferred himself. Echoes have been used with dramatic effect in plays, a scene from Webster's Jacobean *Duchess of Malfi* being one of the most effective. The echo sends back a far more sinister meaning than the original words sent out.

ACT V, Scene iii: *Milan, part of the fortifications. Enter* Antonio *and* Delio. *There is an* Eccho *from the Dutchesse (of Malfi's) grave.*

ANTONIO . . .	But all things have their end: Churches and Citties (which have diseases like to men) Must have like death that we have.
ECCHO	*Like death that we have.*
DELIO	Now the Eccho hath caught you.
ANTONIO	It groaned (me thought) and gave a very deadly accent?
ECCHO	*Deadly accent.*
ANTONIO	Eccho, I will not talke with thee; For thou art a dead Thing.
ECCHO	*Thou art a dead Thing.*
ANTONIO	My Dutchesse is asleepe now, And her little-ones, I hope sweetly: Oh Heaven Shall I never see her more?
ECCHO	*Never see her more.*

The same situation can arise with a bat. It can get incorrect information back or nothing at all if it lets the signals being sent drown out the much fainter ones coming in. Obviously they must not be allowed to confuse each other: The creature needs to get back the echo to its first signal before sending the second one, and also it must not deafen a sensitive ear waiting for a faint echo with a loud outgoing noise. If you shout at a very near rock face, you do not hear the echo because you have desensitized your ear with the shout. The bat has overcome this problem by having a muscular device that neutralizes the ear as the signal is being sent out and then immediately restores it to normal, ready to record the echo. It is a most ingenious and useful attribute but, even so, not unknown to man. If, while listening to a boring speaker, you yawn heavily—a thing all too easy to do—you put your ears out of action and will not hear for a blessed second or so!

At times bats travel in flights of considerable numbers, and it is strange that they do not confuse each other with their ultrasonic signals and echoes. That they do not, seems to be because each bat has a distinctive voice of its own, which it can recognize. Moreover, unlike radar (electrical)signals, the ultrasonic pulses die away quickly, as their effective range is about five yards. Bats can turn very quickly when in flight, enabling them to avoid danger (a cat, for instance) or seize food, such as an insect in flight or a spider on a twig ahead. Rarely do they make mistakes, but naturally errors can occur. For example, a bat may dive at a fisherman's artificial fly as he is making a cast, and sometimes they are caught in that way. Such a hooking is nearly always in the bat's wing, not in the mouth as one would expect, possibly indicating that the signals coming back informed the animal at the last moment that the object was not an insect with which it was familiar but something strange that had better be avoided, and the turn away was not quite fast enough to avoid the hook entirely. Barbed wire is another of our artifacts sometimes fatal to bats. The barbs are so much stronger than natural thorns and can impale a bat.

The ultrasonic pulses require considerable effort on the part of a bat, and its larynx is a strong, well-muscled organ. Trumpet players—in fact, pretty well all persons playing wind musical instruments—know that more effort is needed to get the high notes than the low ones; still more energy must be used to get the ultrasonic vibrations, which are inaudible to us. However, most bats have two audible voices as well. The fine ears of the young can hear the high-pitched squeak, and there is also a low-pitched buzz. The first voice is a kind of language and serves much the same purpose as the squeaks of mice, that is, it passes information around the colony as to sources of food, threats of danger, and so on. The buzz is a product of the ultrasonic vibrations being given out in short bursts. The buzz is not the ultrasonic signal itself but an additional sound, audible to us. When it is heard, it means that the bat is using its echo-sounding facility. On a bat's nose is a wrinkled organ known as the "nose-leaf," which is connected with its sonic-sensing abilities.

Bats have yet another strange attribute, as yet unexplained: an awareness of objects coming near them. It has nothing to do with echoes, because it may be seen when the animal is torpid or asleep and thus not sending out its ultrasonic pulses. It is a kind of feeling at a distance. A sleeping or hibernating bat will become aware of an object coming near it and draw itself up out of the way, even though it may be too torpid to fly. It appears to be a reaction to the approach of an enemy. The creature is attempting to make itself less conspicuous, or getting ready to drop off or spring away from its perch. This reaction is most noted when the animal is enveloped in its big wings. There is then a comparatively large area of sensitive skin exposed, which possibly senses any sudden, even slight, change of temperature, such as one caused by the approach of a warm cat or a cold stick.

Bats vary greatly in size according to the species in question. Two kinds were found at Bartons over its existence: the little brown bat, with a wing span of about 9½ inches, and the big brown bat with one of about 14½ inches, but neither of those measurements is a world record. For instance, the Indian flying fox has a wing span of nearly four feet and the English pipistrelle is tiny.

Bats have a rotary action to their jaws, rather like that of a human, which enables them to cut up the hard carapaces of insects. Bats seem to be very furry because they have two kinds of coat, the first long and silky, mostly standing out straight from the skin, and the second a downy undercoat. The animal thus looks bristly. Most bats are a dull brownish color and there is no color difference between the sexes. They have large ears, enabling them to use the sound location system described above. Their eyes are small and not particularly adapted to night or twilight flight. Echo-sounding largely replaces sight in the bat's world. Bats' powers of flight vary greatly between species. Some, such as the two species found at Bartons, have a vigorous, swift flight full of sudden turns, whereas other species flutter about near ground level. Bats tend to adopt a regular flight path at specified times, which naturally is when their particular insect food is available. They may parade up and down a woodland glade snapping up insects, or back and along the edge of a wood, or skim over the surface of water or through a farmyard. They like to break into flight from a height, but they can take off from the ground if the need arises by using arms and legs at the same time. Although they prefer to hang head downward from a perch, they approach the site head up and then turn around and hang down by their feet.

Bat matings take place in the fall and the sperm is stored in the female during hibernation. Mating may take place again in the spring when ovulation occurs and the egg is fertilized by the stored sperm. Apart from these periods, most bats roost in separate male and female groups and have separate summer and winter quarters, often many miles apart.

Bats have a low birthrate: The females are two years old before they breed and they only produce one offspring per birth per year. The gestation period is about six weeks. The young bat has milk teeth at birth and accompanies its mother in flight for some ten to fourteen days by gripping the false teats in the region of the groin. By the time the baby bat is fourteen days old it is too heavy for the mother to carry and is left in the roost. Sometimes the mother, on her return, suckles the first baby she finds and at others she seeks out her own particular offspring. By July the young will be on the wing and finding their own food, mostly insects caught in flight. They have to build up a considerable store of food, mostly as fat, in their bodies to keep them going during the long hibernation.

The food of bats is almost exclusively insects and spiders, though the famous Gilbert White (the eighteenth-century naturalist of Selbourne) accused them of feeding on his bacon hanging in the chimneys for smoking. It was far more likely that the bats were feeding on the bacon beetles and were thus helping him preserve his food from loss. Bats capture most of their food in flight, and if the insect is too big to eat at once, the useless parts (such as the wings and legs) are bitten off and discarded while the juicy bits are tucked into a special receptacle—the interfemoral pouch—formed by the tail being bent forward. Such pieces can then be consumed at leisure in the roost. Water can be picked up when flying over streams and ponds. If a bat makes an error and falls into water, it does not exactly swim, but by flapping its wings, it usually reaches the edge and escapes.

Insects, some of them, have not remained passive in the face of danger from bats. The push and pull of the evolutionary gene battle has given some Noctuid moths an ability to hear the bats' ultrasonic signals and take avoiding action by following a suitable darting, zigzag flight and foiling the monster chasing them.

Bats are popularly supposed to be very dirty creatures, but in reality that is by no means the case. As soon as a bat gets back to its roost and is hanging upside down, it starts a thorough cleaning operation, combing the fur with its feet and cleaning the feet with its incisor teeth. Of course they suffer from parasites. One is a strange wingless fly of the *Nycteribidae*, feeding on their blood. Somehow these flies have induced the bats to tolerate them. They are never removed and eaten but, as the bat is combing itself, just come out from the fur and quickly move to another spot. As L. Harrison Matthews pointed out, it is as if we were to tolerate several large crabs hidden in our clothing.

The life-span is about seven years, considerably longer than that of other mammals of similar weight, such as mice and rats. The main reason for their longevity is that they hibernate; the activity of their machine is thus spread over a longer period. As bats live almost exclusively on insects, which are scarce in winter, they have either to migrate or hibernate and they have chosen to do the latter. Or to some extent both, for

in America bats hibernate in winter quarters usually some
distance from their summer roosts.

The natural hibernation sites of bats are caves, though sometimes hollow trees may be used, particularly for summer roosts.
Such spots are not very numerous in nature, so that the arrival
of man, particularly those from Europe, was advantageous for
bats for two reasons. First, his activities encouraged insect
life, and second, he provided lofts, cellars, barns, church roofs
and spires, all splendid roosting places where the creatures
could be fairly undisturbed. Moreover, bats like damp and
often choose spots so humid that droplets of water form on
their fur.

They hibernate in considerable masses, hang downward
from a suitable perch, reduce their metabolism and become
torpid, thus enabling the food reserve (mostly a layer of fat
beneath the skin) to maintain them through the winter and
leave some for the spring sorties.

The hibernation is remarkable. The heart beat and respiration are so much reduced that the bats' oxygen consumption
is but one hundredth of the summer rate, when they are active
and hunting. In hibernation the creature has alternate spells
of breathing and ceasing to breathe. For instance, in hibernation a bat will breathe at thirty inhalations per minute for three
minutes, stop for from three to eight minutes, and then start
again. The summer inhalation rate, when the bat is active, is
two hundred per minute, with no pauses. In hibernation much
of the blood is put into the spleen, and the circulation of the
blood is thus much reduced while the food reserves are drawn
on only slowly.

So advantageous to the bat's general economy is that facility that it is sometimes used in summer when the creature
can enter a semi-torpid state and husband its food supplies.
Naturally this is usually during the daytime, when they are
inactive. During activity their appetites are large, and if they
were active all the time, they would need to eat their own
weight of food daily. In a summer colony not all the bats are
in the semi-torpid condition at the same time: Many of them,
usually more than half of the numbers present, stay in the
active state as a precaution against surprise from an enemy.
Though the sentinels can thus warn their torpid companions,

it must be remembered that it takes some time fully to awaken a completely torpid bat, from half an hour to an hour. Its temperature must rise from about 48°F to the normal of 98°F, and the respiration to the normal rate of two hundred mentioned above. The blood must be taken out of the spleen and circulated in the usual way by the heart. Though the bats alerted by the sentinels are not completely torpid, they nevertheless would take an appreciable few minutes to become fully normal, and the main function of the sentinels is less that of sentry than acting as part of a defense force. All rising at once, they can mob a cat, fox, or owl, for instance, and drive off the attacker.

Not only can some bats go into semihibernation in summer, they can also come out of it in winter for short periods if the air warms up. They may fly about their cave or even emerge into the open air if the evening is mild. Naturally they take any insects or spiders unwise enough to have emerged at that time, which food revitalizes them. They then take up their winter sleep again.

The ability to hibernate is an important aspect of the bat's food economy. The bat is a warm-blooded animal and has a large weight-to-surface-area ratio, meaning that the heat loss of a bat is big compared to that of a larger mammal, such as a man or cow, even though the bat is well insulated with fur. In addition, the bat catches its food while flying, an activity requiring a great deal of energy, all of which has to come from food. Moreover the food—flying insects mostly—is very specialized, and catching it on the wing requires much effort. Entering the torpid condition means a considerable economy in the use of food and food reserves in the body.

Some consideration now needs to be given to being the right size for the particular kind of life being led. Let us compare two mammals, bat and man. If one takes, say, the weight of 1,120 bats as equaling that of a 140-pound man, the former, when active, would be eating 140 pounds of food per day whereas the latter, using 3,400 calories plus 75 grams of protein, would take in only about 4 pounds. It is an advantage to be our size and not to have to fly by means of our own efforts to collect our food. Had we to do so, our muscles would be enormous and our daily food intake several times our own weight.

The push and pull of evolution has set certain average weights as being the best for certain animals. The smaller the ratio of weight to surface area, the fewer calories per kilogram will the animal require to keep it warm, but as size increases so must the size and cross-section of the bones increase to support the weight, which in turn means bigger muscles to work the limbs and then more food to drive the muscles. A compromise is reached between small weight with easily moved limbs and low fuel consumption, but big heat loss, on the one hand, and large size with but little heat loss per unit area, on the other.

A man needs forty to fifty calories per kilogram of body weight per day and the active bat wants about seven hundred calories per kilogram—a considerable difference. By introducing torpidity, the bat drops its calorie need to about fifty-eight, a figure approaching that of the human. Torpidity has the disadvantage of exposing the bats to attacks of enemies, but by choosing roofs of caves, lofts, church spires, and cellars, the bats have chosen sites where predators are rare.

High feeding during the late summer insect flush, followed by a fall temperature drop, is what induces bats to return to their winter quarters and enter hibernation. Bats are sensitive to special temperature levels; for instance, they will not emerge from the roost for their regular hunting flight if the temperature is below 40°F or if it is windy.

The low reproductive rate of bats has already been mentioned. The actual birthrate—one per year—and the approximately equal numbers of the two sexes born is comparable with that of man, but other, naturally different factors vary. Breeding starts at two years and the lifespan is about seven years on average, though twenty years is not unknown for some species. If the number in a species is not to decline, every female must be succeeded by one surviving female of breeding age, which is to say that the net reproductive rate must be unity. To get a rate of just over unity, each female bat must live to an age of over four and a half years to have the necessary three offspring. As bat populations tend to be stable, something like this must be happening.

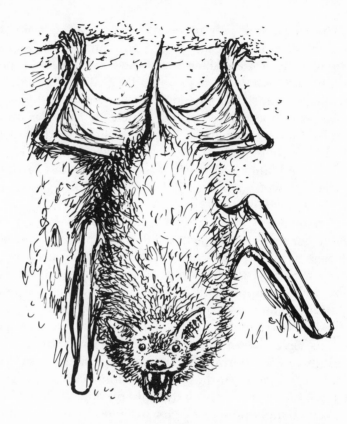

Big brown bat

Big brown bats flew around the house and farm from the early days of the settlement. They appeared to have an affinity for man and made roosts in barns and under eaves of roofs as well as in their natural habitats, such as hollow trees and over-hanging branches. They did not gain access to the house itself until it was vacant of man in 1783. The previous winter a storm had broken a pane of glass in the window of an attic, allowing the bats to establish their summer breeding roost there, but they had spent some time at the house before then. Some of them in the 1720s had used the porch as a night roost, leaving it at dawn to hunt and then return to their main daytime roosts in hollow trees and the barn. The droppings they left behind in the porch seemed very mysterious to the house-proud

Bashuah Barton, as there seemed to be no animal with which they could be associated. Forty years ago, she speculated, it would have been put down to witchcraft and she wondered if the old folk had not been right. However, the mystery was solved in 1729 by her seven-year-old daughter Tryphena's finding a fallen bat on the floor of the porch early one morning. She rescued the creature and kept it as a pet.

Try, as she was usually called, was very interested in animals and plants. From an early age she was thought to be a queer child and a bright one too. She could read and write well at seven and was learning the Indian language from friendly Indian women in the neighborhood and by puzzling out words in an Indian Bible.

When she rescued the young big brown bat from the floor of the porch, she put the injured creature into an empty room and gave it the name of Carolina, in honor of the new Crown Colony to the south which she had heard her parents discussing—they deplored the slavery there both from the moral point of view and for the competition slave agriculture could offer to theirs.

Tryphena kept the bat in the closed room for two weeks before her parents knew anything about it. She fed it on beetles, grubs, and scraps of meat and started to breed mealworms in a bowl of corn flour so as to have food for her pet. Soon she would call, 'Carolina," and throw a mealworm into the air which the bat would seize before it fell to the ground. The bat would sit on her shoulder and wait for food, and it usually responded to the call "Carolina" even from another room. One day Tryphena opened the parlor door, called her bat, and showed this trick to her parents and the "hired girl," old Grace Hinson, who at eighty-two years of age was still active. Grace commented that it was lucky the world was now enlightened. Goodness knows what would have happened to her if she had done that in those bad old days when she was accused of witchcraft. Bashuah was always a little nervous of her daughter's eccentricity and lamented the deaths of the two baby brothers who, had they lived, might have restrained her, but Jethro told her to let the child alone; she was doing no harm and her ability to talk to the Indians in their own tongue could be of great use.

Although the big brown bat likes man and can be tamed, he is unreliable. Tryphena had her fingers bitten on more than one occasion, but said nothing to her parents about it. Bat bites can be dangerous because of course the animal might be rabid, though infection is rare today.

When Tryphena was sixteen Carolina just disappeared. Perhaps a predator such as a cat got it, or it joined the fall migration to the south and, not having made the journey for some years, got lost and perished.* The tamed animal returned to the wild usually suffers hardship and early death.

The big brown bats have two kinds of summer roosts. They leave their main roost at dusk and hunt insects over a set path, flying at a height of twenty to thirty feet. After feeding they retire to a night roost in a different spot, from which they emerge at dawn, possibly to feed again but in any case to return to their main summer breeding colony. When they are in flight an audible chatter can be heard, with which they appear to be communicating with close-by neighbors, and of course they are putting out their supersonic emissions as well.

Two late human inventions, one nineteenth- and the other twentieth-century, were damaging to these bats. Big brown bats were frequently impaled on barbed wire; somehow they did not get the signal back in time to avoid it. DDT also proved very dangerous to them.† Sometimes mousetraps can catch bats, but such an event was rare.

As mentioned before, in 1783, when the house was empty, a window in the loft was blown in during a winter storm and gave access the following spring to some little brown bats. They formed a summer colony there, liked it, and used it in following seasons until there were hundreds of them in the house during the summer. They did not spend the winter there, but retreated north, strangely enough, to some very suitable caves in Vermont. Although they left a considerable deposit of dung in the loft, and an objectional smell, they also helped in

---

* There is an amusing misprint in the *Pictorial Guide to the Mammals of North America, III*: "According to the 6th century B.C. philosopher Aesop, avoidance of creditors was the bats' motivation for night flying, and there have been various other explanations." Many a human debtor has adopted night flight for the same reason!

† In point of fact, DDT was first made by Professor O. Zeidler in Germany in 1874, but its insecticidal properties were only uncovered by Müller in Switzerland in 1939, 65 years later [42].

LITTLE BROWN BAT

the preservation of the place by eating large numbers of wood-boring beetles that would have attacked the roof timbers.

The little brown bats came out of the house in the evening —late dusk, slightly later than the big brown bats—and started to forage over water and through woodlands. They kept at a height of about ten to fifteen feet, somewhat lower than the larger species, and they often repeated the same flight pattern. A curious feature was the frequent failure on their return to reenter the house at the first attempt; several tries were often needed before access was gained. Bats often defecate as they enter their roost and these telltale marks on wall or paintwork are a sure indication of the presence of bats within.

Their food was almost entirely insects, though they would not refuse a spider. The female bats gave birth in the early fall, after a gestation of from fifty to sixty days. There were no adult males in the colony until after the young were weaned. Only one single offspring per year was produced, but as the creatures lived a long time—around twenty years—the colony could grow quite quickly. After their Vermont hibernation the little brown bats came back to Bartons about April 1 to establish their breeding colony. They had a fair turn of speed, flying at from ten to twenty-two miles per hour. The females left the winter roost before the males and seemed to act as pathfinders.

They liked rather warmer summer quarters than did the big brown bat, and thus the Bartons' attics suited them.

Bats are very old creatures: Fossil remains found in the Eocene—40 million years ago—show they were fully developed by then, and the long, long force of evolution has placed this strange pattern of life on them. The North American bats are insectivorous, but overseas, particularly in the tropics, they feed on other foods: There are the notorious vampire bats of Central and South America who suck the blood of mammals (they weaken but rarely kill their hosts) and the flying foxes of Australia who eat fruit. There are even fish-eating bats. The American bats are highly specialized feeders and take advantage of one particular supply of food—insects. The numbers they destroy are enormous, and while many beneficial insects as well as pests must be eaten, there is no doubt that bats were friends of all who lived at Bartons because they kept down the attackers of the farm, the garden, and the house.

CHIPMUNK

Other mammals came into the house, some as pets, one as a pest—the rat—and one first as a pet and later as a pest.

As has been mentioned before, Tryphena took a great interest in the natural world, and the chipmunks delighted her. She would watch them running down the trees headfirst, then sitting on a tree stump stuffing nuts into their cheeks and quizzing the neighborhood. In 1732, when she was ten years old, she caught a young one emerging from its underground gallery and made a pet of it. Searching for a name—all her pets had to have names—she was delighted to find from her Indian friends that the word "chipmunk" was derived from their word *achitamon*, and so called her new pet "Achit," usually shortened to "Ach." The word, it appears, means "headfirst," the way the creatures come down trees.

The chipmunks lived in galleries excavated in the soil under tree roots and house foundations. The galleries branched to form cavities for the storage of winter food, each one being devoted to one product only, such as acorns, nuts, fruit, grain, or garden bulbs. Chipmunks were numerous around the house and its foundations, but did not (apart from Ach) come into it very much.

When Ach died, Tryphena tamed a gray squirrel, a male who was very attentive to her. Tree squirrels are now protected mammals and may not be shot except by the owner of land on which they are being a nuisance. Unless very numerous they seldom cause trouble, apart from eating through the insulation of telephone and other electrical cables. Flying squirrels were sometimes found in the neighborhood of Bartons; they do not really fly but use a spread membrane to extend their jumps from tree to tree. They feed mostly on meat, are only active at night, and can cause various "mysterious" bumps and rustlings.

Raccoons sometimes got into the house, particularly when it was empty of people, though they are partial to man's dwellings because they can feed on his waste. They are ingenious creatures and can use their "hands" to advantage. It has been said that there is no form of closure for a trash can that the animals cannot open.

A raccoon caused a considerable problem at Bartons fairly recently. In converting the house to a restaurant in 1978, a

SQUIRRELS

fireplace in one of the upstairs rooms was blocked up, but the chimney left open. This proved attractive to a female raccoon, who entered the chimney and made a nest in the shaft. The new owners tried to drive the creature out by tapping the walls, banging the fireplace blockage, and so on, which only frightened the raccoon and made it cling in terror to its nest.

RACCOON

A professional exterminator was called in and faced certain difficulties. Raccoons also are protected animals and the new restaurant manager could not bring himself to shoot such an appealing and attractive-looking animal. The professional was not allowed to do so by law. Raccoons are difficult to trap, but after much effort the exterminator did secure it, and without being bitten, too. He took it in a cage, well south of Plymouth in the direction of Taunton, and let it out in a piece of woodland there. Two days later it was back in the chimney at Bartons. Raccoons—or at any rate this particular one—have a strong homing instinct. It was again trapped and this time taken north of Boston toward Salem, and once more released. A return from there proved too difficult for the animal.

It is a debatable point whether capturing and transporting an animal to a new environment, rather than killing it, is any kindness to it. The creature suddenly finds itself in a strange place, where its fellows most probably have carved out their territories and so resent an intruder, and where it knows nothing of food sources and the presence of enemies. It is no wonder that animals so often try to get home under such circumstances.

As to rats, the first invaders were the black rats coming off the settlers' ships. There were none, or very few, indigenous American rats in New England. Later on, the Norwegian rat introduced and largely replaced the black rat. They were never resident in the house but were unwelcome visitors. Today at Bartons, with so much food about, constant vigilance has to be maintained to keep the premises free of them. Rats (and raccoons) love garbage.

6

~ç

SPIDERS

John Barton III's house was built on the edge of the forest and some cleared land, once Indian, then reverting to bush, from which state it would eventually have returned to its climax condition of forest had not the settlers intervened. Though the first animals to live in the house were the wood borers, since many were present in the very timbers used, the most numerous creatures on the site itself when the first foundations were laid were the spiders.

Spiders were particularly plentiful at the forest edge, and as the house went up during the year 1633 a considerable change took place in their relative numbers as was only natural. The main kinds of spiders originally on the plot—the hunting spiders, sheet-web builders, and those in low bush and grass habitats—moved away or died, and the house and the tree-loving web builders colonized the structure as it rose, offering them more and more splendid sites for webs, snares, and shelter, until finally the house spiders occupied the cellar, dark corners of the rooms, the attic, and thatch in large numbers.

Spiders are not insects; they belong to the family of jointed-limbed animals, or Arthropods, which also includes such beings as crustaceans, scorpions, and insects. Looking at spiders, one sees that they are rather different in appearance from insects: In the first place, their bodies are divided into two main portions (as against three for the insects) having the head and thorax united into one piece, and behind this an abdomen. Secondly, the spiders have eight legs against the insects' six.

They moreover do not have a complete metamorphosis as do most insects—who pass from egg to larva to cocoon, pupa, and adult—but hatch from the eggs as tiny spiders and grow larger by successive molts, forming a new skin beneath the old one, splitting the old skin off, expanding the new skin, and letting it harden. Spiders and insects are similar in that they have no internal skeleton but a comparatively hard external one, to which the muscles and other organs are attached. Like insects they get their oxygen by the absorption of air through tiny vents on the surface of their bodies. Spiders have either two, six, or eight eyes, and as these animals inhabit an enormous range of different sites, from the bright sunlit fields to the deepest sunless caves, their powers of vision vary enormously —as indeed do all their other powers, for their "plasticity," we might say adaptability, has enabled species to develop and specialize in colonizing differing areas, sites, or kinds of food. Some spiders will hunt their victims by day, others by night; some will build webs to catch a certain type of insect; some tiny insects will live in other spiders' webs, feeding on the crumbs which fall from the rich man's table. All this has been brought about by the power of natural selection and enables them to prey on the whole field of insect life.

Spiders have powerful jaws with which to seize their prey, and in most cases the last of the fangs is hollow with a minute hole at the tip, through which they inject the colorless, acid, liquid poison with which they paralyze and kill their victims. This has been secreted by the poison glands within the body. They also have a pair of palps, which serve somewhat as hands, being useful in feeding and other activities.

The best known characteristic of spiders is their power to spin the silk from which they build webs, but it is not a characteristic of all of them. Some live by hunting their food and some by spitting sticky gum at insects, thus pinning them down. The silk is produced from special organs at the rear of the abdomen; and each may have more than a hundred tiny openings (spinnerets) through which the silk is projected. The silk glands secrete a fluid that is squeezed out through the spinnerets in the organ, and the filaments harden on contact with the air. Its relative strength is enormous. The spider can move the organs, which project like tiny short fingers, so that if the tips are separated, a wide band of silk can be formed, or if kept close together, a strong compact thread results. Some spiders have a comb, called the calamistrum, on the hind leg which helps form the sheet silk, and also a special central silk-forming organ with very fine openings, so that sheet webs, which collect dust and fragments in our lofts and old buildings, are easily made. Two kinds of silk may be spun: the first with sticky beads on it on which insects may be caught, and the other plain, strong, inelastic threads.

In addition to making webs, the silk is also used for egg cases, for making tubes or tents in which to live, and as a means of locomotion. On a warm day with a gentle breeze and rising air currents, the spiders—particularly the young ones—climb to the top of twigs, grasses, or weeds, and there, standing on tiptoe, turn to face the wind; a spider will then start to let go a thread which the breeze will carry away. When the friction of the air on the line is equal to the weight of the spider and the line, the animal lets go of its support and floats away into the sky. By this means spiders are dispersed over both long and short distances and may even be carried out to sea, where they perish. The white threads floating away in the blue are a common summer sight: "In the year that L. Paulus and Claudius Marcellus were consuls," says Pliny, "it rained wool." It was 216 B.C., and the wool was undoubtedly a massive flight of spiders, most likely of the Linyphiid family, which frequently inhabits walled gardens.

These animals are extremely ingenious in the use of their threads. They will use them as safety lines, carrying a strand of silk about with them so that they can recover their position after a fall. They will cast them over a large insect struggling in a web to prevent its escape. On sheet webs they will arrange a series of trip lines in order to slow down an insect that is trying to get away, and they will also hold a web back with a line and suddenly let it go so as to entangle an insect more securely.

With eight legs, two palps, and two or three silk lines to manipulate, it is surprising that a spider can be so agile and not become caught in its own snares; they have a remarkable coordination of leg movement and can run across a web at great speed, avoiding sticky threads and trip lines in order to

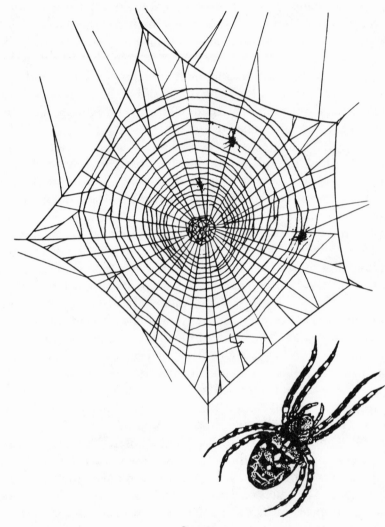

SPIDER

reach an insect and give the quieting, paralyzing first bite.

The orb webs, those magnificent works of art glistening in the morning dew, are composed of two types of silk, and each species of the orb-web builders makes a certain distinctive pattern. The spider squeezes a thread out and lets it float off in the wind; when it catches on an object she pulls the line in tight and then, spinning out a safety line as she goes—in case the attachment of her first line is not too secure—she crosses the first thread, tightens and strengthens it, and then proceeds to make the boundaries of the web. This is all done in hard, relatively inelastic thread, and similar filaments are used to make the radiating spokes of the center and a widely spaced spiral leading to the circumference of the structure. When all is ready, strong and taut, she puts on the evenly spaced series of spiral threads made of sticky silk which is the web proper, and cuts away the temporary spiral threads she first laid down. These last filaments are covered with a coating of gum that draws together to form sticky beads along the length, and these catch and entangle insects. The spider is indefatigable. When part of the web is destroyed by a violent encounter, the spinner patiently repairs it and builds a new web, except for the framework, every day.

In addition to the orb-weavers, there are funnel-weavers, cobweb-weavers or scaffold-builders, triangle-weavers, wolf spiders, and jumping spiders. Then funnel-weavers abound on grass, where the dew can be seen glistening from their webs in the early morning. They construct a sheet supported by the grass, with a funnel-shaped nest at one side in which the spider can hide or retreat if danger threatens from too large an insect visitor; the end of the funnel is left open so that the spider can escape right away if it is necessary to do so. The owner walks on the surface of this web instead of hanging from the bottom as most spiders do. The cobweb-weavers, or scaffold-web spiders, construct a loose tangle of threads, which may have a sheet halfway up the structure. There are usually some vertical threads with sticky drops at the lower end which pull the web down against its tension; when an insect wanders into one of these, it becomes stuck and the thread breaks off at ground level, the spring of the web jerks the visitor up, and probably entangles it in another sticky thread. The spider can then haul the insect up into the main part of the web, bind it with more lines, and dispatch it.

The triangle-weavers make a triangle of threads and sticky webbing attached to a twig at two corners and to a single thread at the third, which is then fastened loosely to a third stem. The spider holds the loose thread, pulls it taut, and when an insect blunders into the sticky webbing she lets the thread go so that the triangle contracts and further entangles the victim. She may do this several times before going into the web to feed, and when all is over another trap of the same nature will be constructed.

The jumping spiders have keen sight and attack by jumping on their victims. They are common on fences and sides of buildings and seem to be examining you very carefully if you stand and look at them. Their jump is amazingly accurate: for instance, they can catch a flying insect by jumping on it, spinning a line as they go, and return to their original position, say on a fence, by means of the lifeline spun out. This again shows an astounding coordination of eyes, legs, spinners, and palps.

Male and female spiders have to be present in considerable numbers on any site if the males are to meet the females, and the species to be continued. The male wanders more or less at random until he finds himself somewhere in the vicinity of a female, when his chemotactic sense will tell him she is near, either from the feel of the ground she has been on, a web she has spun, or a thread she has trailed. In some families the male recognizes the female by sight. Dr. S. Bristowe has shown that if in the case of a small linyphiid spider there were only one male and one female per acre, on an average the male would have to walk 82.5 miles before he found a female, and if both sexes were wandering, the distances they would have to travel would be doubled. Eighty-two miles is a quite impossible walk for a spider and even a mile is an enormous distance. In point of fact, spiders are very numerous per acre. Many *Theridon* were present in the field before Bartons was built; at times there were half a million of this genus per acre and another one and a half million of other kinds of spiders; consequently there was no difficulty in the males being able to meet females. In fact, at that time in New England the weight of spiders per acre, taking the average for the area, was considerably greater than the weight of humans per acre.

Spiders vary greatly in weight: A large adult *Theridon* can weigh several hundred milligrams, a newly hatched one a milligram or less. Very large numbers can occur in an area, a million per acre being quite a usual, even a low, figure. On the other hand, the number of humans per acre at the time of the arrival of the *Mayflower* was very low. Charles Brookes, in his

History of the Town of Medford, estimated that there were only twenty thousand Indians within fifty miles of Plymouth [6]. This enables an interesting calculation to be made. Reckoning the area as two thirds of a circle (two thirds because Plymouth is on a bay) with a radius of fifty miles, we get an area of 3.35 million acres. Taking the weight of an average Indian (man, woman, and child) at ninety pounds, which perhaps is on the high side, and ignoring the handful of settlers who were too few to make any significant difference to the calculation, we get 1.8 million pounds, giving us a weight per acre of humans of just over 8.5 ounces. No wonder the countryside seemed so empty to the settlers. They did not take much notice of the spiders, but spiders, on the other hand, were very numerous. A population of a million per acre and an average weight of four milligrams each, gives us four kilograms, or eight pounds thirteen ounces of spiders per acre. In terms of biomass, spiders were sixteen times more numerous than humans, yet these last "held domain over the whole earth." There is no doubt that we are ingenious creatures.

Today, taking the United States as a whole—mountains, cities, deserts, farms, lakes, and all—its human population now weighs some 10 million tons, giving a figure of about ten pounds per acre, just a little more than the weight of spiders per acre in the old days in New England. It is nice to think that, in terms of biomass, we have caught up with the spiders! But this is because the calculation has been made using the whole territory of the United States—the uninhabited or sparsely populated mountains and deserts included. Today the population of New England (1970 census) is 11.8 millions, weighing some 533,000 tons. The area of New England is 66,608 square miles or 42.6 million acres. This gives about twenty-five pounds of humans per acre.

The food of spiders consists almost exclusively of insects and they will only eat what they themselves have killed. However, hungry spiders will eat insects that would be rejected when more palatable food is abundant. Spiders adapt themselves to the kind of food that is available and their abundance naturally depends on the number of insects present in the neighborhood.

Spiders are able to judge the size of prey caught in a web

by the vibrations set up by the struggling insect. They will jerk a radial line both in order to entangle the insect more securely and also to estimate its kind and size. If it is too large or thought to be dangerous, the spider will approach with great care, leave it alone, or even cut it out of the web, but if it is something good the animal runs down, killing it at once if small, or entangling it with more silk if large, until it is able to approach safely, bite, and inject enough poison to paralyze its catch.

Some insects have managed to make themselves so distasteful to spiders that they are left alone even when caught in a web. Spiders frequently reject monarchs, wasps, *Sciara* flies, and aphids, sometimes after feeling them with their legs or palps—when the chemotactic sense tells them they are unpleasant—and sometimes after actually taking a bite at the insect, when the spider retires to the edge of the web to reject the distasteful morsel. It has every appearance of reflecting, "These monarchs make me sick," literally so. One bite does the butterfly no harm because it lies still, does not struggle, and thus avoids exciting the spider to more activity. In a short while a web-builder will remove the offending but quiet insect from its web, and no particular harm will come to it, whereas an insect that continues to struggle will be entangled in more and more silk by the spider and eventually will be killed, even though the animal is distasteful and not eaten.

Strangely enough, not all wolf spiders, or hunting spiders, have good sight; some find their food by wandering around and feeling for insects with their long chemotactic front legs, which enable them rapidly to estimate the nature, size, and position of the food and then attack.

Insects have been profoundly affected in their development by spiders' voracity for them, since any mutation that gives an insect prey an advantage over a spider, such as an unpleasant taste or the ability to excrete a disagreeable fluid in an emergency, is most likely to persist in subsequent generations. It is frequently found that certain insects (and similar animals) that are readily eaten by birds and such small mammals as, for instance, hedgehogs are avoided by spiders: Examples are lacewing flies, sow bugs, many aphids, and millipedes. It seems that natural selection has acted to protect them against their worst and most constant enemy, the spider. But the spiders must not be too successful—if they destroy all the insects in a neighborhood, then they, too, face future starvation.

Some insects escape spiders because they are very heavily armored. Certain sow bugs—though these are crustaceans, related to lobsters and crabs—can roll into a ball and defy any spider. They are protected by plates of chitin as well as by a disagreeable taste. Finally, other insects have an oily or waxy skin which does not adhere well to the sticky threads of the spider's web and allows the owners to escape easily if caught; examples may be seen in many of the Ichneumon flies, which frequently escape from webs.

Spiders destroy enormous numbers of insects, far more than birds do. At Bartons they certainly slowed down the increase in numbers of the woodworm in the loft, caught a lot of flies, and generally reduced the insect population.

Susannah Barton's house was dark and she was a very busy woman, so that not all the spiders' webs were dusted away. Her daughter-in-law was a bit more active against spiders, but it was Abigail who was their real enemy, dusting their webs away whenever they appeared and throwing the owners out of the house, not killing them. She had a certain amount of superstitious reverence for spiders, even fear of them. After all, one heard of the terrible black widow in the South whose bite could kill you. The black widow, or hourglass (from the mark shaped like an hourglass on its abdomen) spider's reputation is somewhat worse than its bite, so to speak. In the old days it often frequented privies for the insects found there, and when disturbed would bite a human in a tender part, causing intense and agonizing contractions of the abdominal muscles, salivation, then drying, and a black depression, but the victim would recover after several painful days.

The irrational fear of spiders is long-lived. The very word itself is derived from the Saxon and means "poison head." Dr. Bristowe, the British spider expert, used to spread alarm and consternation at times, when on public transit, by picking a spider off a neighbor's coat or basket, identifying it ("Ah yes, a nice little *Pholcus*") and eating it.

That spiders were thought to have powerful properties may be seen by the many references to their use in old medical books. For instance, a "plaister of spiders" is described in a 1671 *Compendium of Physic* [55]. The "plaister" was a paste of turpentine and spiders, and backed with gold or silver foil and "applied to the pulses of both wrists an hour before the fit of a Fever or Ague" occurred, "it effected a cure."

House cleaning makes humans an enemy of spiders, but just as man preys on man, so do some spiders attack their own kind. Mimetids feed almost exclusively on spiders, and these were sometimes found under the roof. A member of this family will creep gently into the web of an orb-weaver, so as not to be noticed; it will then cut away a few threads to leave space for its special method of hunting. The predatory spider hangs down, draws in its legs, and tugs on the lines, apparently giving a signal which the owner associates with the presence of a desirable meal in the web. Down comes the unsuspecting creature; the predator shoots out its long, spiny front legs and traps its host, burying its jaws in a leg or in the body and giving a paralyzing or fatal bite, for these predatory spiders possess a powerful and quick-acting poison.

At the end of the mating season the female spiders eat the males, as is well known, though it does not happen in every species. This is a further example of the economy of the spider system. The male spider represents a store of food, particularly of hard-won protein, which would be lost to the race when the males die, as they would in any case at the end of the season. The father literally sacrifices his substance to help secure the future of his offspring. In general, males do not live long or eat very much after they have reached maturity. Polygamy is practiced and a male will generally mate again if he succeeds in escaping from his first adventure. The pattern varies greatly according to the kind of spider. There are some species where a male and female live peaceably together in the same web, though there is no particular constancy among them.

The destruction of the male by the female is an example of how, biologically speaking, the female is the more important sex—a fact recognized by humans too. When considering the rise and fall of populations, and when the ship is sinking does not the captain call, "Women and children first"? Is this chivalry, or the atavistic recognition of the fact that if the race is to survive, then the women are the more important part of it.

Among the vertebrates the most destructive animals to spiders are the toads, who will feed on large quantities of them; frogs will also eat spiders but not to the same extent as toads. Birds do not consume as many as is sometimes thought, though starlings and tits perhaps eat about five hundred spiders a year each, whereas a toad will eat a thousand. The average frog accounts for about three hundred spiders a year, less than an insectivorous bird.

Mammals destroy spiders by crushing them in the meadows, and cattle, sheep, and horses consume them as they graze. Shrews and bats are fond of spiders, and man, up to about the time of the Revolution, used spiders in medicine. Strangely enough, spiders still have a use in medicine. Peter N. Witt and two colleagues found (1968) that web-makers could be used as test animals in the assessment of drug activity. The amount of web derangement induced by a known dose of a drug given to a spider was an indication of that substance's biological activity [64].

Insects form the main food of spiders but, as a class, are revenged on them by parasitizing their attackers. The Pimpline insects of the Ichneumon family lay eggs both in adults and in their egg sacs. The Pimpline settles on a spider and paralyzes it with a sting—a thing the spider itself often does to insects by means of a bite—then lays eggs on the forepart of the abdomen where the spider will not be able to remove it when the creature regains consciousness, in perhaps a quarter of an hour. The egg soon hatches and the young larva sucks the juices of its host; it avoids feeding on any vital part, and in fact the spider seems to live a normal life. It spins its web, catches its food, mates and lays eggs, but all the time the Pimplinid larva is there, always situated so that the spider cannot remove the "monkey on its back," so to speak. A moment comes when the larva is sufficiently grown and is ready for pupation. First it kills its host, presumably by biting a vital spot; it must do this before moving away from the spider or it would in its turn be killed, even though the spider by this time is feeling the effects of the attack, becoming slow, aimless, and making a bad web. The spider dead, the larva emerges from the body, finishes eating its erstwhile steed, and crawls away along a thread to pupate. It spins a little cigar-shaped brown cocoon; these may sometimes be seen on spiders' webs. From this it emerges as an Ichneumon fly after about a week and sets off to look for a spider and start the cycle again.

Other kinds of insects of the same family attack the egg cases of spiders, as do also earwigs, some beetles, anthocorid bugs, and a number of other species which are not usually numerous.

Many kinds of spiders came and went in the house. The principal species were those liking damp dark places, such as the cellars. Among the spiders found were the daddy longlegs, the house spider, a funnel spider, and various hunting and jumping spiders.

The daddy longlegs, obviously, has just that. Like all spiders it has eight legs, the longest two inches long and the shortest about an inch. In an angle of a wall or ceiling it builds a loosely woven snare, consisting of a tangle of threads crisscrossing in all directions. The creature has eight eyes and may well want them in order to find its way around its complex web! When anything drifts into the snare, the owner violently shakes the structure so as further to entangle the potential meal. So violent is the motion that both web and spider seem to disappear. After a while the motion becomes less because the spider is exhausted; by then the prey is well wrapped up, it is killed and the juices sucked out, the remains being discarded from the web.

The female daddy longlegs makes her egg case, or cocoon, of a very light texture, about June, and takes it around with her. A curious feature is that she continues to carry it for a while after the eggs have hatched, thus showing a degree of postnatal maternal care rare in the world of arthropods. The daddy longlegs was also found in the Bartons roof space, and Ed Hopkins, during his "study year" there, watched them, remarking in his notes on the strangeness of seeing the young spiders scurrying about the empty cocoon and feeding on insects caught in their mother's cobwebs, somehow securing themselves in spite of the violent shaking.

The short-bodied long-leg spider was also found at Bartons.

It is another species and not just a youngster of the daddy longlegs, but Ed was not at all sure about that. They were not very numerous in the attic; the cellar suited them better—it was dark and damp.

The American house spider was found all over the place and various hunting and jumping spiders could be seen from time to time.

The numbers of spiders at Bartons varied greatly during its history, as did the number of all other animals in the place. Spider numbers over the years are shown graphically in Figure III, page 132. It is impossible to be exact about spider numbers, so in the table the population is put at "Slight, Medium, and Heavy."

The house was built on the forest edge, disturbing in the process the spiders on about a fortieth of an acre. Some 250,000 spiders on that area were destroyed by the felling of trees, digging of foundations, and trampling of land. The ancients would sometimes sacrifice an animal, even a child, beneath the foundations of a house in order to ensure good fortune, little realizing that if the sacrifice of an animal were necessary, they already had a holocaust of spiders on their hands.

The cottage nucleus of Bartons of 1633 was small, dark, and damp, and there were many spiders in the cellar and attic and quite a few in dark corners of the bedroom and kitchen.

The spiders in the bush and woods found John Barton's new house a valuable refuge. It attracted insects, so spiders throve and their numbers increased. The hurricane of 1635 checked the increase, as the roof was blown off. The thatch, being new and not very thick, had tended to keep the attic space damp, which suited the spiders. The new roof of shingles led to a small reduction in their numbers, though the original cellar was still damp. The provision of bigger glass windows in 1650 reduced the spider population a little, as it enabled Susannah Barton better to see the webs and clean them away. However, in 1679 the addition of the east wing, with cellar beneath and a porch on the south side, pushed up the numbers again, particularly around the indoor privy, which attracted a lot of flies, good spider food. The creepers and honeysuckle growing over the porch, and the ivy—a special import from

Fig. III. Population of spiders.

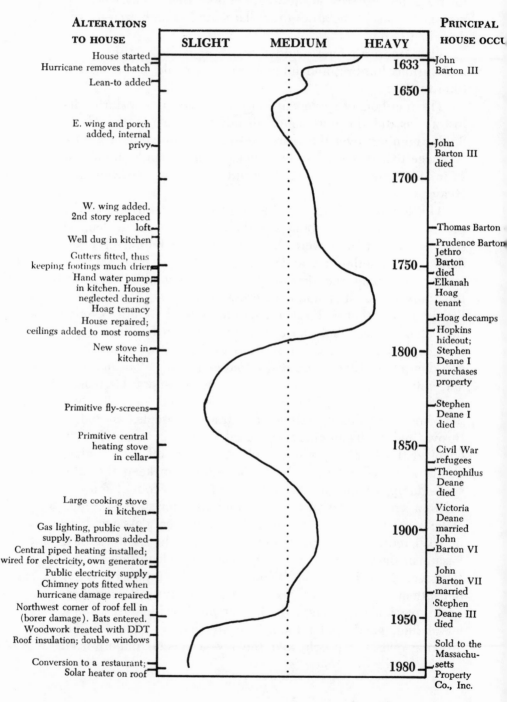

England, growing with vigor on the east wall—also provided cover for the spiders. For almost a century the arachnid population remained pretty constant.

During the Hoag tenancy (1760–1787) the house was much neglected and the spiders increased in numbers.

They had reached their peak by the time Stephen Deane discovered the refugee from Shays's Rebellion. Mr. Deane's alterations and redecoration decimated the spider population as the whole house was cleaned and altered. But the provision of ceilings to most rooms, with cat doors giving access to the floor joists so that the cats could pursue the mice, meant that the spiders had a protected environment and a supply of wood beetles as part of their diet.

The bats in their period of occupancy of the attics also fed on spiders.

After 1800 spiders were rarely seen in the house, for the cellars began to be infested with toads, inveterate enemies of the spider. Moreover, fly-screens from around 1856 meant fewer insects generally in the house. Water tanks in the roof spaces, on the other hand, increased the humidity and favored the spiders to a slight extent.

The vacuum cleaners at work from 1923 onward again reduced arthropods generally, but the real menace to this group was the DDT treatment of 1952. Spiders are not now at all common in the house; the two that best stand up to the dry conditions are the long-bodied cellar spider, already mentioned, and the funnel-weaving *Tegenaria*. A night hunting *Oonops* can be found, as well as another tiny pink *Oonops* stealing around the webs of the larger spiders, consuming small insects and mites considered too small, or too distasteful, by the web builders, but *Oonops* numbers are low and decreasing. The large inhabitants breed but little and the population tends to be maintained by colonization from outside: Floating on their gossamer balloons, these creatures land on the roof and creep upward under the shingles and into the roof space, but the loft, now warm and dry, is no longer the favorable environment it was at one time, so that the aeronauts are not particularly successful in establishing new colonies.

During the two periods when the spider colony was at its height—1635 to 1690 and 1762 to 1786—there were a large number of other species represented. Among them may be mentioned the fierce *Ciniflo*, or *Ciniflo ferox*. This is a large creature with a body about 13 mm long, having a dark carapace and a dusky gray, almost black, abdomen; it is a dark, sinister animal with pearly-white staring eyes and is responsible for many people's being afraid of spiders. They are cribellates and surround the main threads of their webs with sheet silk combed out by the calamistrum on the hind legs, which gives a bluish tinge to the fresh web.

The mouse-gray spider was common during these times as well. It is a fairly large creature, mainly active at night, that builds a silken retreat for itself and its eggs but does not construct a web. The carapace is reddish-brown and the abdomen mouse-gray, thickly covered with fine hair so that it resembles a mouse in this respect. The adults are found mostly during the summer months.

During this period the enemies of spiders also abounded, and among these were the Mimetids, which were mentioned before as feeding on their own kind. They were seldom seen in the house, but they attacked spiders in the fields around it and in the garden and thus kept down the number of migrants. In the damp cellar at Bartons, toads kept down the spider numbers, until the boiler for the central heating was installed, the floor concreted, and the life there considerably altered. The toads which were found were removed and there was no inducement for them to return.

7

BIRDS

WHEN THE BARTONS nucleus was first put up (1634) the bird life in the area was very different from that of today. In the first place, two species of big birds, then found in large numbers, are now extinct—the heath hen and the passenger pigeon. Secondly, the habitat at that time was forest with small agricultural fields and pastures. It had a very low human population and, moreover, until the settlers started multiplying, a diminishing one. There were also wild turkeys, but the heath hens were more numerous. All that has now gone, there is no indigenous forest of any size left, and new kinds of birds have moved in.

As the settlers throve and advanced their hold on the country, so did their demand for wood both for building and for fuel, as logs and charcoal for making lime for mortar and then for smelting iron and other metals. The woodland birds gave place to those from the forest edge, and they in turn were replaced by the house-using kinds and the birds of farms and towns.

Birds as a race have always been able to adapt themselves quickly to new circumstances, because though some kinds disappear, or become extinct, others take their place. The very existence of birds on this planet is due to their successful adaptation through a long period of evolution. After the amphibians crept out of the sea and conquered the land, during the Devonian Age (about 300 million years ago), the reptiles arose, and as they scrambled among the trees, the centuries rolling by, the ability to extend a leap by means of a gliding motion gave such animals an advantage over their competitors. Two such forms of gliding mechanism developed—one in which all four limbs formed the basis of wings with skin stretched between them (in rather the same way as in a bat's wing today), and the other where the forelimbs only were used. In this latter case, the reptilian scales of the limbs began to change and become feathers. Even though this was during the warm Jurassic period (90 million years ago), it is thought that the original advantage of the change from scales to primitive feathers was the greater warmth of the latter, which would be particularly advantageous in the polar regions.

When the colder Cretaceous period followed the Jurassic, the advantage of feathers was yet more pronounced, though the flying reptiles were still existing and in a wide range of sizes from a creature no bigger than a sparrow to the enormous pteranodon with a twenty-five-foot wingspan. This animal, twice the size of an albatross, lived a life similar to that of the modern bird; their fossils are found in deep chalk which must have been deposited far from land, so we know they ranged far out to sea, fed on fish, rested on the water, and only returned to land to breed. The enormous creature, slowly flapping its wings, gliding and soaring over the sea, must have been a strange sight in that distant age. The wings stretched between the immense forearms to the legs and were quite bare of covering; the relatively tiny body was just an appendage to the wings. These and similar reptiles could not compete with the other line—the primitive birds in command of the new realm, the air—even though they evolved many of the advantageous structures of birds. They had hard beaks and no teeth, a large section of the brain devoted to securing balance and control in the air, and strong, hollow bones containing air instead of marrow, which made them much lighter, but they did *not* have feathers, that very efficient covering which retains warmth.

As the Cretaceous age became colder still and gave way to the Eocene, the flying reptiles disappeared and the true birds triumphed. They had developed feathers, which not only kept them warm but gave them great powers of control in the air. A bird is usually a small animal, which again means that it has a relatively large surface area compared to its weight.

A young unfledged bird must eat its own weight of food daily in order to maintain life and grow, most of this food being used to maintain its temperature, so that the advantage to a bird of the warmth-retaining feather covering is immense. The feathers trap little pockets of air, which, if it cannot move, is a most effective insulator; the reason a bird fluffs up its feathers and looks bigger in cold weather is that it is trying to make as many of these pockets of dead air around it as possible.

A typical feather consists of three parts: the quill, the rachis, and the vexillum, containing the barbs and the barbules. The quill, or calamus, is the part inserted into the skin; it is hollow and the lower part is filled with spongy matter. The hollow part of the quills, mainly from geese, after being hardened in an oven formed the quill pens of the Bartons and their successors for a long time. The rachis forms the shaft of the feather and is simply the continuation of the quill; it is grooved on one side, which adds to its strength, and is filled with a soft pithy substance. To each side of the rachis spreads the web which makes up the vexillum, or vane, of the feather. This consists of barbs which are joined together by small hook-like barbules at the top of the feather but not at its base. The structure is a masterpiece of evolutionary development, as feathers are both immensely strong and very light. There are naturally a number of different kinds according to the function they have to perform for the animal.

Quill feathers are found in the tail and wings; those attached to the hand bones are the primaries, and those arising from the forearm, which are smaller, are the secondaries. A small thumb in the bones of the wing also carries feathers, which structure is known as the "bastard wing" and in effect acts as an airfoil by playing a part in the control of flight. The tail usually carries from ten to twelve strong quill feathers known as rectrices, but up to twenty-four may be found in some birds; the bases of these feathers are covered by more short ones known as tail coverts. The body is covered by the down feathers and over these are the body feathers, or plumules, where the barbs are quite free, having no hooks, or barbules.

The skeleton of a bird is very light and compact; like those of the early flying reptiles, the bones are "pneumatic," having hollow air-filled spaces in them. The sternum, or breastbone, in flying birds is very large, serving for the attachment of the big muscles which move the wings and which form the white breast meat in our domestic fowl. The bird's bill now no longer bears teeth; it contains a hard, horny tongue, and the food is conducted first to the crop, then to the gizzard, where it is ground up by the action of the strong muscles and the presence of grit and small stones which the bird continually picks up for this purpose. From here, the ground-up food passes to the true stomach, gut, and anal vent.

The respiratory organs include not only the lungs but also the air spaces in the bones, and the extensive air system in the bird's body allows a quick intake of oxygen into the blood when the animal is in active flight and using up energy very rapidly. A bird has a four-ventricle heart and a blood circulation similar to that of a mammal.

Birds have only one functional ovary, which is surprising, as egg laying can be most active. The yolk is first formed; then, moving down the egg-tube, it is covered with the albuminous white and toward the end of the passage receives its hard shell, consisting mostly of carbonate of lime; from here the egg passes to the cloaca, and then out of the vent. The young have a hard knob on the upper half of the beak which enables them to break their way out of the egg. Some birds, such as the domestic fowl, have precocious young that can feed as soon as they hatch, and others have nestlings that must be fed for some time by their parents.

Birds live in nearly all climates, and in any one spot may be residents, migrants, or gypsy migrants (those that move from one district to another in search of food, but have no fixed migration pattern).

Bird life has many strange sides to it; at times they seem to have mysterious powers of doing things for which man would require complicated apparatus, and on other occasions they seem unable to solve the simplest problem. The difficulty in understanding the behavior of birds is that we are human and we try to do so if not in anthropomorphic terms, at least in anthropocentric ones. Man is the most highly developed and thoughtful of animals and we must be on our guard against seeing human behavior in animals, for in fact we should look at it the other way around. What we take to be human behavior in animals may only be animal behavior in ourselves.

Not the least of these strange powers is that of migration over vast distances and the return to the same nest again the following year. Why does the swallow go in the first place, and how does it find its way out and back in the second?

Many of the seemingly inexplicable actions of birds may really be due to their quicker reactions to a stimulus and to the fact that, without postulating any mysterious extra sixth sense, birds do have some of the existing senses more acutely developed than man—their hearing is over a bigger range, particularly at the lower frequencies, for they can hear distant gunfire inaudible to us, and their sight is more acute, particularly for distant movement, as is that of many other animals.

Though "lower animals," birds have two characteristics of higher ones: a freedom to move to new conditions and, usually, an ability to live under those conditions, for when one considers the range of climates and surfaces, from the tropics to the pole, from the dry desert to the vast ocean, there are very few zones which do not have some bird life. It is the struggle for existence that has forced birds into all possible climates and shaped their seemingly strange ways. These ways all have a survival value and enable the creature either to get its food or rear its young under advantageous conditions. Even so, it is in birds that we see the first appearance of play—not that this may not in reality have a survival value. Birds definitely play, chasing each other about in the air, diving and soaring and playing a game similar to tag with a favorite perch, such as a flagpole or roof. It seems they are so full of vitality that at times their surplus energy boils over into these games, and while these and other actions appear to have no obvious biological significance, they may in fact be a means of keeping the necessary muscles and nerves up to the mark.

A bird's reaction to a stimulus may be seen to be a mixture of the automatic and the emotional; there is likely, in the final analysis, to be far more of a straight response to stimuli than the thinking out of a best course of action, because birds do not think in the way that we do. They feel and have emotions, but no ratiocination. For instance, a flock of starlings flying north may all suddenly turn and fly west. Why do they all turn at once? Is there some mysterious power of thought transference, or some signal given by the captain? The explanation may well be a combination of two things: a far keener sense of time intervals than ours, and a simple follow-my-leader reaction. A man's natural speed over the ground is some three to ten miles per hour (though a champion sprinter can do a hundred yards at twenty miles per hour), and his sense of time intervals corresponds with this pace—perhaps that is one of the reasons that he is so dangerous in a car. A bird may well travel at thirty or fifty miles per hour in the air, and with a thirty-miles-per-hour following wind it can have a ground speed of eighty miles per hour; consequently its appreciation of time intervals must be so much the more critical if it is to maintain control, avoid collisions, land on its perch accurately, and so forth. A bird possibly sees in a hundredth of a second something taking a man a tenth of a second or longer. Moreover, it is not burdened with a developed brain and consequently does not have to think out what it will do; it responds almost automatically and at once (perhaps birds, given suitable controls, would make better car drivers than men). Finally, since the bird is smaller than man, the actual distances the signals sent by the brain along the nerves have to travel are that much shorter in the animal; consequently the time interval between sending the signal and resulting action is that much shorter as well. This means that the apparently instantaneous turning of the whole flock of starlings may well be only apparent and that really they are following one after the other but at intervals of time too small for us to appreciate. Such movements are not always completely unanimous; sometimes a flock will split as it turns, a minority breaking off in one direction, but the gregarious instinct is so strong that this splinter group will soon wheel around and rejoin the main party.

Birds live in the present, and while they are keen and lively they have no knowledge or thought of either the past or the future. They will build a nest as a preparation for the future family, but that is an instinctive reaction to certain stimuli, not a thought-out process. It is man's ability to think out a course of action for the future that enables civilization to progress; at the same time, man has lost instincts and consequently the quick automatic responses to outside factors that so often are advantageous to animals.

Migration, the formation of territory, song, flocking or solitary life, commensalism with man, all have a survival value. By migration, birds can exploit a much larger territory and a particular food, and consequently support a bigger population of their species than they could without. Apart from considerations of winter climate, such insect-eaters as the swallows, swifts, and purple martins would not find their food here in winter, so that they must either migrate, change their food, or live only in the tropics, where a constant supply of insects could be found.

We may well say, "Why not then live only in the tropics? It must be very pleasant for a bird." The answer is that the tropics are already full of birds who have become especially adapted to tropical life, apart from the question of whether the tropics are agreeable to birds or not. Bird populations extended their zones by, some of them, moving from the tropics to temperate and arctic climates, where the competition was less fierce, and the migration pattern fixed into hirundines (swifts are not hirundines, though they have a superficial resemblance to them) has enabled them to exploit a special food in the two temperate zones. The struggle for survival has forced on them this pattern of migration over half the world as the best answer to the problem of continuing their existence.

When the food begins to fail, then they must go, and the stimulus which drives them to migrate is the shortening day length. They have taken advantage of a particular supply of food, have exploited it to the full, and now they must do so again in the corresponding antipodean conditions across the equator.

Any particular area can support only a certain number of animals, and they are mostly all competing one with another for it. Birds will get their living in this area and there will be competition both between species and within the species for the food and nesting sites. In order that the species survive, a mechanism must be brought into play to ensure that the area does not have to support too many birds, because if there are many more than the zone can feed, the result will be that all the nestlings are inadequately fed, do not reach maturity, or grow up as weaklings, and the species will be prejudiced, if not extinguished. The device of territory overcomes this: In the spring the males of many birds establish a zone for themselves, seek a mate, and drive out all other birds from their special area.

The purpose of song is to advertise the possession of territory and to warn other birds to keep away. After the male has secured a female, both the birds defend their territory from intrusion by others. Of course the stronger birds secure the best territories and sometimes a strong bird may drive a weak bird out and adopt his territory, or the strong one may carve a territory of his own out of two or three neighboring areas, but generally, once a male has established his territory, he is able to keep it; still more are a mated pair likely to maintain their own private feeding ground, as usually they have to expel only solitary intruders. If there is a surplus of birds some will not get territories; they will tend to be the weaker and less enterprising creatures. Neither will they get mates nor, of course, breed. This device of territory thus prevents overcrowding, and ensures that the area available is used to the best advantage and that the nestlings of all those birds which do manage to secure a territory will have a good chance of being adequately fed.

After the nestlings have flown, the device of territory breaks down, and the birds join up in a social community again.

It is only the smaller passerine birds that form territories in this way, and it is an immense change in their lives every spring when they pass from the intense social life of the flock to the solitary one of the territory. The pattern is imposed by the need for survival, for not to conform to it means eventual extinction. In spite of this, however, some birds do not need to make the annual change of habit, because they have a bigger or a more varied food supply, or are strong fliers. The swallows, swifts, and similar birds fly so well and range so far in three dimensions that they do not need a private estate but can get their food from, in effect, the public domain—the swifts may easily rise two thousand feet in it.

If it is such an advantage to birds for each pair to have its own private estate, we might well ask: Why do they form flocks? To which, of course, the answer is that these flocks also have their advantages. They afford protection against hawks and other enemies, as a flock can keep a far better look-out than a solitary bird. Moreover, by means of "mobbing," an enemy such as an owl or a cat may be driven off. Flocks also ensure the mixing of different blood lines and are a help in long migration, as often birds will come down and try to help forward a fallen comrade. They also ensure that a newly discovered source of food can be used by a large group rather than by the original discoverer alone, a factor which tends to the benefit of the race as a whole.

The song of birds is often complex. Many have about as varied tones and sounds as has the human voice, but there is no true conversation in birds. The different calls, songs, sounds, and notes serve to send signals of alarm, of love, of intention to fly, to return, to do this or that, but there is never any answer given to such a signal other than a repetition meaning only, in effect, "message received." In other words, the song expresses the emotions as well as definite danger signals; these emotions may be a feeling of well-being, of anger, of excitement, of joy at a successful rearing season or the discovery of a good food supply. They are not languages which can be translated, except by our interjections such as Oh!, Hi!, Beware!, or by the lines of old folk songs like "Fol-de-loll, fol-de-loll, loll, loll, loll." Birds will also express boredom by means of song, and indeed this is the chief reason that cage birds sing. Many birds mimic other sounds, including the human voice, and these activities seem to be part of their play; they can also recognize the voices of their mates and enemies.

The newly established Bartons, particularly Susannah and her first two daughters—Humility and Experience (the latter named after her godfather, Mr. Experience Mitchell)—were much cheered by the range of new and beautiful birds they found on and around their little farm. The eastern bluebird was one of the most striking, and the robins were enormous compared to the ones they had known in England; they called them robins although they were really thrushes, the only *Turdus* species in America. The striking cardinals had not yet reached New England from the South, so they were deprived

BLUE JAY

of that stirring sight. Nevertheless, one doubts if it would have cheered them all that much, at least if the bird had been known by that name, because both name and color would suggest what they so feared—the Church of Rome. Over the years, particularly over the last fifty, the cardinals have gradually colonized the area, being much aided in the process by the provision of feeding tables by bird lovers all along their route. They are now quite common at Bartons. Blackbirds, crows, jays, and many other species were there and formed a facet of the settlers' New England life. Thoreau thought the crow the most intelligent of New England birds and Theophilus Deane agreed with the writer's remark that "it [the crow] produced the perfect New England sound [56]." Eagerly the early Bartons watched for the return of the migrants in the spring and summer; they seemed to come with a rush that ended with the swallows, the same graceful birds they had known in the Netherlands and England. There was much speculation as to where the birds went in the winter, and the true facts of bird migration were not accepted, so strange and seemingly impossible were they, for about 150 years. As late as 1755 Dr. Samuel Johnson, the great lexicographer, contended that "swallows certainly sleep all the winter. A number of them conglobate together by flying round and round, and then all in a heap throw themselves under water and lie in the bed of a river." By 1832 the great American ornithologists Alexander Wilson and C. L. Bonaparte in their magnificent book appeared to accept the hibernation idea. They wrote:

The barn swallow (*Hirundo rufa* and *H. Americana*) is forced when winter approaches, to descend to the bottom of lakes, rivers and mill-ponds, to bury itself in the mud with eels and snapping turtles [60].

But they were being sarcastic and mocking the naturalists who still maintained the conglobation theory. The two authors then went on to describe what really happened—migration to the South.

The birds around Bartons during its long history fall into three classes: those that actually nested in or on the house

BARN SWALLOWS

(residents), those that occasionally used the place as a perch or a source of food, and those that were used as food by the humans themselves.

The first resident bird was a male serin, or canary bird, brought across the Atlantic in a tiny cage by Susannah Palmer when, aged eighteen, she crossed with her parents in the summer of 1632. By careful attention she managed to keep it alive, and the bird's lively singing cheered her, her family, the crew, and the other passengers on the long journey, uneventful though it was and quite unlike the ordeal of the first *Mayflower* passage.

Swallows, purple martins, and swifts were originally cliff breeders and have attached themselves generally to man's dwellings and buildings because these same structures provide better, more numerous, and more permanent nesting sites than do cliffs and banks. Cliffs constantly crumble away, even granite ones, but the walls of a house or barn last, and moreover, usually have eaves over them giving additional protection. Then again, man's activities—his gardens, farms, and dung —breed insects, the birds' food. The swifts' and hirundines' adoption of man was thoroughly practical and was only challenged later by the English sparrow. At Bartons the abundant springs in the neighborhood formed streams feeding ponds and marshes and so provided plenty of mud for the nests of these birds. The swallows and swifts were conservative creatures and, having found a good site, came back to it year after year. As they were such strong fliers and insect feeders, they had no need to form territories in the conventional sense. Their territory was, in fact, a three-dimensional one, measured in cubic miles, not acres, for they rose in the air to a great height, in contrast with the feeding area of other nonterritorial birds, such as the English sparrows.

Swallows were constantly sweeping the air for insects, though they did not exploit such a large volume of it as did the chimney swifts. Swifts range so high and so far that it is sometimes thought that they spend the whole night on the wing, sleeping while soaring in the air; even if not true, it is a charming fantasy that this powerful bird should really live in the air as its medium, something in the same way that a fish lives in the sea.

Chimney swift

Certainly the male swifts may be seen on a summer evening chasing the hen birds back to their nests and then all getting together, screeching and circling higher and higher till they can no longer be either heard or seen. There are reports of them coming tumbling out of the sky at a mad pace just about sunrise, to dash off in all directions when only a few yards from the ground.

Swallows, swifts, and martins are peaceable birds, safe from hawks by their speed. Animals such as skunks, squirrels, and rats will take eggs and nestlings, but the birds' real enemies are the English sparrows, which will take possession of the nests and even throw out the eggs in them. Many battles took place under the eaves of Bartons for possession of the nests, and still do, both species of birds screaming and twittering with rage. Results vary. If the swallows or swifts lose the battle they usually construct new nests nearby. Winter feeding of sparrows by man adversely affects the swallow group, as it makes the former birds that much stronger and thus more able to take over the swallows' nests. It is perhaps being anthropomorphic to say so, but is to some extent true, that it must be most disconcerting to find, after a six-thousand-mile flight from, say, Uruguay, one's fine American residence taken over by some cheap, immigrant squatters whom one is unable to evict. How did the birds find their way over this enormous distance, and how did this habit arise?

In the first place, birds, being free to move where they wish, have a natural tendency to wander; if a hard winter constantly eliminates stay-at-home birds, then those that move away and survive the journey will be the future perpetuators of the species, which will thus tend to have this pattern of migration stamped on it. Then there is the question of distance. From Bartons, martins, swifts, and swallows went to South America—a journey of some six thousand miles—but birds of these species habitually fly enormous distances every day. Swooping up and down, using the air currents in the same way a glider pilot does, the chimney swift does not need to expend much energy in his constant travels from a summer's dawn to the same day's dusk; he can cover forty miles in an hour or easily five hundred miles a day, so that the journey to Buenos Aires is put into another proportion when we see five hundred miles as a regular daily beat. We notice the long distances between the two centers and overlook the daily circles and swoops over our heads. The birds will feed as they go if they have the chance; they do not fly particularly high—usually under three thousand feet—nor very fast, about forty miles per hour being the speed of most of them. They seem to possesss a sense of general direction and to follow coastlines while avoiding mountain ranges. They may easily have some sense of temperature gradients and thus be guided southward. They eventually learn to recognize local objects at both ends of their beat. Young birds do not learn the way from old ones, because the young leave first; it is instinct that drives them on, and they must memorize the route so that they can return to the same spot when the time comes. It is noticeable that young birds only come back to the same locality, not to the identical nest from which they left.

Instinct—today the biologist is constantly referring to "instinct." It is a dangerous word and perhaps one that were better abolished, for it is imprecise and thus can be given any shade of meaning desired. When psychologists argue, "instinct" is frequently thrown in as being a sufficient and final proof of a favorite theory, according to the arguer's personal convictions. The word "instinct" arose in the eighteenth century to mark the distinction between the behavior of man and animal. The age of reason saw man as the ultimate of creation and as activated by God-given reason; by contrast, the animal was moved by an equally God-given but very different concept— "instinct"—which enabled animals to do things without first learning how to do them. There seems no occasion today to make this very fundamental distinction, whether one adheres to the theories of Darwin, Lamarck, or Lysenko; there are few biologists—or indeed laymen—who would consider man as anything fundamentally different from the rest of creation. The same basic laws of behavior should apply to him as to animals (though the vice of scientists is to find universal laws); consequently we can do without the concept of "instinct" as an animal-held, mysterious, inexplicable thing.

I must point out, however, that Ronald Fletcher has come to the defense of the word "instinct" in his book *Instinct in Man* [19]. There is nothing wrong with the word, provided we accept a definite meaning for it. Fletcher describes instincts as the "trains of unlearned behavior . . . which are activated in a coordinated manner when the animal encounters the various situations of its environment. . . . Instinct is simply a concept used to denote a certain correlation of these features."

Mankind has instincts. For instance, the baby knows how to suck milk as soon as he is born, though he must be taught how to handle solid food. In man most behavior is conditioned not by these inherited tropisms, but by the higher brain centers —by the process of thought. His instinctive behavior is over-ridden by a thoughtful one. The same is true in a greater or lesser degree with animals. Some, such as most insects, are almost completely controlled by the inherited pattern; others show increasing degrees of independence from this pattern, until we reach man, who has comparatively little instinctive behavior left in him and is, or should be, entirely controlled by thought.

The chirruping of the male crickets irresistibly draws the females to them from far away in the fields; the song of the sirens was equally irresistible to Odysseus and his men, but his higher thought processes enabled him to realize the danger of the song and to overcome it by having himself tied to the mast and filling his crew's ears with wax. The crickets come to the sound even if it means falling into a trap. The humans can take steps to avoid danger, because they can overcome their tropisms with a thought-out course of action.

At Bartons the swallows would fly down to the streams to select the mud for their nests with great care, for it had to mold properly, to dry without cracking, and to be strong. The foundations must be particularly well laid, and once this is done the rest follows easily, the birds using pieces of straw to give the structure strength. Nest construction is only done in the morning, for each addition must be left to dry and harden; if too much were built, the wet clay would pull itself down by its own weight. When sufficient mud for the day has been put on, the birds are free to feed and amuse themselves, which they do with marked expressions of joy and pleasure.

At Bartons, the nests were placed high up on the wall, beam, or projection, so that the overhang of the thatch protected the entrance. The eggs were white, three to five in number, and two broods were usually raised, with sometimes a third, both the cock and the hen sitting on the eggs in turn. The older of the young birds helped in the feeding of the subsequent broods, and the fledglings were not only fed but also had their excrement, a tough kind of jelly, carried away by their parents and siblings. When three weeks old, the fledglings became ready to fly and for a short time they were fed on the wing.

Swallows and their cousins are much attacked by parasites, so that it is not necessarily an unkindness to the birds to destroy the old nests, since they may well contain the eggs of mites, bugs, and lice, which creatures take a heavy toll of the birds' blood.

The swallows were always welcome and protected at Bartons; that they made the place lucky was acknowledged by all. It was a well-known fact that, if one took swallows' eggs from a nest, the cows would give bloody milk. John Barton III, after the hurricane of 1635, was not really happy until he found, in the following year, that the swallows had come back and were nesting in suitable spots under the shingle roof and in the barn, just as happily as they had under the thatch. But as that sounded superstitious, he had to give a more rational explanation for his feelings and spoke of the great quantity of noxious insects the birds consumed. Moreover, the birds continued to build in the house when it had another story added to it on the south wall in the Stephen Deane improvements.

The chimney swift was not as early a resident as the swallow, because in the first days the house had only one chimney —that of the kitchen—and the kitchen fire burned in it all the year round. When the east wing was added in 1682 two additional fireplaces were installed, and the following summer some chimney swifts built in the easternmost one. In the fall of that year Patience Barton refused to allow a fire to be lit in either of the new rooms until she was quite sure the swifts had gone.

The chimney swifts made their nests of twigs which they broke off in flight, then carried to their site and cemented into nest form with a thick saliva they secreted in their throats. Many nests could be found in any one chimney. These swifts are related to the edible nest swift of Malaysia and China, which creature makes its nest almost entirely of saliva. The nests are a much sought after and expensive delicacy. Fortunately for the American chimney swift, no one has yet thought of using their nests for soup. The twigs could easily be strained out. No doubt such a development, should it take place, would put yet one more bird on the sad road to extinction.

The chimney swift has been called "the cigar with wings." It is blackish, long, and swallowlike, has slightly curved wings and no apparent tail. A curious characteristic of the wings is that they appear to beat alternately, a situation which would offer considerable mechanical advantage by spreading the energy load. The downward thrust of the wing calls for more effort than the upward recovery, so that if only one wing was going down at a time the work done would be more evenly distributed. However, motion pictures are said to show that alternate flapping does not take place.

Chimney swifts circle in thousands over their chosen chimneys and as dusk deepens they drop out of the sky, twittering away and forming funnels of flying birds over the chimney into which they eventually drop. Such circling and massing was an action supporting the winter "conglobation" theory.

Mr. La Flèche loves his birds, but also finds that they—particularly the cardinals and swallows—have a powerful appeal for his customers. The tradition still survives that swallows are lucky, so for both motives he puts out bird tables said to be "squirrel proof," although the nuts and nodules often fall to the ingenuity and adaptability of the little gray robbers. The food on these tables during winter and early spring mostly benefits the English sparrows, concentrating them on the house where they tend to occupy the swallows' nests while the owners are on the other side of the world.

Farmyards are now rare in the area, it being largely country residential, and in any case farms are now so much cleaner; the dung is properly stacked so that it does not breed flies to the same extent as before, and the cow sheds are sprayed to kill any that do appear. Pests of gardens and farm crops are now mostly kept under control, with the result that there is not the same insect abundance in the neighborhood as formerly, meaning less food for the swallows and swifts. On the other hand, rats, which are enemies of birds, taking eggs and young from the nests, are now controlled to a greater extent than in the old days, but as the nests of swallows and swifts were mostly too high up on outside walls to be at much risk, the decline of the rat was not much to the advantage of the Bartons birds. The restaurant, *cuisine française* and all, may well lose its swallows unless they harden their hearts against the winter English sparrows. In the battle between swallows and sparrows for nests and sites, the sparrows have the advantage of being resident the whole year round.

Glass is a phenomenon birds have not yet mastered. Every now and then, especially in the spring, a bird such as a robin would be found dashing at a Bartons window as if trying to force a way in. The bird, nearly always a male, sees its reflection in the glass, and taking the picture to be an intruder into his territory, tries to expel him from it by adopting the threat attitude. But the intruder does not obey the rules. Knowing he was trespassing, when threatened he should retire, but what happens? The intruder, so it seems, has also adopted the threat attitude, so the defender dashes at him and suffers a resounding blow on the head, an experience leading to considerable bafflement. Knowing how to deal with glass may have some survival value, but so few birds meet this particular problem that no instinctive knowledge of the subject has yet been acquired. It is interesting to note that the observant James Thurber, poor though his sight was, put the swallow (in one of his *Fables for our Time*) as the bird most likely to come to terms with "crystallized air [57]."

Woodpeckers built in the house when it was left empty except for Edward Hopkins. A northern flicker took advantage of a hole under the eaves of the west wall of the original house, where the wattle-and-daub filling behind the painted clay facing was decayed. He and his mate enlarged the hole and made a nest inside. They also got into the double walls of the icehouse that Stephen Deane built on the grounds. Ice was a summer luxury in New England that came easily if proper provision was made for it. Tryphena Barton's husband, Theophilus Chilton, even made a lot of money shipping ice to Europe. In 1775 the more decorative pileated woodpecker—it has a red crest and black and white coloration—enlarged holes in the wall of the west wing and nested there. The drumming of the birds in the fall as they dug holes and rammed acorns and nuts into them in the early morning was as good as an alarm clock and made sure that the hired hands woke up early and got to work.

As the ivy grew up the eastern side of the house, it provided cover for certain birds. The first, about 1680, was a wren. This tiny, shy little bird was a great joy to the young Barton children; they were strictly forbidden to approach the nest or even to watch it too persistently.

The next resident bird, the English sparrow, reached Bartons much later, in 1872. It is an example of an extraordinarily successful animal, and its colonization of New England—in fact of America—warrants some comment [54]. It is a very plastic, adaptable bird and has exploited a particular ecological niche in both Europe and America, one almost vacant in the latter continent, namely the use of food raised by man, and odd bits of his living space. It can be seen to have done this in two main fields, the sentimental and the practical. Moreover, for a bird, the sparrow is very intelligent and quickly

WREN

learns from experience. For instance, scientists studying birds capture them in traps in order to examine, weigh, and ring the creatures. Many birds, such as finches, wrens, tits, and pigeons as well as sparrows, can be caught in this way and released after being studied. They all may be repeatedly trapped—that is, except the sparrows, who will never enter a trap a second time. Moreover, sparrows will find their way out of funnel traps, whereas other birds cannot. A funnel trap is just that. A funnel into a glass or wire box, with the stem of the funnel cut off, leads into the body of the trap where food is put. Only the sparrows can get out of it by their own efforts.

Thoreau, in the woods at Walden, may unwittingly have contributed to the enthusiasm for the English sparrow. He wrote:

I once had a sparrow alight upon my shoulder for a moment while I was hoeing in a village garden, and I felt that

I was more distinguished by that circumstance than I should have been by any epaulet I could have worn [56].

But he was not writing about the English sparrow. That great naturalist had died before the immigrant had reached New England; he was concerned with one of the American species, probably the song sparrow. The distinction was not properly realized at the time. If Thoreau admired sparrows, so should everyone else.

The birds have now become unmitigated pests. They take a lot of small grains, though it must be stated in defense of the creature that much of it is spilled seed that would have been eaten by rats or mice, or wasted. It is true that they also consume a number of weed and grass seeds, but not all are destroyed. Some seeds can resist bird gut activity and thus are excreted to germinate elsewhere. Such plants are using the sparrow as a distribution agent. Sparrows take sown seeds and seedlings, attack fruit, and open pea pods. They tear flowers, particularly the yellow ones, such as the crocus. They drive out desirable birds—the swallow group, for instance. They foul buildings and pathways with their droppings and carry and transmit pests and diseases to man and animals.

In spite of all this, the English sparrow was deliberately imported into America and the sentimental aspect of its success story was prominent here. Although to today's eyes the bird is not a particularly attractive one, yet in 1850 the inhabitants of Brooklyn, nostalgic for things from the old country and seemingly fascinated by the creature, deliberately imported eight pairs. In order to oppose objections, they also put it about that the birds would destroy the snow-white linden moth caterpillars, then causing much damage to shade trees from Brooklyn to Philadelphia. When the English farmers heard of the birds being imported into America they were amazed and could only account for it ". . . on the assumption that America had been visited by a wave of temporary insanity [54]."

The birds of the first introduction failed to survive the winter of 1850–51 and a further fifty pairs were introduced the next year, so determined were the Brooklynites of that age. These survived in sufficient numbers and the species became established. Commercial interest and the press pushed the

business, and an English sparrow boom developed in which
Stephen Deane II was caught up. Having sparrows around the
house became fashionable, and Stephen found it cheaper to
import birds direct from England rather than pay the high
prices demanded by the New York breeders. In all fairness it
must be said that the English sparrows did seem to keep down
the caterpillars for about fifty years, but the area had ex-
changed one pest for another. The expectation had not, as so
often happens, been fulfilled just as had been imagined. As
Alexander Pope once put it:

> Hope springs eternal in the human breast,
> Man never is, but always to be blest. [46]

In the early years of the twentieth century the shade trees
were badly attacked once again, and G. W. Herrick, at the
Cornell Agricultural Experimental Station, wrote, "It may well
be that the great and wanton destruction of birds is one cause
of the abnormal abundance of the insect [23]."

Stephen Deane's English sparrows throve. They built their
dome-shaped nests in any holes they could find and also
pushed their nests up under the eaves and gutters. A pair
would have four or five broods a year, and with abundant food
available the young spread out all over the state. Boston became a very paradise for them. On the afternoon of November
20, 1906, at Boston the sunset was at 5:24 P.M. and Mr. C. W.
Townsend was watching a tree roost site in the center of the
city. Sparrows started to arrive at 3:45 P.M. and then came in
enormous numbers. Later Mr. Townsend described the scene
at 4:15 P.M.:

> It is now raining birds. The trees are a scene of great activ-
> ity and the noise rises above the roar of the city's streets.
> The birds are crowding together in the trees, constantly
> fighting and flying about as they are forced from their
> perches.

By 5:00 P.M. the event was over [31]. Sparrows go to roost
early and, like Charles Lamb, compensate for it by getting up
late.*

* Charles Lamb (1776–1834), writer and Government employee, when
reprimanded for arriving late at the office, stammered out the excuse, "Yes, sir,
but I make up for it by going early."

The sparrows were "sedentary" birds, that is, they did not migrate in the fall but built themselves winter roosting nests, and there were able to defy the cold. Their food around Bartons differed a little from that taken in Boston and Springfield. In the fall, in farming areas, they took quite a lot of small grains (wheat, oats, and barley) and a certain amount of corn, too, not venturing far into the fields. A strip some five yards wide anywhere near a hedge or shelter could be cleared by those birds. For the rest of the year they relied on man and, up to the 1920s, the horse. First their "cuteness" induced man to feed them; second, they took part of the food being fed to domestic chickens and pigs, getting to know the time of day these operations took place and assembling to await the free-lunch handout. In the chicken yard, if the person scattering food chases the sparrows away, they come back almost immediately and start again; however often the operator drives them off they always come back, so that in the end the human just gives up and accepts them as one of the facts of life.

An adult sparrow needs about seven pounds of food a year, and as in Massachusetts alone there are some 5 million of them, they need about 17,500 tons of food a year. The sparrow-to-man ratio is about 0.33. Garbage, dropped food, and now bird tables supply a lot of it. The horse was once a major asset to the birds. They took grain spilled around the stables and from the feeding bags and picked out undigested or half-digested grain from the droppings. In the spring and summer, sparrows feed their young mostly on insects, but take those useful or harmful to man quite indiscriminately [31]. They will pick insects out of spiders' webs, but the Bartons' sparrows were a bit wary of the actual spiders themselves.

Being so adaptable, sparrows quickly take advantage of new sources of food. At night they capture moths and other insects attracted to light traps, driving to fury many an entomologist trying to make a census of insects. They also collect insects from neon signs, window displays, and even the radiators of motor cars. Unlike the insects, sparrows are not dazzled by this unnatural lighting. They can catch insects in flight, but are clumsy compared to the flycatchers, swallows, swifts, and martins. They have learned to soak hard bread crusts in water to soften them and will even drop hard bread into water and return to eat it later, when it has softened.

Naturally they have enemies, being subject to diseases caused by viruses, bacilli (anthrax, for instance), protozoa, and fungi. Worms and flukes attack them, as well as mites, the red chicken mite being particularly common. Sparrows are a source of infection of domestic poultry; the mite can carry the protozoa *Lankesteria*, causing the death of many young birds. Feather mites living close to the skin are also found. Lice, fleas, and ticks can be present on the birds and in the nests. The English sparrow brought its own particular flea with it, thus adding another creature to the continent's Insecta. Considerable numbers of fleas can be found in the nests. Up to eighty have been counted. But the fleas do not have it all their own way; when they are numerous a beetle may also be found in the nest, preying on the parasites. These fleas are now found on poultry and many other wild birds. The bluebottle flies and their larvae were also found in the nests.

The commonest tick present on the Bartons sparrows was (and is) the snowshoe hare tick: It can be very dangerous, acting as a vector for relapsing fever as well as being able to inject a poisonous saliva into its host. The tick found the sparrow a great blessing, because when the number of snowshoe hares was low the tick turned to birds, particularly to the ruffed grouse. As it eventuated that the tick could also feed on the sparrow, the new introduction helped the arthropod survive and overcome a shortage of its main host. This tick, being an Argasid, can suck blood from its host very quickly and so does not need to attach itself to the bird, but can live comfortably in the nest waiting for its food to return and present itself. There is a corresponding drawback, however, in that it can more readily be eaten by the bird or the beetles in the nest preying on fleas. Nevertheless, the English sparrow undoubtedly helped the snowshoe hare tick survive and thereby reduced the numbers of its host.

Sparrows were attacked by predators: hawks, owls, skunks, rats, snakes, and so forth, but its most dangerous enemy was undoubtedly the cat, both wild and domestic. However, a new unconscious predator has become a major cause of death to sparrows in the last thirty years—the automobile. It approaches too rapidly for the birds always to avoid it, but on the other hand, the machine knocks down insects and offers some of them, caught in radiator grilles, as half-cooked tidbits, and thus perhaps more nourishing for the young. Even so, the most far-reaching effect of the internal combustion engine on the sparrow population is not its direct killing of the birds—compensated to some extent by the insect food it supplies—but that it replaces the horse, a major provider.

Sparrows incorporate feathers and hair in the linings of their nests and both can prove dangerous; feathers because they bring mites into the nest, and hair, if it is long, because it can get entangled around a foot or wing and hold the bird captive till it starves to death, though usually in such circumstances the bird's mate (they mate for life) will supply food. A new danger is string, particularly nylon string, which unravels easily and ties birds down.

By 1880 the tide of enthusiasm was beginning to turn against the sparrow and a few years later Stephen II realized he had made a mistake in introducing the birds. He endeavored to reduce their numbers by destroying and removing the nests on his house, no easy task for several reasons. For instance, a pair can have four or five broods a year, and if a nest is removed the birds will build another one in the same place or near it. Sparrows show great devotion to their nests. One, removed from the eaves by Stephen's gardener and containing a few unnoticed eggs, was thrown undamaged onto a rubbish heap; the pair continued to use it and hatched out the brood. Also, when Stephen II was at Bartons the farm itself was no longer his, and the sparrows used the farm buildings as nest sites. The farmer there was far too busy to set about destroying sparrow nests several times a year and, to Stephen's exhortations, used to reply that the birds kept his fields free of insects, and he didn't believe the creatures were infecting his poultry with nasty diseases or pulling up seedlings.

In any case, destroying the nests at Bartons and the farm would not have had much effect on the total population of the area. It would merely have meant that there would have been a greater survival of birds from other areas who would have flown in and used the Bartons food supply.

Stephen II encouraged cats and was in two minds about destroying rats, but the sparrows had their answer to that.

They tended to feed in groups, keeping a watch for predators; no sentinel was posted, as with the crows, but all were wary, so that a universal lookout operated. The alarm call—a nasal "quer-quer-quer"—from any one bird alerted the whole group and a cat would be "mobbed" and driven off. Moreover, as they were sedentary birds, the area became well known to them, especially among the older birds (some seven years of age is common). They got to know the habits and whereabouts of predators. Sparrows, for instance, will follow the movements of a rat, keeping just out of its reach, in order to get knowledge of its life-style. The alarm call is a powerful weapon; it will even silence the brood in the nest squeaking with all its might for food.

Stephen II's anti-sparrow rage produced an idea that could have been successful. It was the commercialization of sparrows as food. Sparrow pies, he maintained, were delicious and why buy *ucelli* from the Italian shops when sparrows could be had for nothing, at any rate on his land. Pushing his case, and in a throaty aside to his male listeners and with a dig in the ribs to the nearest one, he would point out that the great Linnaeus had said they were an aphrodisiac, adding, to show his erudition, the great botanist's Latin comment on the bird's sexual activity: "*Salacissimus qui vigesies saepe coit.*" But Linnaeus or no, the idea did not catch on. There is not much food on a sparrow in the first place. The dressed bird goes to perhaps half an ounce and much of that is bone. About twenty birds would make a modest dish; these have to be plucked, eviscerated, and dressed, requiring a great deal of labor even by Stephen II's standards. Moreover, in New England then there were not many people of Italian origin who might have liked the tiny spitted birds, popular in Italy to this day. There was also a psychological block. Crunching up a songbird, bones and all somehow seemed wrong, though eating heath hens, turkeys, and poultry raised no qualms. Also perhaps there was a guilt feeling, and the sparrows did help control pests, a sentiment such as that expressed by Ralph Hodgson:

I saw with open eyes
Singing birds sweet . . .
Sold in the shops of

Stupidity Street.
I saw in a vision
The worm in the wheat,
And in the shops nothing
For people to eat,
Nothing for sale in
Stupidity Street [25].

Even so, robins were being sold in Boston in 1880 at 60 cents per dozen, which price for those days suggests they were something of a luxury. There would be two or three times more food on a robin than a sparrow.

Stephen Deane II gave up the struggle to eliminate sparrows and eventually even allowed them to be fed by his grandchildren.

The reasons for the English sparrow's success, not only in America but all over the world, warrant a brief examination. Some of the causes have already been mentioned, and here they and other reasons will be summarized. The bird exploited a vacant food niche. No form of life to any extent was using the surplus food rejected by man and horse. Nor was any bird using to the full the nesting sites provided by man, though the swallows and chimney swifts did compete for those places to some extent. The sparrow was sedentary and so got to know its area well, particularly the habits of its predators. Being sedentary, it saved much labor in that it did not have to build a new nest every year [62]. The sparrow was plastic, wary, and intelligent, so it could take advantage rapidly of any new conditions favoring feeding (bird tables, food-factory waste, dockside spillages, and so on). It was a social feeder and thus was less likely to be attacked by predators, and its alarm call was distinctive and heeded by the whole flock. Finally, at least to begin with, it had a sentimental appeal for humans. Much indignation was expressed at the end of the century when sparrow clubs sought to extinguish the English sparrow.

The second class of Bartons birds were those using the house as a perch and observation post. Naturally there were many casual visitors of this sort, the commonest being the New England crow. Starlings, introduced to America in the 1890s, also used the house fairly regularly, though the early settlers found "stares" in America on arrival and commented that they were much darker than the bird they had known in Europe. The starling they found was the eastern blackbird. Feral pigeons (the rock pigeon) introduced from Europe, also perched on the house.

Let us now turn to the third class—the birds used as food. The wild turkey at once springs to mind; the creature was smaller than the domesticated turkey and had brown tips to the tail feathers instead of the white tips of the domesticated bird. The first Bartons did not eat many of them, partly because the heath hens were much more numerous, and also because of a report, emanating from the French (was it an early conservation measure?) that consuming turkeys gave one leprosy. In passing, it is interesting to note the use of the word "turkey." Anything new or from a foreign country in those days was often referred to as Turkish, even American plants and animals which the settlers must have known were not at all from that far country. The Indian corn (maize) was known as Turkey wheat and the scarlet runner (pole beans) as the Turkey bean. Captain Standish carried four books with him on the *Mayflower*, one of them a history of Turkey [9]. So at once the very American *Meleagris gallopavo* was called "the turkey" and William Wood described it as ". . . a very large bird of a blacke colour, yet white in flesh [65]."

The heath hen, or American grouse, a small speckled reddish-brown bird the size of a domestic chicken, was a popular food with New Englanders from the *Mayflower* onward. It was tastier than the turkey (and in the Bartons' view, safer to eat), was abundant over the whole area, and was easily shot or captured. And they tended to advertise their presence with a call like a foghorn booming through the mist of morning. They were an easy mark. The settlers had no concept of a close season and captured them indiscriminately any time they could. Thus in the breeding season the shooting or trapping of a hen bird meant that her young, too, perished.

In the eighteenth century their numbers began to fall, and by 1870 Martha's Vineyard was the sole place any could be seen. In 1890 the famous naturalist William Brewster could find only 200 on the whole island, and a reserve for them was established at Tisbury. For a while they prospered, but fire,

HEATH HEN

probably started by tourists who came to watch the birds'
curious courtship rituals, nearly wiped them out. Blackhead disease, introduced into the island with domestic turkeys, attacked
the few survivors of the fire. In 1927 there were thirteen of them
on Martha's Vineyard and none, as far as was known, anywhere else. In 1931 only one bird, a male, was left and he was
last seen on February 9, 1932. The species is now extinct.

The passenger pigeon fed on insects, nuts, small grains,
and corn. It assembled in vast flocks in the fall in preparation
for the migration south, roosting in trees at night; the weight
of them would often break branches. They were easily caught
or shot by the early settlers. One discharge would often kill
four or more birds. In 1643, though, the assembly started early
and the huge flocks ate "a very great quantity of English
grain," as Henry Winthrop wrote [63]. Famine very nearly
overtook the settlement. The pigeons came again in 1644 but
the harvest had already been taken, so they proved a blessing,

"it being incredible what multitudes were killed daily."

The squabs were taken in great numbers and pigeon oil, or Indian butter, pressed out of them. Quite a commerce in squabs and adults developed. In the early nineteenth century they were still numerous; Alexander Wilson talked of a swarm containing more than 2,230 million birds, eating some 400,000 tons of nuts, mostly acorns, a day [45]. Two things led to their extinction: cutting the forests and overexploitation. By 1914 they were extinct, the last bird dying in the Cincinnati zoo on September 1 of that year.

Finally, geese and ducks formed part of the settlers' food and they soon established domestic poultry. In the nineteenth century, chicken was a luxury food and not the commonplace of today. "A chicken in every pot" was a slogan set out by Henri IV of France in an effort to quiet discontent in the laboring population. It was adopted by Herbert Hoover. It helped lose him the 1932 election! The expression is no longer a rallying cry, chicken being one of the cheapest meats on the market.

8

~✍

THE DRY-LITTER
COMMUNITY

U NDER NATURAL CONDITIONS there is a rare group of animals
belonging to the dry-litter habitat—rare because of the
scarcity of dry litter in nature. Wet litter is very common, particularly in the woods, at the foot of cliffs, and so forth, where
rotting vegetation, dung, and animal remains may be found,
together with its own special fauna—earthworms, wood lice,
springtails, mites, millipedes, etc.—living in and on these wet-
litter substances. By contrast, dry-litter habitats under natural
conditions are found only in the nests of certain birds, such as
those placed on cliffs or in dry caves, or in a few dry deposits of
dung from bats or birds—all very rare positions compared to the
wet-litter sites, but nevertheless containing their own special
fauna.

The dry litter tends to consist of high-protein material such
as waste hair, feathers or fur, or dung having a high nitrogen
content, and the creatures living in it—or some of them—were
first of all predators on other small animals and then became
scavengers of such discarded materials of higher animals as
molted feathers and hair, cast snakeskins, and dung. They lived
a highly specialized life within their unusual realm and had to
perfect devices which would economize water, the scarcest
material in their chosen environment.

When man came on the scene he had a considerable effect
on these rare animals, because he was a great creator of dry
litter. He liked dry places—caves, huts, castles, houses—which
he would keep warm and, to begin with, not particularly clean,
so that dry litter began to collect in depth and a vast new dry-

litter habitat was created. Even though he was not covered with fur, did not molt or cast his skin, and left his dung in the wet-litter habitat, yet he started to wear clothes, and scattered bones with meat still adhering to them about the floors of his caves, huts, and castles. His first clothes (skins and fur) were to those dry-litter animals a huge supply of their chosen medium, and as man began to weave coverings of wool and keep them in chests and cupboards, the animals began to move out of the birds' nests and bat dung and take to clothing as their main means of livelihood.

As man moved forward to improve his world, so he influenced the life of many other creatures; he greatly increased the opportunities and numbers of these erstwhile scavengers (a step which caused considerable annoyance to their hosts). They have not, however, abandoned their old sphere and are still found in birds' nests and deposits of dry droppings, and frequently it is from these sources that the creatures spread into man's stores of food and clothing.

What we now call clothes moths are members of the dry-litter community. They belong to the family Tineidae, of which there are about 130 species in North America. All are small and plain-colored. They are scavengers, feeding on waste materials, fungi, and certain fabrics. However, there are a few exceptional Tineidae that live on leaves. The three commonest clothes moths at Bartons were the case-making clothes moth, the webbing clothes moth and the tapestry moth. To these pests must be added the spider beetle and the carpet beetle, or woolly bear, both operating in much the same way as the clothes moths. The furniture mite is another animal belonging to this community, and there are many more that have specialized in sharing man's stores of food, of which the flour beetle was the commonest when Bartons was built, but to which others, such as the Indian meal moth, the grain and rice weevils, the fruit moths, and the bookworm have been added as trade and commerce interchanged both animals and goods from one part of the world to another.

These were the main dry-litter creatures that fed on man's goods in the house, but they were not the whole dry-litter community, for there were a number of other creatures that benefited from these sheltered conditions. Silverfish gradu-

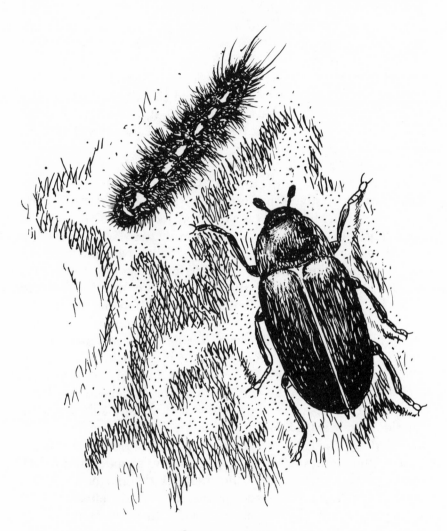

CARPET BEETLE

ally developed in the house, but did not do much damage; they
are the most primitive of all insects and can be described as
living fossils, though very minute ones. The Bryobia or clover
mite frequently came into the house to pass the winter and was
fond of the thatch, the lower and upper layers of which formed
part of the dry-litter habitat. However, the thatch at Bartons
was short-lived (and illegal for some time) and caught fire
after the hurricane of 1635. Before the fire many of the lower

layers of the young thatch were moist, because it was not very thick and after rain not all of it dried, so only the more sheltered bits of thatch and that around the chimney can be considered as part of the dry-litter world. Not even all of this was acceptable, because the Bartons were so nervous about the chimney area thatch catching fire—and the kitchen fire burned summer and winter—that they dressed it with a mixture of seawater (as a source of salt) and some of their precious lime to make the reeds fire-resistant. These chemicals discouraged the dry-litter animals.

In the dry, non-saline areas of the thatch such creatures as mites, psocids, silverfish, springtails, fleas, Protura, and even sow bugs flourished. It was not ideal food for them, being a comparatively low-protein, high-carbohydrate zone, but they used it to some extent, as it was an excellent shelter. Many of the scavengers here were actually living on molds growing on the reeds and grass rather than on the thatch itself. Strangely enough, the top layer of thatch is more often dry than wet, because wind and sun dry it so quickly after rain, but the variation makes it unattractive for the animals as a permanent habitat. Melting snow keeps the thatch damp for a considerable time, to the distress of the dry-litter world.

Clothes moths were well known to the settlers; their clothing was of wool, linen, and leather with a little silk provided for the most wealthy, and all these except the linen would be attacked by the clothes moths. Brushing, airing in the sun, putting the clothes away clean, and laying lavender and laurel in the clothes closets were the methods the Bartons used to combat the ravages of these insects. They were effective, too (except perhaps the lavender, though this may have some slight repellant action on the adult moths) and remain so to this day.

Through the centuries as the house was improved, so was it kept that much warmer and so did the clothes moths thrive increasingly, but now that the present owners have the place centrally heated there is another crisis in the lives of the clothes moths because, though they like the heat, it is becoming too dry for them. Moreover, moth-proof carpets and clothing are an additional brake on an increase in their numbers, as are also artificial fibers such as nylon and polyester. Neither are modern manufactured woolens all that a clothes moth wants, for it is found that it will breed much more quickly on raw wool, which obviously contains some vital substance in relative abundance compared with the manufactured article. It is only the clothes moths who have completely adapted themselves to living on fabrics; if these are clean they can live on them, but they prefer soiled material containing sweat, food, or excrement which enables them to obtain supplies of vital elements (possibly certain fats, vitamins, and amino acids) more readily than from clean fabric alone. That is one of the reasons that putting clothes away clean helps to protect them from moths.

Finally, moth powders and sprays based on modern insecticides are a serious threat to their continued survival as a race. Together with their enemies the spiders, they are declining, though by no means extinct as yet. They have overcome many setbacks in arriving at their present way of life, and breeding as fast as they do, they may yet overcome these new difficulties.

Here again we can see the struggle for survival imposing a pattern of life on the clothes moth. A medium containing food material, protein, carbohydrate, vitamins, and water—albeit this last was comparatively scarce—offered itself and was duly colonized. To do so, the creatures had to acquire some unusual and special habits, for they had to be able to digest the fibrous proteins found in wool, hair, and leather such as keratin, fibroin, and so forth, which are digested by few animals. Nevertheless they have done so; they had to, or else leave the field untouched. Measurements have shown that about half of the fabric consumed is actually used by these animals and the rest excreted as waste. It is a large percentage in view of the difficult nature of the medium; such food passes through the gut very slowly because it is so hard to digest, for if a larva is first starved for a while and then fed, it will be two days before anything is excreted.

The creatures can readily obtain oxygen from the air, and have a large surface area compared to their weight which makes this easy, as they breathe through pores in their skin (spiracles), not by means of lung books. The larvae live on or in the medium the whole time, so the question of water supply is important. As they breathe they lose water; they obtain very little with their food, for wool and hair do not contain much of this substance so essential to life. To overcome this difficulty they have acquired the ability to absorb water directly from damp or dampish air. By this means their vital supply of water is maintained. They are able to vary the length of their larval life considerably, which fact also has a notable survival value. When food of the right kind is scarce or water cannot be obtained either from the food or the air, the larvae can rest or develop more slowly and into a much smaller adult, perhaps a tenth of the weight of a normal insect, though still able, if a female, to lay fertile and viable eggs.

As mentioned above, the drying of the atmosphere of the whole house by the central heating system is a big threat to the way of life of the clothes moth and wood-boring beetles, for it makes the question of water supply acute. On the other hand, it does provide warm conditions all the winter, thus shortening the life cycle and enabling the generations to succeed each other more rapidly, allowing their numbers to build up again. The balance between increase and decrease is a narrow one; very small things may make all the difference to the success or failure of an animal. However, clothes moths are not very likely to become extinct at Bartons as long as birds are encouraged there; while sparrows can force their nests under the guttering or eaves, and swallows build on the walls, there will always be a supply of various of these moths ready to find their way into the house, with its vast supply of dry litter. As soon as a dry-litter animal finds itself in a favorable position in a house, its numbers will build up very quickly. Similarly, the numbers will decrease equally rapidly as soon as measures are taken against it, but in spite of these, the birds' nests, together with antique furniture (frequently with old baize or stuffing in it, full of moth) form a constant source of material for the renewal of the population.

The first of the clothes moths at Bartons was the common or webbing clothes moth, brought in with the settlers' first goods. In the dark and damp conditions of the early house they throve and extended their territory by spreading into birds' nests, such as those of the swallows, wrens, and chimney swifts. The tiny eggs of this moth are oval and ivory-white in color; found singly or in groups of two or three, they are laid on the surface of tight-woven fabrics or between the strands of wool in blankets and looser woven cloths, or at the base of hairs in furs. Some fifty eggs are deposited by each female, but the quantity naturally depends on how well-fed the moth was before pupating. After laying the eggs, the female dies; the eggs hatch in a week or ten days' time. The larvae are white with yellowish-tawny heads and are about three eighths of an inch long when fully grown. As soon as they hatch they begin to feed on the "dry litter" on which the eggs have been laid. When faced with mixtures of animal and vegetable fibers, the moths seek out and consume only the animal ones. The material, if colored, shows through the skin and makes the larva inconspicuous, a fact having a considerable survival value. Many of the maids and mistresses at Bartons were not sharp-eyed enough to notice the beginnings of an attack on the blankets, jerkins, hose, and multitudinous succession of garments in the long history of the house, and so gave the tiny, vulnerable caterpillars opportunity to develop to maturity.

The webbing clothes moth larva usually builds a tube of silk and the fibers of the food medium on which it has been feeding at the time, projecting its head from either end to eat. When a new area is to be browsed, the larva either extends the tube or abandons it and constructs another one. Not all larvae do this; a few are free-feeding over the area, or just spin a little web silk to protect themselves. Here again is posed a question as to the balance of advantages to the race. The tube protects the larva against certain parasites but renders it more conspicuous to man, while the free-ranging larva is less conspicuous to man but more exposed to attack from Ichneumon and Braconid parasites. Which is the greater danger?

The noise of the moth feeding, when amplified by microphone, is very startling: a vast tearing and rending of fibers heard in a rhythm of three or four bites followed by an interval of two or three seconds' silence, and then repeated. It is indeed fortunate for the moth that our unaided ear cannot pick up this sound, for such an alarming noise would not only advertise the presence of the moth but lead to instant defensive action as well! The larvae of the common clothes moth by no means confine their feeding to wool and fur. At Bartons poisoned mice sometimes died behind the wainscots and these were attacked by a number of insects, including the clothes moth. They proved a valuable source of moisture to them, for not only was the fur used, but also the drying but still moist flesh on the mouse bones was colonized; however, this attractive source of food also had its dangers for the moths, for those that attacked the stomach and viscera were killed by the same arsenical or phosphorus poison that killed the mice. The moth attacking the dead mice helped destroy the body more quickly and were advantageous to man in that respect. The action of the humans at Bartons to reduce one animal obnoxious to them had the effect of increasing the opportunities for development

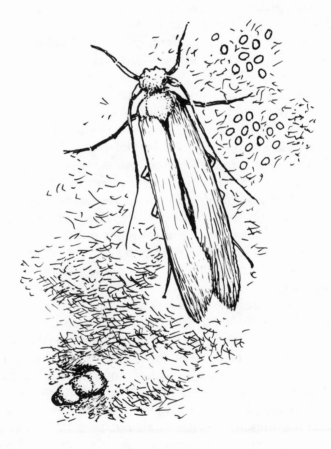

CLOTHES MOTH

of another equally objectionable. The moths also occasionally
made experiments in living on purely vegetable materials. In
the early days of the house, they successfully managed to
develop on a few porridge oats lying neglected in a sack, and
on some crushed barely fallen into a corner in the brew cellar;
however, in these cases they always concentrated on the high-
protein portion of the vegetable material. They also attacked
silk and leather.

The ancestors of this moth seem to have lived as predators
on the larvae of ticks, mites, and similar creatures, and from
this to have adopted the scavenging way of life as being
easier; they then pushed a branch out to attack man's goods.
It appears a most adaptable animal and may well have genes in
its makeup that will again face man with a new development:
Nylon may perhaps fall into its power, or the ultimate threat
(imagined by Stephen Vincent Benét of a termite)—one day
an entomologist may find a clothes moth larva starting quietly
to eat into a steel girder. It has already attacked the insulation
of telephone cables in New York.

After the larva, comes the pupa; first a silken cocoon is
spun, and attached to it are threads of the material on which
it has been feeding. This economizes on the silk it has to spin,
leaving more food reserves for the succeeding adult and the
future generation, and is also an aid to concealment. The pupal
case is formed within the cocoon, and the duration of this
stage is again very variable, lasting from two to six weeks, a
lower temperature prolonging the process. At the end of the
due time, the pupal case projects from the cocoon, splits at
the end, and the moth emerges.

The newly-hatched moths are a bright golden-buff color,
the wings free from markings and with rather loose scales,
some of which easily become detached. The wing expanse is
about half an inch, the males being a little smaller than the
females. The female is full of eggs and rarely flies, as she is
so heavy; moths seen on the wing are nearly always males,
or spent females who have already laid their eggs and are
thus light enough to fly.

At Bartons the humans always chased and killed any
small moth seen fluttering in the house, which did very little
to keep down the population of clothes moths, because some

were garden moths drawn to the lights at night or, if clothes moths, were the males or empty females who were about to die in any case. Of course, if enough males could be killed, the future population would be affected, but killing a few males will make very little difference to the numbers of the next generation, a fact which is true of most of the animal kingdom and is no doubt the reason that only men used to go to war and women did not. The moths, particularly the females, try to escape danger by running for shelter in quick, dodging, characteristic dashes, though sometimes they take short flights as an additional measure.

The length of life as an adult moth is again very variable: The males live longer than the females, the former averaging about four weeks and the latter half that time or a little more, but in cold winter weather females will live some five weeks. The adult moths tend to be abundant in early summer and in the fall, but now at Bartons they may be met with all the year round due to the central heating, though not in the large numbers that were known in the past.

Much was the damage and many were the minor tragedies that these moths caused the humans at the house over the first three hundred years of its life. When young Abigail Gifford married Experience Barton in 1674 her grandmother-in-law, Susannah Barton, arranged a magnificent reception in the new wing of the house. Two days before the ceremony the old lady called Abigail to the house, saying she had a special gift for her—a silk shawl brought from France twenty years ago and kept locked in the old close-lidded mothproof chest John Barton III had brought from England. The shawl had been locked away, as it was considered to be a needless vanity for farmers such as they—indeed it was illegal for the lower order to dress in the fashion of their social superiors. "But now times are changing," she told Abigail, "and this magnificent shawl will show we are no longer poor farmers but established citizens. Now open it, my child." And she gave Abigail the key.

"Oh ma'am," said Martha, the hired girl, "the chest has not been opened for five years." Nor had it. When the box was opened the result can be imagined—the silk had been ruined by an attack of moth.

The old lady's temper was not improved by the knowledge that she herself had always refused to allow the chest to be opened, for fear of the temptation it might provoke, and though the maid tried not to look at her mistress the thought was in the air: "Lay not up for yourselves treasures upon earth, where moth and rust doth corrupt . . ." for the Bible then was on the tip of everybody's tongue [2].

Martha was quick-witted; she thrust the remains of the shawl into a basket and plunging to the bottom of the chest, brought out a silver mug and some yellowing but untouched linen napkins. "Mistress," she said, "here is the christening cup of your dear father, Mr. Steadfast Palmer, which will also serve for their firstborn. And I will cut up the shawl and make the most magnificent patchwork quilt and surround ever seen for the cradle."

Abigail quickly seized the cup and admired it, and Martha showed that much of the shawl was still sound. The situation was saved. Needless to say, the quilt, with its special pattern for the bridal bed, had already been made; otherwise the shawl would have been incorporated in that. It was a lesson she never forgot, though she lived to a ripe old age, ruling the family with a rod of iron to the last.

The incident was not unlike a custom of those days when certain things, usually unpleasant, were done to impress the minds of young people at some important event in order that they should not forget it. A fourteen-year-old boy might be asked to witness a will or a contract and then be beaten or thrown into a pond, for in remembering this undeserved punishment, he would also remember the will or the contract.

Not only did Abigail (now Barton) remember the danger of moth, but the happening also taught her that she must always at least consider the opinions of others, though she might not accept them. It was a turn of events that brought prosperity to the farm, for many new ideas were adopted to the great benefit of the family.

Small events have larger consequences; the moths had crept into the chest through an ill-fitting lid and a warped board and had prospered in a comparatively isolated world. Their very success nearly spelled their doom through the next ninety moth-generations or more, for Abigail never forgot to order the common precautions against moth. Abigail made one important observation on this scheme which was a little in advance of her time, considering her social position and her sex.

It was generally concluded in those days that insects and creepy-crawlies in general were spontaneously created out of "corruption," that rotting meat engendered maggots, that dung engendered flies, and shut-up clothes, moths. Abigail accepted this to some extent, but noted first that the clothes were not rotting and, secondly, that the maggots in the clothes turned into moths; hence she argued the moths could turn into maggots. There was even some confusion over the name, for the word "moath" had once meant the maggot, but now meant the flying creature—which to her suggested a close association between them. Ever practical, she decided to try keeping the moths away from the clothes by having a chest made with a very tight-fitting lid; fortunately, the clothes she put into it were free of eggs and larvae, so her theory was triumphantly vindicated. But one of her daughters was not so successful with "mother's mothproof chest," which she left unopened, full of clothes, for two years, because moth eggs had gone into the chest on the clothes when first put there and throve in their closed community—for it happened that no parasites had gone in with them, nor could they get in to restore the balance. Mother's mothproof chest became a family joke.

Abigail's ideas were in the air. William Harvey, the king's physician, published his book on the engendering of animals thirty-seven years before Abigail died, and his dictum *"Omne vivum ex ovo"* had appeared in one of the newsletters which they received from London from time to time and had greatly intrigued her—though it did seem to flout the Old Testament, for did not the Book say, "Out of the lion came forth sweetness"?

How often at Bartons did the humans go to their stores to take out a special garment and find it moth-eaten! What feverish last-minute repairs were made; what firm resolutions were passed never to let it happen again, only to be broken and the cycle to repeat itself. The moth population grew to its height during the tenancy of Elkanah Hoag. This was because anything unwanted was pushed into a corner or a loft,

a minimum of cleaning was done, and all the scavenging creatures throve. The clothes moth population dropped dramat-
ically when the house was empty, from 1782 to 1788. It was
no longer warm and the almost inexhaustible supply of dry
litter continually provided by man ceased to come forward.

A change took place from 1788, when Stephen Deane purchased the house. Though it was restored, painted, and cleaned,
the clothes moth population again rose a little; food was once
more available. However, a hundred years later it had risen
yet again for three main reasons: First, the heavy nineteenth-
century drapes and furnshings supplied plenty of food. Second, gas lighting and central heating, primitive though they
were, kept the house much warmer and thus shortened the
life cycle of the species. Third, the English sparrows' nests
and winter roosts provided a constant source of reinfection,
whatever measures the house-proud ladies took against their
enemies.

Because the clothes moths have proved such a continuous
menace to man's goods, they have had at least one far-reaching
effect on him, for the insecticidal properties of DDT were
uncovered in 1939 while Dr. Paul Müller, a Swiss chemist, was
looking for new mothproofing agents for fabrics. It is interesting to note the long delay between the first making of that
chemical—which was synthesized by Professor O. Zeidler in
1874 at Strasbourg—and the discovery of its insecticidal properties—sixty-five years. DDT started a new epoch; it is such a
powerful insecticide and can kill so many disease-bearing insects (malaria and yellow fever mosquitoes, plague fleas,
typhus lice, and houseflies, to name a few) that millions of
people who would in the ordinary way be dead from those
causes are now alive and healthy [42].

DDT is a complex organo-chlorine molecule, its name being
derived from the initials of its chemical formula. An anonymous
English pest-control expert composed an ingenious, nicely
scanning limerick combining a tribute to the substance's insecticidal powers with its chemical name:

The mosquito was heard to complain,
That the chemists had poisoned his brain.

The cause of his sorrow
Was para-dichloro-
Diphenyl-trichloro-ethane.

Nowadays the side effects of DDT (by means of food chain accumulations in wildlife) are thought to make it too dangerous for general use in the United States.

In wartime, soldiers are particularly liable to infestation by insects, including lice, often carrying some of the fatal diseases mentioned above. The treatment of the Allied armies' men with DDT (and HCH) saved the lives of thousands, as it did also of the civilians in Naples after the German withdrawal in the second World War. In that conflict, for the first time in the history of war, more people were killed by bombs and bullets than by disease. One of the major errors Hitler made was in not treating his soldiers with DDT. They became heavily infested with lice, enabling the Allied Medical Command, after comparing infection rates of the opposing armies, dryly to comment that "for every infected allied soldier there were 300 lousy Germans."

Would the insecticidal uses of DDT have been discovered so soon had the clothes moth not been so persistent? Taking this into account, we can perhaps say that the moth has been beneficial to man, for the discoveries (DDT and other synthetics) engendered by the moth's activities has both kept down many murderous diseases and has shown what could be done, thus leading the way to the discovery of alternative methods of insect control.

The other clothes moths were also found at Bartons, though they were not so numerous as the "webbing" variety just discussed. The casebearer clothes moth is very similar to the webbing moth and has adapted the habit of the feeding tube to the point where this article forms a permanent home, carried around by the larva. The case is made of silk and pieces of the food material, and in this respect is similar to the feeding tube of the common clothes moth. It is broader in the middle than at the ends which allows the larva to turn round and feed from either end at will; rarely is the insect able to live without its case. It is white, four tenths of an inch long, and has a dark head. It feeds in much the same way as the common clothes moth but can adapt itself to feeding on a stranger variety of vegetable products than can the common species. Dried aconite root, cayenne pepper, horseradish, mustard seed, ginger, and similar drugs and spices it seems to relish, as well as the more common high-protein vegetable foods used by its cousin, the common clothes moth.

The larva pupates inside its case and usually the adult does not emerge from it until the following spring. The moths themselves are mainly found from June to October, though there is much overlapping of generations. They are about the same size as the common clothes moth. The wings themselves —the forewings—are dusky brown with three well-marked spots on each. The male moths usually hold their antennae erect, while the females fold them flat along the wings. They shun light when disturbed and run to cover rather than fly, in much the same way as the common species.

The third clothes moth, the carpet moth, was only occasionally found in the house, though it was fairly common in the stables and harness room of the farm, as it has a definite preference for feathers and skins, especially if they are raw. It is sometimes called the tapestry moth, since when found in houses it is frequently in these hangings. Horse collars and the hair stuffing of carriages were once much attacked by this creature.

The adult moths have a wingspan of about three quarters of an inch, the males again being smaller than the females. The head is white, as is also the base of the forewings; the lower halves of the wings are white, sometimes speckled with black. When the moth is at rest it has a protective coloration suggesting a bird dropping, which points to the fact that it is a bird-associated insect and has turned to man's "dry litter" comparatively recently. The larvae are similar to, though rather bigger than, those of the webbing and casebearer clothes moths.

Both this creature and the casebearer only throve under the crowded and strained conditions in which Elkanah Hoag lived. Bartons does not know them at present except for a stray introduction now and then from a bird's nest, or from an occasional one flying in from the farm buildings.

The brown house moth entered Bartons as a scavenger of

vegetable remains, then turned to man's vegetable food and finally to his animal products. The adult female has a wing span of about an inch, the male again being rather smaller. The forewings are dark brown in color and have blackish spots on each, two together near the center and the third halfway between this and the wing tips; a number of small black dots are found at the end of the wing. The general outline of the moth when at rest is much broader and more oval than that of the pointed or narrow clothes moths.

The fully grown larva is about three quarters of an inch in length, of a shining white color with a tawny-yellow head. It constructs no feeding tube, but moves around freely in its medium, occasionally spinning a little silk webbing.

The brown house moth first established itself in the attic at Bartons, from whence it passed to the hall, where it lived on straw, chaff, rushes, and waste grain left in old sacks and skeps. Once in the house, it turned to such food as peas, oats, and barley, and any dead insects it came across.

From these successful beginnings it turned toward the drier litter in the house, attacking the stuffing of the chairs, furs, and the leather bindings of books. When it attacked books, those on the lower shelves were the first to suffer, for the moth rather liked damp situations. Consequently it was very much at home in the cellar, which was always damp until the boiler was installed there. It now has such a wide feeding range that it is capable of causing much damage to man.

It did, indeed, cause the Deanes considerable annoyance. The family in the nineteenth century were becoming more and more prosperous, and the Civil War did their business no harm, as they supplied many goods needed by the Union Army (and, rumor had it, to the Confederates too). Stephen II (born 1791) was not a hard drinker; in fact, he considered himself a temperance advocate and urged that everyone should drink wine instead of hard liquor. His father, Stephen I (born 1765), had experimented with the local indigenous grapes and made a considerable quantity of *labrusca* wine, which he (Stephen I) much enjoyed. Stephen II, from his Harvard days onward a man of the world, rather despised the native vintage and drank only imported wines, becoming quite a specialist in the vintages of Bordeaux and Oporto.

To celebrate the peace he imported three barrels of *premier cru* claret from Chateau Margaux, France, and a hogshead of port. His shipping contacts greatly facilitated this transaction. The consignment arrived safely at Bartons and was put in the east wing cellar. When it had settled, elaborate measures were taken for its bottling, one difficulty being to find corks.

In November 1865 a team was assembled to bottle the wine, to drink the health of the united country and the brave new world opening up before them now that secession and slavery were dead. Some nine hundred bottles of the best wine were laid in the cellars in racks and bins, and the brown house moth set to work on the corks, for that is another substance the ubiquitous insect can digest.

The damage was not noticed for some time, for the wine was stacked in the new, specially prepared wine bins, bottle on top of bottle, most of them with a dab of white paint on the upper side, thus enabling the bottle to be brought to the dining room without disturbing the deposit, especially in the case of the port wine. Stacked in this way, the bottles were used from the top downward while brown house moth was working the corks from the bottom upward, in the same way as with the books.

An elderly black butler was employed by Stephen II, and when Stephen was informed by his servant that he had found a half empty bottle of port, the master took no notice. But when the butler reported that he had found four more partially empty bottles the worthy merchant was convinced that old Joseph was drinking more of the wine than any old servant might reasonably be expected to do and remonstrated with him. Joseph, the soul of honesty, who drank only the leftovers, was most upset and he and Stephen started a grand investigation.

Old Joseph's cry of "There's maggots in the corks, sir," nearly caused Stephen to have heart failure. What seemed like hundreds of the bottles had been attacked; where a larva had started to bore inward, a little frass might be seen, and where the creature had bored its way out, to pupate, there the little silken case and more frass appeared. As cork is full of cells containing air, no problem of the insects' breathing when deep in the cork arose, and if they required moisture they had but to turn to the damp side of the cork, holding back, as it was, a vast reservoir of liquid. This indeed was their undoing, for the cork was holding back a strongly fortified wine, one containing some 18 percent of alcohol, and no animal is likely to live for long once it tries to inhabit such a world.

After the excitement had died down, old Joseph and Stephen made a closer examination, and it was seen that the damage was really very little, for any larva that had penetrated far enough to reach the wine was very soon too full of port to continue its activities, suffering a fate akin to that of the memorable Duke of Clarence. In fact, most of the insects were repelled by this dangerous fluid. A few larval mines reached so near to the end of the cork that wine seeped into it and slowly penetrated to the outside, accounting for the five half-empty bottles that had been found, but there were no more than a dozen similarly affected and these were in bottles that had poor quality cork in them, or corks that had already been used once and had been penetrated by a corkscrew.

"This has got to stop," said Stephen, "and the remedy is wax, hot wax."

The necks were all cleaned with a rag and the corks carefully painted with a mixture of beeswax and tallow, a task which took them a good two weeks. This treatment preserved the corks from further attack. The brown house moth's experiment was not a very successful one for the race, nor was Stephen and Joseph's work with the wax very necessary, because the wine was slowly seeping into and penetrating the corks, a fractional separation of the water and the alcohol taking place as the alcohol penetrated more rapidly than the water (in fact, this was the "partition effect" which is the basis of the modern chromatographic methods of analysis). Consequently no moth would have been likely to lay eggs on the cork after the wine had been there for a year, nor after this period would any larva get far in a cork, even if eggs had been laid on it, before it was overcome by the fumes. After the two men had treated the port wine bottles they had a look at the Bordeaux section. Here the brown house moth had been much more successful, because of the lower alcohol content of the table wine. Those bottles were then waxed.

Today, of course, commercially bottled wine has the corks protected from the moth with a metal or plastic capsule. It is quite possible that wines improve more in noncapsuled bottles than in capped ones, because there is a very slow exchange of air through the cork which cannot take place when a capsule hermetically seals a bottle. Today one often finds that capsules of expensive wines (particularly German ones) have a few holes punched in them, over the end of the cork, which allow this gas exchange to take place—and the moth to push an egg or so into the cork, too!

Nonalcoholic fluids would have been still better for the moths, as in fact proved to be the case at Bartons, for Stephen's father, Stephen Deane I, had great faith in the mineral water from Stafford Springs as a corrective of his gouty condition and had imported and bottled a considerable quantity of it. Stephen II always maintained that the local water was as good as or better than the Connecticut fluid, and considerably cheaper. After the old gentleman died, Stephen II forgot about the fifty or so Stafford bottles still left in the cellar, but when examining the wine corks, Stephen and Joseph also inspected the dust-covered remains of his father's Stafford bottles. Nearly every one was empty, the corks having been eaten out by the brown house moth.

Three other creatures—spider beetles, hide beetles, and carpet beetles or woolly bears—also attacked man's goods in the house in much the same way as the clothes moths, but specialized in high-protein materials such as leather, wool, dried meat, skins, stuffed birds, and so forth. The most important family is the Dermestidae and nearly all the damage is done by the larvae of the insects, as many of the adults feed only on pollen and nectar from flowers or scarcely feed at all. Like the clothes moths, they are adapted to living on foods with low water content, are great scavengers, and would clean up the bodies of dead rodents and birds found in the house. In fact, they are sometimes used to clean a skeleton before it is mounted for lecture and scientific purposes. In the nests of birds and rodents they would live on any high-protein discarded material, such as hair and feathers. Nests and dead animals served as a source of infective material for their attacks on the human stocks of food and clothing. The bacon hanging in the chimney was colonized at times by the bacon beetle (which gave rise to the story that bats eat bacon). Stuffed birds were only another dead animal to these creatures and were soon attacked, but the greatest loss they caused was the destruction of the mask and brush of Stephen Deane I's fox—a trophy mounted and hung over the fireplace to celebrate a famous run made when he took over the mastership of the pack in 1857. Four years later it had been so eaten by hide beetles that it had to be burned, an event which annoyed the intrepid master very much more than the capture of Fort Sumter by the Confederates. Carpets and felting under carpets were also attacked, and the woolly bears are still occasionally found when old felt is taken up, but in general the vacuum cleaner has reduced the population to very small numbers, as it removes eggs, young larvae, and adults.

The larvae of these beetles have one habit that causes damage to man. When ready to pupate they bore passages to points near the surface, so that the adults can easily emerge into the open air. In so doing they may need to pass through inedible substances. They often penetrate the wood of boxes containing food, and they have been known to eat into lead-covered electric cable, which may short-circuit wires or lead to telephone breakdowns. They frequently attack hides, and the woodwork of vessels carrying these is particularly liable to be bored into by Dermestids; for instance, in 1593 the timbers of the good ship *Thomas Cavendish*, bringing back a cargo of penguin skins, were so used for pupation galleries by these insects moving out of the skins that she took in water and was lost.

The clothes moths were not the only dry-litter insects that benefited from the presence of man at Bartons. A number of other insects that attacked his food were also found from time to time, particularly in the early days. Some of them showed a considerable adaptation to very specialized environments, and all of them were able to economize their water resources.

In the early days of the farm the Bartons stored large

quantities of grain and flour in the house, in addition to the grain stored on the farm both in bins and unthreshed in the ricks. Regular visits were paid to the water mill in the village with one or two hundred pounds of grain which was returned as flour a week later, and as the roads might be very bad in winter, a considerable stock of flour was held in the house, at least in the cold months, to provide against the family having to go hungry in bad weather.

The miller was Experience Barton's uncle by marriage, by name Mark Gascoyne; he had married John Barton's younger sister, Jane, and had been put into the mill by his brother-in-law, it was said, on account of the size of his thumb. The thumb that went *inside* the measure of every peck of grain or gallon of flour handled was that much extra profit to the miller—except, of course, when the miller was measuring grain or flour which he took, instead of money, in payment for the work done. Then he used both hands to grasp the measure, thus keeping his thumb out of it. The right to grind corn and the size of the miller's thumb were both recurrent causes of dispute and constant jokes of the countryside.

The preservation of the grain sound and wholesome throughout the year was ever an anxiety to the settlers. There were three dangers: the first, that it might not be very healthy to begin with; the second, that it would go moldy; and the third, that it would be spoiled by insects. Wheat, barley, and oats could be attacked by the bunt disease, or stinking smut, which causes the grain to be filled with a black dust of fungus spores instead of flour. When the attack was bad the release of this black dust into the flour, when the grain was ground, gave it a fishy taste and violet color that were much disliked; such flour was frequently used for making gingerbread, in which the taste and color could be disguised.

Wheaten bread was rather a luxury and usually the Bartons used a mixture of corn, wheat, barley, and beans. If any of these came too moist from the threshing, or were kept in damp places, they would go moldy, and in fact, farmers and millers frequently had to dry the grain to prevent this loss—"drying with ashes" is an item often found in millers' accounts.

The third danger was the attack of insects in grain and flour, and the first insect to take advantage of what was for it a large stock of food in the house was the grain weevil. The weevils are a family of beetles having long blunt snouts that bear antennae about halfway along their length; and the grain weevil belongs to the subfamily of weevils that has come to be particularly objectionable to man, for many of them attack his crops, and others the harvest in storage. The bean weevils destroy both seed and plant, the cotton boll weevil is notorious, and the turnip gall weevil, palm weevil, and rice weevil are a few more.

The grain weevil spread round the world in the train of explorer, trader, and conqueror. The adult weevil is just under a quarter of an inch in length and is dark brown or black in color. It is a very strongly protected insect, being well armored with a coat of thick chitin—the insect integument—and a strong pair of wing cases, or elytra, which are possessed by all beetles and are really the forewings. Owing to its sturdy construction, the beetle is able to resist the crushing action of great weights of grain and so survive in conditions that would squash softer insects. When once the beetles get into grain they feed on it, boring in with their long snouts, sometimes consuming the whole of the contents of a grain and at others taking only a taste. After mating, the females are ready to lay eggs and show some skill in selecting suitable sites, for the seed chosen for this purpose must not only be

GRAIN WEEVIL

big enough to nourish the larvae, but must also contain enough water.

The insects show something of their southern origin in displaying a preference for warm places for depositing their eggs. The female bores out a deep hole in the selected seed with her snout, then turns round and deposits an egg in it, immediately sealing over the hole with a gelatinous excretion which hardens at once. The females prefer grain that offers easy access; the most attacked is hulled barley, next to which they prefer rye and then wheat. They do not like unthreshed grain. Up to about five eggs per day may be laid, with a total of about two hundred per season. Only one egg is deposited in each seed of such small grains as barley and wheat, but two or three may be laid in such large grains as maize and beans. The adults live about seven or eight months. The eggs hatch in a week to ten days according to the temperature, and the larvae live entirely within the grain, eating out all the interior until only a shell of bran is left; the larva literally creates its own living space by eating away its surroundings, which takes some four to eight weeks unless a cold period intervenes, when activity ceases, to be resumed with a rise of temperautre. The larva pupates within the grain, taking about a week, when the tiny weevil is formed within the cavity, which it quickly breaks open to reach a more generous supply of oxygen on the exterior. The insect is very vulnerable at this stage, as it is soft and can easily be crushed by any movement of the grain. It is at first a light brown in color, but after about four days, darkens as the skin hardens. It is then ready to mate and start the cycle over again; there may be from one to four generations per year. These weevils not only consume a lot of grain but foul much more with their excrements, on which bacteria tend to develop, raising the temperature of the grain store and further hastening the development of the weevils.

In the bad years at Bartons all this weevil-infested and broken grain had to go to the mill, where it made a very poor flour and a worse bread, but in good years with abundant harvests the damaged corn was set aside for feeding poultry and pigs. The Bartons and their successors were well aware of the damage weevils could cause them and the difficulty of

188 ¾ THE LIVING AMERICAN HOUSE

assessing the extent of the attack, because the female weevil, in laying the egg, covers her tracks so well that it is almost impossible to see which grain is sound and which potentially wormy. A rough and ready test had been devised, however: When a handful of grain was thrown into a bowl of water, the good would sink and the attacked would float.

The Bartons took certain measures against these losses; they knew that grain kept in sealed vessels would remain free from weevil, not only from their own practical experience but also because it was a measure recommended by the classical authors (it can be found in Pliny's *Natural History*). What happens is that the living grain is respiring, as are also the insects. Oxygen is taken in and carbon dioxide given out, and in a sealed vessel, the latter heavy gas accumulates and eventually kills the insects. The Bartons kept a reserve of grain in tightly closed barrels, in stone ewers, and sometimes in open barrels on the top of which a layer of dry sand and road dust was placed. That method was successful, provided the grain went into the barrel sufficiently dry, for if it were damp the grain would be free of weevil but would be ruined by mold, or by an attack of grain mites.

One of the advantages the settlers found in America was that the grain from their harvests was much drier than that they were accustomed to find in Europe, so it was not so likely to go moldy and it resisted the weevil too. But of course it could absorb moisture during the long cold winter, and so had to be watched. When the water content of grain reached 14 percent the weevil liked it, though in fact it can breed in grain down to 10 percent moisture, but much more slowly. The insect finds it almost impossible to live in grain with 5 percent or less of humidity. But temperature was also important. The weevils were quiescent when the grain took on the winter temperature. If the grain is also treated with an inert sharp dust such as gypsum or road dust, which is mostly ground-down flint, the dust will absorb water from the grain and will also scratch the skin of the beetles and break the prot ctive layer sealing in their water. This has the effect of increasing their need for water and making them that much more vulnerable, and of slowing or totally destroying their development.

These facts were known in an empirical way to the ancient Egyptians. Joseph, when he collected the surplus harvest of the seven fat years, seems to have stored the grain in the ear in pits beneath a layer of Nile mud, which in that climate would rapidly become dust, so that he was able to feed good grain to the population during the seven lean years. In the ancient world people lived close to nature and could solve some problems in an unscientific yet effective manner.

Spilled grain around the farm buildings and in the house is the great reservoir of population for the grain weevil. Little piles of it in corners by the bins, carried down into holes by mice and rats to their winter hoards, and so on, are the places where the insect continues to breed, whatever man may do to keep his main stores free from attack, and where they are still found to this day in spite of the many improvements on the farm. Nevertheless, the population has slowly fallen from the time when the house was first built, because, as civilization developed, less and less whole grain was kept.

Experience Barton, who died in 1723, was the last person to send his own grain to the mill and bring it back as flour. Prudence Barton purchased flour by the sack from the local store and baked bread once a week. Sophrinia Deane (1840–1905) was the last in the house to bake her own bread as a regular thing, though the restaurant now bakes its own rolls, using fairly sophisticated machinery, as it adds to the appeal of the establishment.

All this led to scarcely any grain being kept in the house, other than tailings for chicken feed; the small grain in that is not very acceptable to the weevil, both because of its size and because, being small, it dries more readily. There was scarcely any grain weevil in the house during the late nineteenth century; it was one of the few animals whose numbers grew less at that time. By 1902 there were no grain weevils at all, because all the reserves of grain had been used up, mostly by the mice in their efforts to continue their existence in such desirable quarters.

When John Barton VII ran the place he kept chickens and fed them largely on a purchased grain mixture, as well as on "laying mash." Though this mixture was mostly tailings, it did contain quite a proportion of corn, large enough for occasional invasion by the grain weevil even though it was of poor quality. Consequently, the insect is still found at Bartons from time to time but never in the large numbers common during the first hundred and fifty years of the house. The adult insects either fly in from the farm, are brought in on sacks, or are actually in the chicken food when purchased.

When the grain had been converted to flour the material was by no means secure from attack. The grain weevil could still feed on it, though it seldom does, but there are other insects more adapted to living in this loose medium. In nature, such insects follow the attack of the grain weevil, consuming

FLOUR BEETLE

the loose flour that falls from corn damaged and broken by the weevil.

The common followers of the grain weevil—the mealworm, the adults of which are known as the cellar beetle, and the dark mealworm—are the larvae of two species of beetles, not weevils. The adults of the mealworm are black in color and lay eggs (from about eighty to five hundred each) in all kinds of flour, bran, middlings, biscuit meal, and so forth, each egg or parcel of eggs being carefully wrapped in a covering of flour kneaded into a paste with saliva to protect it. The larva is known as the yellow mealworm from its shining yellow color, and when fully grown is about an inch in length, thin and cylindrical, with a number of bristle hairs on the body segments that help it force its way through the floor. This larval stage lasts one and a half years, so that the insect does not breed very quickly compared with the increase in numbers of the grain weevils. It grows fastest in the damper and warmer portions of the medium and can turn to other food as well as flour, as it also eats scraps of meat; this insect has even been found in association with the deathwatch beetle, following up the softening of the wood started by that well-known borer. The dark mealworm has a very similar history; the larva is darker and tinged with brown and its larval stage takes longer—two years. Much smaller, though similar, grubs sometimes found in the flour as well were the larvae of the common flour beetles.

Little Tryphena Barton used to hide a jar of flour at the back of the cupboard in order to encourage mealworms which she used as food for her animal pets, particularly her tame bat; but she also fed them to robins and some toads.

These insects were only found in the house when considerable stocks of flour were kept, or where much grain had been split and neglected. As mentioned above, grain stopped going to the mill around 1723. The Bartons still bought flour, a sack or two at a time, and this often contained the eggs, if not young larvae, of the mealworms, although they were not at all common insects in the house except when specially bred for the purpose of feeding animals. They reached their peak with the Hoags, who were careless and spilled grain and flour all over the place, forming ideal centers of population for this type of dry-litter creature. The insects are not found in the house today, because though the restaurant keeps considerable stocks of flour, it comes from mills which are regularly cleaned and disinfested.

As international commerce increased, so did the opportunities for these once rare animals, for wherever man moved his supplies of food, there went also the creatures living on it. All the time the people at Bartons were living on their own resources—on food they themselves raised—they had to preserve it from attack of only the indigenous animals, but when food from other countries started to arrive in quantity, new creatures were introduced with it. Many of these died because they could not live under the new conditions, but a few throve because they could and because their natural enemies had been left behind and did not exist in the new environment. One of these was the Angoumois grain moth, so called because it did so much damage to wheat in the district of that name in France in the mid-eighteenth century. The insect's ravages were an important factor leading to the French Revolution

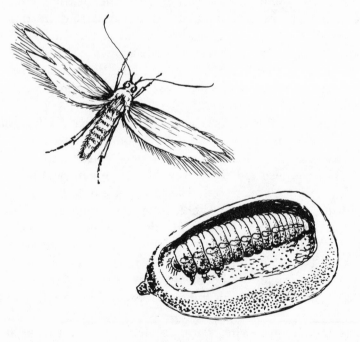

FLOUR MOTH

because, with their crops destroyed, the farmers were unable to pay their taxes, from which the "aristos" and clergy were exempt. The distress was relieved to some extent by a scientific study made by a M. Duhamel du Monceau [38]. He advocated heating the grain in kilns, or exposing it to the sun in thin layers. Both practices spread to New England and helped control this trouble.

Beans were an important food for the Indians and the immigrants and considerable quantities were stored over the winter and spring. Boston, of course, was famous for them. Beans and peas were particularly liable to attack by storage pests, especially the pea bug (also called the bean weevil). The pea bug belongs to the family *Bruchidae*, the members of which are able to attack legume seeds both in the field and in storage.

Some of the early farmers took the usual remedies against them, such as storing the seed dry in closed stone jars and frequently shifting the beans around to disturb eggs and adults. One practice in the seventeenth and early eighteenth centuries was to take off one's "go-to-meeting" boots on a Sunday afternoon and fill them with seed beans, which thus acted as boot trees, keeping one's best pair in good shape. The following Sunday the seed was emptied out and the boots drawn on. The constant movement did much to upset the life cycle of the pea bug and preserve the seed for the farmer.

At the house in the 1680s, where putting beans in the boots was practiced by Experience Barton, one of the hidden penalties for not going to meeting every Sunday was an increase in the infestation of the seed by the weevil, because the insects were able to grow in the undisturbed conditions. Experience never knew the real reason for the increased infection of his seed and put it down to the Lord's disapproval and punishment for not going to meeting, which in a way it was, for wearing his "go-to-meeting" boots and rebeaning them every Sunday would have halved his losses.

In 1848 one of Stephen Deane's cousins (also a Mr. S. Deane) wrote an article on this insect; it was printed in the *Boston Cultivator* [14].

The Mediterranean flour moth is actually indigenous to

Central America but it reached the United States from France, carried in ships' stores. Both moths found the New England conditions suited them: Nuclei for infection were in spilled grain on the farms and in stores accumulated by mice in their burrows. Neither are found at present in the house, as everything is kept so much cleaner.

9

~

ADAPTERS

THE INSECTS of the dry-litter community were not the only
animals at Bartons that found a prosperous new environment in man's goods; there were many others as well who
did not come originally from a dry-litter world but nevertheless
adapted themselves to living in or on houses. Some birds and
mice are obvious examples, but there are a number of other
animals that find life in a house very advantageous, though
usually in places rather damper than those selected by the
true dry-litter animals. Mites and insects were the chief
creatures that took advantage of man's providing himself with
better food and shelter. The short-lived thatch at Bartons
harbored a considerable community of mites at one time, some
of them parasitic on other animals, but there were three mites
which were numerous on food and furniture from time to
time.

Mites are not insects; they are very small creatures with
eight legs and are related to the spiders. On animals and man
they can cause mange and scabies, but at Bartons the principal
mites were those attacking grain and flour. The grain and
flour mite followed on the attacks of the grain weevil. They
can occur in vast numbers. In grain they bore into the seed
and destroy the germ, and in flour they select this part upon
which to feed and thus deprive it of a valuable constituent.
They give a musty, tainted flavor to cereals when even comparatively small numbers are present; in the early days at
Bartons when complaints were made about the quality of the
bread, it was not all due to the stinking smut disease in the

wheat but in part to mites attacking the flour. The flour or grain has to be moderately moist in order for the mite to thrive—they need about 12 percent of moisture—and a high humidity in the atmosphere. Surprisingly enough, the mites do not require very high temperatures, being content with a range between 65° and 75°F, and as a consequence only certain parts of the flour, such as a damp surface layer, may be attacked.

The mites are very small and look like dust when they fall from a sack of grain; the adult mites are oval, grayish creatures with eight legs and about one fiftieth of an inch long. The females lay minute eggs in the flour at a rate of some twenty-five a day, each one some five thousandths of an inch in diameter. These soon hatch out into six-legged larvae, which at once start to feed and reach their first molt in a few days, after which they emerge with four pairs of legs, feed and grow and molt again. From the second molt they can emerge in one of three forms, either as an adult mite or in one of two kinds of resting stages. In one of these last, the legs are somewhat reduced and the abdomen is provided with a sucker by which they can attach themselves to other animals frequenting their environment, such as mice, flies, beetles, and so forth. In the other resting stage, the legs are much reduced and the body becomes very compact and light so that they can be carried into the air by the wind. In both these states they can endure successfully much more adverse conditions than as eggs, nymphs, or adults, for they survive both cold (below freezing-point) and heat (over 100°F). As they also resist dry conditions more readily in this form, these resting states are a means by which the animal can be widely disseminated.

When these mites became numerous in damp flour, molds were also found; the movement of the creatures about the flour helped spread the spores of the fungus and so further spoiled the Bartons' hard-won supplies. The flour mites did not have it all their own way though, because they in their turn were preyed upon by other creatures, which kept their numbers down. Their biggest enemy was a rather smaller diamond-shaped mite which fed on the flour mite and thus got its food from man at second hand. The predatory mites throve best under warm conditions, whereas the flour mites were more

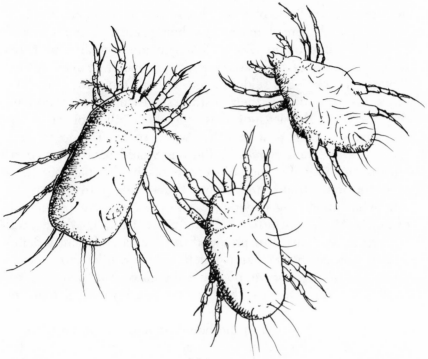

MITES

sensitive to humidity, with the result that their relative numbers rose and fell with the seasons. The flour mite numbers tended to rise in the winter, and this rise was followed by an increase of the predatory mites in the summer, due both to the ample supply of food and to the increase in temperature.

These mites were quite serious pests of grain and flour in the years of bad harvest weather, because the grain would be damp, as would also the resulting flour. After the beginning of the eighteenth century little grain was kept in the house (though plenty of flour was still stored there), so the mite population began to fall. The decrease was accelerated by the false scorpions, or *Cheliferidae*, which feed both on the actual flour mites themselves and on their predatory associates. These false scorpions are quite small creatures, about one eighth of an inch long, and bear a pair of strong claws very like those of a scorpion. They used to come into the house in the sacks of grain, from whence they would spread to any flour being attacked by mites. They were not very numerous when the only grain actually kept in the house was the chicken food.

The population of mites and their predators in the house again fell when bread was no longer made regularly, as naturally the stocks of flour kept there were much smaller; nevertheless the house has seldom been without them for long. The mites are ubiquitous; their resting stages can be carried on the wind, on the legs of flies, spiders, clothes of man, fur of animals, and a host of other ways, so from time to time the cooks and housewives at Bartons would have the experience of opening the flour bin (particularly if it had not been used for some time) and seeing the surface move gently—a somewhat unnerving experience—due to a massive population of mites. This is encouraged at the present day by the central heating in the house, for provided the flour is sufficiently damp (a bag may easily get damp if left near a window, from condensation of the hot air on the cold glass) and a few mites reach it by some means, the heat ensures a rapid increase of population.

Another mite found in the house, though not in large numbers, is the cheese mite. It is very similar to the flour mites in appearance, requirements of moisture, temperature, and life history, except that no resting stage is formed. Small pockets of mites in such cheeses as Stilton add to the "ripeness"; they are found as small holes with an accumulation of brown dust in them, which dust contains living mites, their cast skins, and excreta. In some cheeses, such as the German Altenburger, a colony of mites is deliberately added to the cheese in order to give it its characteristic flavor. Cheese mites must share with oysters and similar shellfish the distinction of being among the few animal foods still eaten alive by man. The cheese mite population had two peaks, one during the time of Stephen Deane and the other at the present moment, as one of the specialities of Bartons House Restaurant is very ripe cheeses. Stephen Deane II used to "feed" his cheese with port wine, which tended to delay the ripening, for the alcohol at first inhibited the growth of fungi and animals, but as it evaporated it left the cheese pleasantly moist with several cracks and pockets in which mites could develop.

The fourth mite found in any numbers in the house was the

furniture mite. It was common in hay and straw on the farm and from there had soon established itself in the thatch, where it throve, together with the predators mentioned above. From the thatch it spread at times to the grain and flour in the house and to birds' nests, but its greatest effect on man was when it established itself on the stuffing of Stephen Deane's Victorian furniture. The "horsehair" sofa of the drawing room was actually stuffed with a common substitute for horsehair—green Algerian fiber—and as the room was seldom used, it got very damp; the mite blew in from the farmyard and crept inside the upholstery, where it found an ideal environment, feeding on a mold growing on the fiber and the leather. The mites would crawl out of the cracks in the furniture and be seen as a gray dust on the dark leather. Alice Deane often accused her help of neglecting to dust the parlor, until one day she actually noticed that the dust was moving. She was most concerned and wanted to have the offending article burned; however, her husband had all the leather furniture moved into the barn and sent for the upholsterers, who took out all the stuffing, painted all the cracks with turpentine—which killed the mites in them and some of the wood-boring beetle larvae as well—dressed the leather, and replaced the old stuffing with horsehair. There have been no further outbreaks in furniture, but a haybox was made during the second World War, in order to conserve fuel. At the end of the war it lay in a cupboard, damp and forgotten; the molds started to grow, and soon the mites were thriving again—a short-lived triumph that ended on a bonfire after they had betrayed themselves in the usual way by "dust" falling from the attacked article.

Just before the first hurricane (there was another in 1938) the thatch was about one year old and the lower layers were rather damp. Mites accumulated here in considerable numbers, but most of them were destroyed in 1635 when shingles replaced the thatch. As the shingles aged and as moisture gathered where they overlapped, the mite population began to grow again, especially near the chimneys which kept the area warm during the winter. These mites were also found in the damp parts of the cellars until the original one was dried out by the installation of a coal-burning boiler in 1860.

The clover mite, or *Bryobia*, invaded the house from time

to time. It tends to form conspicuous bright red patches on a damp wall or piece of dark furniture. It is not really doing any harm; it does not attack humans or animals, though it may spread the spores of molds and bacteria. An interesting characteristic of the species is that it appears to be able to do without males; at any rate, none have ever been found and the species thrives, at times becoming a pest of clover and other crops. Whether there is any lesson in this for modern man (literally man, as distinct from woman) is difficult to say. Several of these red patches, some of which seemed to be gently heaving as the creatures moved around looking for food, greatly alarmed Mrs. Hoag in the fall of 1775 and induced that already overworked woman to a spate of extra activity in cleaning the house. A temporary improvement resulted, but the house fell back to its neglected condition again during the difficulties of the Revolutionary War. Patches still appear from time to time in the roof but are seldom seen, so cause no alarm. Other mites are, however, still to be found in the house. Molds still grow in damp corners in the roof and in old birds' nests, and winter condensation from time to time provides damp pockets where these and similar creatures establish themselves; they have been known to make a colony in the restaurant's choice Stilton alongside the true cheese mites.

The roof also harbored a number of insects known as bristletails and others called springtails. The bristletails soon found their way into the house, where they throve much more readily than in the roof. These insects are very primitive, having survived from remote geological time almost unchanged. They normally live in soil, under stones, on rotting wood and so forth, but having been introduced to man's environment, some of them—in particular two kinds known as the silverfish and the firebrat—find the new circumstances a good field to exploit, one living on sugary and starchy substances such as the binding of books, and the other exploiting any very warm situation, as under stoves and behind firebacks.

Being primitive insects, they have never possessed wings, which makes life simpler for them. Insects have no internal skeleton but rely on a strong outer skin to form a support for their organs, having, as it were, an external skeleton; they grow by casting their outer skins. The old skin is split off several times in the course of an insect's lifetime and each time a new, soft one beneath takes its place, becoming a size larger as it hardens, the creature growing in a series of molts and replacements. Wings, apart from wing-buds, are too complicated to take part in a molt, and the change to a fully winged stage is the last molt a to-be-winged insect makes. After it has become winged it can grow no more. The bristletails, never having had wings, wing-buds, or any semblance of such organs, do not have this complication in their life cycle; they can go on growing by this series of molts for as long as they live, and moreover they can regrow a limb that has been lost or damaged as well. As a result, they can vary considerably in size.

The adult silverfish is about half an inch long, shaped like a carrot, and with silvery pearl-like scales which are scattered from time to time as the insect moves around. On the head

SILVERFISH

they bear long antennae and have three large bristles at the rear. They have a pair of compound eyes and somewhat primitive mouth parts. After mating, the females lay eggs, either singly or in groups of about three and usually placed in cracks or protected spots, but some are casually dropped as the creatures move about. The eggs are very small, about one twenty-fifth of an inch long, and soon hatch, each female laying about one hundred eggs.

Silverfish like carbohydrates and are particularly active where books and papers are found, scraping away the paper to get at the starch paste and actually digesting some of the cellulose. In order to form the substance of their bodies and to lay eggs, they have to obtain protein as well, which they get from the glue and size in bookbindings and from feeding on the bodies of any dead insects they may find, such as remains cast out by spiders or those creatures whose life spans have come to an end, together with unconsidered trifles such as the empty egg cases of cockroaches, and so forth. Silverfish shun the light and when uncovered, as for example when a book is removed from a shelf, they stand still for a moment and then run quickly to shelter. Their greatest difficulty in their new medium is to obtain water; consequently they seek situations which are likely to be damp, such as behind loose wallpaper, under sinks, and so forth. The paste on the paper tends to be hygroscopic and remains damp, and not only water is spilt from sinks, but scraps of starchy and sugary food as well.

Silverfish came into Bartons from the thatch in the early days of the house; as the books accumulated they throve—the first volume they attacked was Herebach's *The Whole Art of Husbandry* which had been given to John Barton III by his father—and they were most numerous there in 1946. In 1952 they were considerably reduced by the insecticidal treatment given to all the woodwork in the house to kill the wood-boring beetles. This did not affect those silverfish actually in books at the time of treatment, nor those behind old wallpaper, and as the insecticide residue on the bookshelves wears off, the silverfish are beginning to build up their numbers again, particularly on the lower, and thus damper, shelves. Their numbers will decline as the newer books replace the old, for pastes and glues made of synthetic resins, used for bookbinding and wallpapering, are replacing the old vegetable and animal products that used to give many insects certain essential elements in their food. Once again a change in the availability of food is more important to the survival of an animal, as a species, than are any of the direct measures taken against it.

The other bristletail eventually found at Bartons was the firebrat, an insect similar to the silverfish and, like that creature, able to continue to grow as an adult; as many as sixty moltings have been recorded under laboratory conditions. It was not as long-lived as that at Bartons; it did not thrive in the old kitchen with its open fireplace, because there were no warm enough cavities for it, but with the installation of the eighteenth-century kitchen and a number of closed spaces behind the stove, the firebrat found an ideal environment, though eventually it had to compete with the cockroach for it. Here the creature increased its numbers very rapidly, as it can develop in much drier situations than the common silverfish. The firebrats would come out at night and feed on the food scraps left in the kitchen, on shelves, fallen to the floor, and so forth. When an electric cookstove was installed in the kitchen in 1932 the old kitchen range was no longer used and the firebrat, which so loves the warmth, gradually faded away there. By this time they had already established themselves in the brickwork beneath the central heating boiler in the cellar, a site which suited them well and where again they had to compete with the cockroaches, more successfully as it turned out because they were more adapted to living on food found in the cellar than the roaches, who had to journey to the kitchen for most of their nourishment. Though cockroaches have now been eliminated from the house, the firebrat is still found in small numbers.

Firebrats have a curious courtship procedure, not unlike that of the display of birds. The male dances in circles round the female and repeatedly touches her with his antennae. The actual mating is somewhat akin to that of spiders in that the male deposits a sperm bag in front of the female and then retires, while the female herself undertakes the necessary movements to absorb it if she so desires. There may well be a parallel here between the action of the female firebrat and the artificial insemination of women, which is at present causing so much controversy.

The books at Bartons, in addition to serving as food and shelter for silverfish, were also occasionally attacked by other insects. There were book lice, bookworms, and the clothes moth. The book lice, or *Psocoptera*, are primitive insects related to the true lice found on birds. Those that occurred in the house came from three sources: the first, the thatch, by way of the birds' nests; the second, in a Bible and some other old books brought to the house when John Barton got married; and the third, from the natural habitat of these insects—the kindling and logs brought into the house where they lived under loose bark, in moss, and in various damp cracks in the wood. They are small insects, about one eighth to one sixteenth of an inch long, yellow or gray in color, and in many cases they are able to dispense with males, the females laying viable eggs without any preliminary fertilization—they are partly parthenogenetic.

The book lice tend to live on molds and other fungi growing in their habitat, so that a certain degree of dampness is needed before they can attack books. In order for the book lice to get the necessary protein, some of the fungi must be living on substances containing nitrogen, such as the leather or the glue of the bindings. Although the females can reproduce without males, these are sometimes present and can make tapping sounds not unlike those made by the deathwatch beetle, and serving the same purpose—that of a mating call.

The book lice increased in the house because of the warmth and shelter it provided, though they never became very numerous. During the time it was empty of humans, they still continued there because so much rubbish had been left behind. As the house dried, due to the installation of the central heating, their numbers declined, but they are still there and take advantage of any damp condition to build up the population. For instance, a large colony was found recently living in the sawdust filling of the partition wall between two of the bedrooms in the house which had become damp from a "weeping" water pipe, and a lot more are slowly consuming Beulah

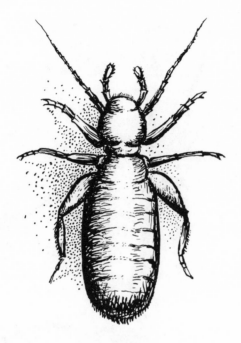

BOOK LOUSE

Beane's juvenilia, lying forgotten at the bottom of a tin trunk in the loft.

A few books were also penetrated by the bookworm, or bread beetle. This is an insect closely related to the common furniture beetle and was originally a grain-feeder, finding it easier living on the debris fallen from broken grain rather than attacking the whole seed. From this field it started living in the stores of food accumulated by hoarding animals, such as mice, rats, and squirrels, but soon found that man had bigger and warmer hoards than any animal and so exploited them as far as possible. It has adapted itself to a wide variety of substances, including such strange ones as belladonna, aconite, and strychnine. In bakeries it often attacks bread; of course, this must be left neglected for some weeks if the insect is to complete its cycle of development, so that at Bartons it bred only in neglected crusts. The eggs were sometimes laid on the old books and the larvae penetrated down into the pages until

BOOKWORM

a full-grown fat grub, turning first to a pupa, then to an adult, would burrow out again to the surface to fly around, find a mate, and start the cycle again.

When Stephen Deane was improving and repairing the house in 1788 and discovered Edward Hopkins (see p. 72), Stephen also found that the strange recluse was reading one of the Bartons' old books—Sir Walter Raleigh's *History of the World*, which had somehow got into the loft and been left there. The book had been much read because, after Raleigh's death (1618), he had become one of the heroes of the settlers in the New World. His *History*, limited though its range was, was an arsenal of political ammunition for the overthrow of absolutism, the divine right of kings, and the encouragement of Puritan feelings in New England [47]. The book was in its original binding, the authenticity of which was shown by the bookworm burrows coinciding in both covers and pages. The care Hopkins had taken in cleaning the book was an additional factor in inducing Stephen to forgive his intruder and offer him employment. Thus the worm galleries were not wholly detrimental to the work, which is now a prized and valuable item in Angela Barton's (b.1960) Boston library and is much coveted by Harvard University.

Another insect which adapted its ways to living in a house was the house cricket. It was a creature that was regarded with affection and even encouraged on account of its cheerful song, and it is still sometimes found in the house. The cricket did, in fact, sing for its supper, though now it lives mostly in the cellar and is only occasionally seen in the upper section of the house. At one time crickets would come out at night from behind the big stove in the old kitchen and feed on the scraps of food dropped during the day; they were very numerous around the bread oven and old hearth.

This insect, belonging to the same family as the locusts and grasshoppers, has its original home in the hot deserts of such regions as Persia and the Sahara, where it finds the climate to its liking. From these areas it has spread in the course of international commerce, concealed in bales of silk, wool, with grain and so forth, but it has also been deliberately carried from place to place by people who enjoyed the sound of its chirruping. The early Chinese much admired the sound and had beautifully carved cages made for their pets. They were popular in Europe too. When Bartons End in Kent, England, was built, crickets were often given to children as presents. At New Bartons the crickets spread out of doors in the summer where they enjoyed themselves in the dry grass and cornfields, and sought cover in the fall. Those that reached a warm house survived, but others that only found a hedge bottom, or even a barn, were rarely able to endure the winter. Some of them got into rubbish dumps, which if they were fermenting were warm, and thus allowed the animals to live through the cold weather, but in the neighborhood of Bartons the race only survived from year to year by colonizing houses for the winter, from which bases they invaded the fields again when the warm weather arrived.

The house crickets, which became such a feature of life at Bartons in the nineteenth century, were not known to the early settlers. The indigenous black cricket and katydids were common and added considerably to the noises of the countryside. The snowy tree cricket even gave an indication to the wakeful at night of what the weather was like outside the tightly drawn curtains and firmly closed windows, for night air, as was well known, was poisonous. It was, too: not on account of the dangerous "miasma" that rose from the soil, as was thought, but because of the mosquitoes which could be carrying malaria, encephalitis, or yellow fever. As to the weather outside, crickets would not sing during rain, and the colder the night the slower were the chirps.

The black crickets sometimes came into the Bartons' house, but never established themselves there. Nevertheless, they could be a nuisance to the humans at times, as was found after the hot summer and good harvest of 1792. In the fall of that year large bands of black crickets invaded the house from the fields and started to consume human food wherever they could find it, bit holes in the damp washing (for the purpose of getting water) and almost deafened the Deanes, who swept them up day after day with brooms until cold weather and food shortage had reduced their numbers to the level of an odd cheerful chirrup from time to time.

The domestic crickets—the "cricket on the hearth"—got to New York in the first quarter of the nineteenth century and spread quickly. By 1875 they were in Bartons, living behind the big stove in the kitchen. Sophrinia Deane used to tell wonderful stories to her grandchildren—Edward, Victoria, and the two youngest sisters—as they sat around the fire on a winter evening. The children loved them and would give the old lady no rest, but at the end of a story, when they pressed her for another, she would say, "No, I must have some quiet and you must listen to the crickets; perhaps they have a message for you." Victoria Deane, encouraged by her grandmother, became a good naturalist; she was interested in the house and the strange story of Edward Hopkins.

The house cricket is another example of an animal successfully adapting itself to a new environment. The reasons for its success were once again both sentimental and practical. It was a creature regarded with affection by the humans and even encouraged on account of its cheerful song. It supplied a background noise, raising a curious parallel with one of today's fashionable practices, by which the production of "mood music" from records or radio is considered essential to any social gathering, study, or the completion of children's homework. Somehow one cannot help feeling that the crickets' chirping would be much pleasanter and less disturbing than today's replacement.

The house cricket is still sometimes found at Bartons in the boiler room, under hot water tanks, and in the kitchen. It is only occasionally seen in the public rooms and even then is taken to be something that has flown in from outside. Today very rarely is its song heard in the house.

On the practical side, the house crickets found warmth and fed on the food scraps dropped during the day. In the 1890s they were very numerous around the old kitchen hearth.

Young Victoria Deane, fascinated by the idea of the message her grandmother spoke of, captured a cricket and kept it in a small Chinese cage her uncle Theophilus had given her. She was very disappointed because it never sang—which was not surprising, since it was a female, for only the males chirrup away. It is a mating call to the females. Victoria soon discovered her mistake and got a whole colony of house crickets together in a big cage, moved into the yard in summer. The singing of the males attracted a few of the females that had escaped into the gardens, farms, and woods. She encouraged them in the house by scattering food and hollowing out spaces beneath the hearths where they could breed. At the age of sixteen she was making a serious study of the Orthoptera and had ventured to criticize the famous Thaddeus William Harris, who had stated there were no crickets in America [20]. Admittedly he first wrote this in 1841, forty-seven years before she was born. "But," she contended, "he repeated his error in 1862," which was only twenty-six years before she appeared

[21]. Alas! She could not forgive such an error, even though her uncle Theophilus showed her that the 1862 statement carried a footnote pointing out the mistake, and that the learned gentleman had died in 1856, and in 1840 perhaps there were few house crickets around Milton, Massachusetts. "And," said Uncle Theophilus, "remember, the State only paid him a hundred and seventy-five dollars for that tremendous work, so what do you expect for that kind of money?"

Victoria had always been rather haunted by her grandmother's remark about the crickets' message, and when she was a young mother she found out what it was—they were proclaiming what the weather was like! She had picked up the information that the chirp rate of the snowy tree cricket, one of the commonest crickets in the woods, gave the temperature at that moment, if one added forty to the number of chirps in thirteen seconds. Twenty-one chirps in thirteen seconds meant the temperature outside was 61°F—a cool summer night—but forty chirps in the same time meant it was 80°, still hot outside.

Not everybody likes the crickets' noise. Victoria's younger sister Eugenie gave it as her reason for leaving home at the age of seventeen to live with her aunt in Boston, and one of the Barton cousins was said to have committed suicide because of the continual noise of the creatures at night. To our ears it sounds something like the squeak of unoiled machinery, and maybe this is more disturbing to modern man than to his forebears, for our ideal is to live surrounded by well-oiled apparatus which never goes wrong.

The adult female cricket digs a pit (as a locust does) about half an inch deep in soft earth, in which she lays her eggs. The spot chosen must not be too dry or the eggs will shrivel up, or too wet, when they will become moldy. After hatching, the nymphs go through a number of molts, till at the final stage the fully winged insects emerge, in the species having wings. The creatures never fly, but the winged males have an important modification in the wings. The fore pair each has a serrated rasplike edge which can be engaged with a hardened ridge on the softer hind wings, so that these two wings rub against each other as they are held aloft at an angle of forty-five degrees, and produce the sound. On a still warm day, that can be very powerful and has been known to travel a mile or more.

The house crickets had enemies: Cats used to catch them, among other creatures, but the most pernicious from the crickets' point of view were the cockroaches. It was a serious competitor for the same food, that scattered around by the humans.

Cockroaches have become serious pests of towns and seaports. A curious feature is that they have been given peculiarly misleading popular and scientific names. The small German cockroach (*Blatella germanica*) is a native of northwest Africa; the large American cockroach, the Croton or water bug, (*Periplanta americana*) comes from tropical Africa, and the oriental roach (*Blatta orientalis*) is probably indigenous to America.

The German cockroach reached America in ships coming from Europe; why it was stigmatized as being German is not really known. There are many injustices in this field (see p. 49). The American cockroach, together with the brown-banded cockroach, might be called the slaves' revenge (arguing on the same lines as an attack of diarrhea in Mexico being called "Montezuma's revenge," and a great one, too) because they reached the south of the United States from Africa via the West Indies in the slave ships. Perhaps the slaves deliberately spread the cockroaches around as they were sold up and down the river. Such an activity is a recurring trait among the resentful. In the second World War, prisoners of war in the harshly run Colditz camp in Germany used to plant pieces of the dry rot fungus (obtained from the cellars) in the roof rafters, hoping that in due course (a few years) the roof would rot away.

The German cockroach likes warm, moist places such as kitchens, food service areas, and fermenting garbage dumps. It is a great pest of restaurants and Mr. La Flèche has tangled with it, and with the American cockroach, on many occasions. The German roach is small, 10 to 15 mm long, light brown in color with two dark stripes running down the shield of the thorax, or pronotum. The wings reach to the end of the abdomen in both sexes. The feet have sticky pads at the ends, so the insect can climb up smooth surfaces; it will roam far and wide in a building if it is warm and food is available.

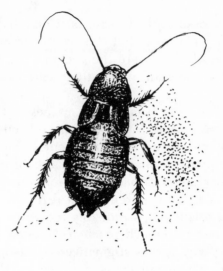

COCKROACH

The American cockroach was called the Croton or water bug, because in the 1840s in New York, when the great public water supply system from the Croton reservoir was installed, the pipe runs greatly facilitated the spread of the insect. It became a much castigated nuisance. In fact it still is one. It is large, 28 to 44 mm long, red-brown in color with a pale yellow area around the edge of the pronotum. The wings also reach the end of the abdomen in both sexes. While it can live out of doors in summer, or in a warm climate, it now thrives in restaurants, bakeries, and food shops. It does not climb so readily as its German cousin and is usually found in basements and on the first floor. An unusual feature of the species is that unmated females can produce egg cases, but the eggs in them do not hatch.

When the *Mayflower* reached Cape Cod the oriental roach was to be found in the woods, sheltering under dead logs and stones. A few would have been in Indian huts and would have fed on the adjacent rubbish heaps, but at that time the Indians were few and wasted very little food. The insects soon began to frequent the settlers' houses. John Josslyn ("Gent") visited New England in 1638 and wrote two books about the country, discussing some of the animals and their drawbacks. Among these were:

> A stinking red and white *Bug* called a *Cacaroach* or *Cockroach* and a little black *bug* like a *Lady-cow* that breeds in skins and furs and will eat them to their utter spoil . . . Likewise there be infinite number of *Tikes* hanging upon the bushes in summer time [30].

A great user of italics was Mr. Josslyn. The second insect mentioned was the Dermestid hide and skin beetle, and the third creature was one of the numerous ticks waiting on grasses for a suitable host to pass by.

The brown-banded cockroach, too, was from Africa and was a fairly late arrival in North America. It reached Florida in 1860 from the West Indies, also having been carried there by the slave ships. From Florida it spread far and wide over the country in consignments of fruit. Being an active climber, it gets into heated rooms in upper stories. It uses its wings much more frequently than other species and when disturbed may escape, or attempt to escape, by flying.

The brown-banded cockroach is small (10 to 14 mm long); the edge of the pronotum is transparent, and as its name implies, there are dark brown bands on the body. It was not found at Bartons House until quite recently; an infestation broke out shortly after the restaurant opened. Egg cases had reached the food stores in corrugated cardboard boxes. The professional exterminators soon got rid of the pest, but a constant watch has to be kept, for not only can they come in, in all sorts of containers—baskets often conceal an egg case—but they can fly in as well.

Cockroaches are a very old group of insects: Their fossils have been found in deposits going back to the Carboniferous strata, where the insects are abundant. They seem to have hit on the right formula from the start and, like the ants, have hardly changed over their 250 million years of existence—a period which could have produced many changes. No mutation became established, however, because the first roaches were just right for their particular niche, which was *not*, of course, feeding on man's garbage in those far-off days. That achievement came much later.

Cockroaches will eat almost any vegetable or animal matter. They will attack and consume young bats falling to the floor of a cave in the same way that they will eat vitamin-deficient white bread falling from the kitchen table. They will eat any of their own kind that are injured, unable to escape from an old larval skin during a molt, or recently dead; this habit is of advantage to the race, as it ensures that the valuable and scarce food material, particularly the protein, is not wasted. But such cannibalism today now operates to their disadvantage. Man often fights cockroaches with poisonous baits, arsenic once being a favorite killer for that purpose; a dying or recently dead insect affected by the bait will often be eaten by an active roach, the poison in the meal being enough to kill the attacker (or scavenger) as well. Even a third insect may be killed by the same poison in the second victim.

Today in houses the cockroaches' chief difficulty is getting water, an acute problem where central heating dries the building. The popular custom of installing humidifiers, of course, makes life just a little easier for cockroaches. They like sweet materials with plenty of moisture in them and they leave traces of brown liquid excreta where they have been feeding. Roaches are often found stranded in bath tubs and ceramic basins where they have gone to get water, subsequently finding the sides of the vessel too steep for their escape; the German roach, with the sticky pads on its feet, is an exception and can usually get out of such places. They will eat damp washing, more for the water than anything else.

These insects prefer to feed at night, being most active two to three hours after darkness comes on and then for some two or three hours more, reducing activity to a low level for the rest of the night. However, keeping the lights on at night will not stop them feeding; if all is quiet they will come out into a lit room. The creatures are sensitive to both light and sound, particularly the latter, which they detect by means of cells (ears) on their long antennae. They are also sensitive to touch, and when at rest the cockroach likes to be in a small crack or burrow so that both its back and legs are in contact with the sides of the refuge at the same time. This preference means that the insect is in a small, comparatively safe place and thus the custom has considerable survival value. A cockroach will station itself at the entrance to such a hole with only its long antennae projecting into the exterior world; by gently moving these delicate and revealing sensors around, the insect learns a great deal about the world outside—for instance, the presence of possible mates, the movements of other animals, such as its provider, man, and whether food is available.

The cockroach is sensitive to smell. Humans are, too, when the creatures are numerous. We regard the smell they give out as unpleasant because of its association with those disliked insects. Whether it really is, per se, is another matter, difficult to decide upon. Civet, obtained from the anal pouches of the civet cat and similar animals, is important in perfumery. Has anyone tried cockroaches as a base for a new scent?

Among cockroaches, smell has two functions. First, it is a feeding marker: the smell draws others of the tribe to a site. Second, the smell is a sex-attractant put out by virgin females to attract males, in most species. The male deposits a package of sperm, known as a spermatophore, which, if conditions are right, the female takes into her body. The female receives several of these during her life and thus maintains the heterozygous nature of the species, which is a kind of guarantee for its continued existence. The eggs are produced in egg cases called oötheca, and the particular species can be identified by the size and shape of the oöthecum, the large American roach having a comparatively small egg case. Usually the egg case is deposited by the female in a safe spot some time before the eggs hatch, but the female German cockroach carries it around with her until the eggs are ready to hatch.

While cockroaches were, and are, universally detested, in the past they did do a little good to man, for they had a great appetite for bedbugs—a yet more unpleasant insect.

The oriental cockroach entered Bartons from time to time, seemingly attracted by the lights there. In 1750 the insect established itself in the west-wing quarters for the hired help, where the same standard of cleanliness did not obtain as in the main part of the house. From the west wing the orientals started to move into the main part of the building and, much as Tryphena Chilton (née Barton) liked studying natural history, the smell and mess of the cockroaches were too much for her. She decided to take measures against them. One such was to spread the crushed leaves and fruits of the love apple or cockroach-apple (that is the tomato) about the place, as the smell was said to kill them [7]. This was another example of the suspicion attached to the Solanaceae in that age; no New Englander ever dreamt of eating tomatoes, except perhaps in small amounts as a love charm or aphrodisiac. The smell was held to be so disagreeable that they were never allowed to grow near a house [37]. The fact that the Spaniards and Portuguese deliberately grew and even ate them was considered to be very strange, but there was no accounting for tastes.

The love apple smell had very little effect on the cockroaches, and Tryphena and the help began looking for other remedies. They would surprise the insects at night, sweep up large quantities, and destroy them. Constant collection kept down their numbers but did not eliminate them. Nor did the "infallible" Mexican remedy put forward by one of the hired hands. It was:

> Catch three cockroaches and put them in a bottle, and so carry them to where two roads cross. Here hold the bottle upside down, and as they fall out repeat aloud three *credos*. Then all the cockroaches in the house whence these three came will go away [27].

Tryphena was very sarcastic about such "ridiculous superstitions" when she heard about these measures being used. She enquired of her hired man whether he had said the *credos* in Latin, Spanish, or English. Perhaps the failure, she intimated, was due to using the wrong language. All this was quite over the man's head. Why, he thought, should the boss be annoyed because he had tried to get rid of her cockroaches? Truly there was no understanding of bosses.

Nor were the baits made up of wormwood and bran of much use. However, later, some white arsenic obtained from a Boston apothecary—the poison being mixed with bran and molasses—began to be very effective. Tryphena got very nervous about having such a dangerous substance in the house; some of the cockroach bait once got mixed in with the chicken mash and killed six fine birds. Tryphena then added soot to the bait mixture to make it distinctive in color. The soot did not repel the cockroaches, which avidly consumed the bait and died. But she noted that chickens and turkeys would eat dead cockroaches and thus could easily be poisoned as well. She gave up using arsenical bait.

From watching them so much, Tryphena hit upon an effective method of control. She noticed that when disturbed at night, a few hours after darkness, they ran to their hideouts: cracks in walls, gaps between the floor and skirting boards, cavities under the stove and hearths, and similar places. She called in one of the men and got him to work with plaster and putty sealing up all possible hiding places. It was a very effective remedy, but of course, as the temperature varies from day to night, from winter to summer, and the atmosphere from wet to dry, so does the house structure expand and contract, thus opening up the holes and cracks for the cockroaches again. However, Tryphena carried out regular inspections and resealed any refuge that opened. The oriental cockroach troubled them very little after that.

The expansion and contraction of hot-water piping (thus of central-heating pipe runs) is still one of the difficulties of cockroach control, as it is always opening up gaps, giving the creatures access to new territory. Glass wool sometimes fills these apertures, but a gap between the wool and the pipe, big enough for a roach, will develop after a time. A watch has to be kept on doors, because the insects can easily get through quite a small gap between the bottom of a door and its sill.

When the house was empty except for the recluse Edward Hopkins, the cockroaches abandoned it. It was cold and Hopkins was careful to leave no traces of his presence, so there was no food for the insects.

Although the American and German cockroaches also got into the house from time to time, they never became very numerous at this period. A factor in such an unusual failure of the cockroach potential was the presence of toads in the cellar. They have a great appetite for cockroaches. A toad can clear a room of roaches in one night [49]. At Bartons the toads, having cleared the cellars, managed to get into the kitchens from time to time and dispatched most of the roaches there as well. Unfortunately, Beulah Deane in 1805 found a toad in the kitchen one morning and some more in the cellars. She maintained that this was disgraceful and gave orders that all these animals were to be removed and that their means of access to the house—a gap in the cellar flap—was to be closed. This done, the cockroaches were freed from the attentions of their predator and began to multiply again.

The second half of the nineteenth century saw yet more frequent outbreaks, the American, German, oriental, and brown-banded kinds all having their turns. About this time some were even blamed for damage they did not do. *The Domestic Encyclopaedia*, of 1803, said that the American cockroach seldom appeared until nightfall, when it entered houses, infested beds, and bit the people sleeping there. The bites would, in fact, have been caused by bedbugs or fleas. The roach attacks were due to the fact that, with the big cellar stove and gas lighting, the building was that much warmer, and a lavish style of living meant that plenty of good food was scattered about. All sorts of proprietary remedies were tried, such as "Johnson's Perfect Roach Trap" (a balanced metal leaf gave way from the weight of the insect and precipitated it into a vessel from which it could not escape). "Schweron's Annihilating Powder contains no poison" shows how nervous people were about arsenic. This powder was probably based on pyrethrum, a powerful vegetable insecticide. "Dutcher's Dead Shot Bug Killer" was also tried. They had a certain amount of success, but in those days the really effective remedy was still the one used by Tryphena Chilton—sealing up the refuges, keeping them closed, and sweeping up all fallen food.

From the 1940s to '50s the problem was much simplified by the use of the synthetic insecticides DDT and Lindane. As both are now banned, more expensive substitutes are used. The pests never became numerous until Bartons House Restaurant was formed and then only for a short time, as the exterminators dealt with the problem.

Insects are short-lived creatures. Cockroaches live from, say, ninety to five hundred days, according to species and the prevailing temperature. The American cockroach is the longest-lived. The females breed very quickly, producing some eighty to five hundred eggs per lifetime, the American again being the leader in this activity. The generations of cockroaches succeed each other very rapidly; three a year are common. Some twenty generations of humans have lived since John Barton built the house, but during that period there have been well over a thousand generations of the oriental cockroach, living in the woods and houses. This means there have been five hundred times more opportunities for genetic change in cockroaches than in humans. Cockroaches being fairly heterozygous—each female mating with several different males—offspring are produced from time to time having characteristics a little different from those of their parents, due to the genes being sorted into a new combination because of the heterozygous nature of the parents. So far, as mentioned above, these different offspring have not dominated the various species to any extent, because the ancient model seems to have been the best under the circumstances, and the "changed" offspring, having no advantageous survival characteristics, did not survive.

Recently, however, a change has come to the fore. It seems there was in the gene pattern of most cockroaches (and insects generally, too) a gene, or combination of genes, bestowing a certain amount of resistance to chlorinated insecticides, such as DDT, Lindane, and Dieldrin. As a result of the spraying and dusting of roaches, the insects containing these spray-resistant genes survived to a greater extent than those not having them, and races of cockroaches resistant to these insecticides began to appear. Cockroaches, having existed on earth for millions of years, it would seem, were not going to be ousted by such a parvenu as man. So that even if the chlorinated insecticides had not been banned, their use, in all probability, would have been given up because they no longer were effective against the newly emerged resistant races.

The new insecticides now in use have not yet selected out a fresh resistant race, but they may well do so. The roach does not give way lightly. Finally we must remember that the cockroach has entered literature [36]. Archy, at present a cockroach, in a previous incarnation was a *vers libre* poet. At night Archy used to communicate with Don Marquis, a journalist, by typing messages to him on a sheet of paper left ready in the typewriter. The machine was worked, so the author said, by the roach jumping off the type bar onto the letter keys (one feels Archy must have been of the large American species, as it is heavier than the others). The messages, of wry philosophical interest, were all in lower-case letters, as Archy could not jump onto the capitals key and the required letter key at one and the same time!

Another creature that occasionally was found in the house, taking advantage of man's goods and way of life, was the vinegar eelworm. Eelworms are small free-living worms often found in the soil and in decaying vegetable matter, though some of them, such as the potato eelworm and the sugar-beet eelworm, can cause serious loss of man's crops. In nature, as fruits ripen, their sugar content increases and on the skin the "bloom" develops; this is a wild yeast, and as soon as the fruit cracks with ripeness, the yeast attacks the sugar and multiplies itself, at the same time turning the sugar into alcohol and carbon dioxide gas, which is the basis of wine making. As the alcohol forms in the pulp, it is in its turn attacked by other bacteria and converted to an acid and water. This reaction is the basis of making vinegar. In the wild state certain eelworms or nematodes thrive in this acetic acid produced by the decaying fruit.

The tiny fruit flies which are attracted to ripe fruit may carry on their legs and bodies the spores of yeast, the vinegar bacteria, and the eggs of the vinegar eelworm, and can thus deposit all three to set the process of decay going, converting the complex fruit back to the gas and water from which it originally came; but man has again interfered. From the fruits and cereals he makes wines and beers, and from these, vinegars; and if the eelworm finds its way to some vinegar, it will multiply very rapidly there, for its food is much more abundant than in the wild state in a rotting fruit.

Vinegar was very important to the Bartons, as it enabled food to be preserved and relishes prepared to relieve the tedium of the dull winter diet; they regularly brewed it by the old bulk, or Orleans, process, starting from any leftover beer or wine they had. The procedure was to add some liquor, which had started to "turn" naturally, to a half-empty barrel of beer or wine, keeping it in a warm place, when the vinegar bacteria would start to multiply, at the same time converting the alcohol to the acid. Meanwhile, the liquor was frequently invaded by these worms, and a considerable struggle developed in the turning wine, between them and the vinegar bacteria. The bacteria require a great deal of oxygen—in fact, they need about half as much in weight of oxygen as there is alcohol in the tub; a pound of alcohol needs half a pound of oxygen to turn it to the vinegar acid, and the bacteria form a gelatinous film over the surface of the liquid. The worms swimming in the mother liquor also need oxygen, like all animals; any oxygen dissolved in the liquid is rapidly used up, so the worms cannot get this much-needed gas from the surface where the bacteria have established their skin of bacterial tissue. The worms struggle to break through the film by repeatedly throwing themselves against it. If the bacteria are active and growing well, the skin on the surface will be too tough for them and the worms will either die and fall to the bottom or migrate to the sides of the vessel around the orifice, where capillary action raises a little of the liquor and allows the worms to breathe and a small population to survive. If, however, the worms are successful in penetrating the bacteria film when they charge at it, it will be broken up, sinking to the bottom of the vat, and will stop the liquor's turning to vinegar. It used to be thought by the Bartons that the process would only be successful if there were plenty of vinegar worms around the bung hole of the fermenting barrel, which in a way was true, though they were confusing cause and effect. The vinegar could have been formed without any worms present, but the presence of worms clustering around the vent hole meant that the bacterial film was strong and whole and the process going well. Today vinegar is made by a similar fermentation process, though a much different procedure is used and vinegar worms are excluded from it. Nevertheless they are still found at times, for the eggs blow about in the air or are carried by the small fruit flies mentioned above.

10

~❧~

THIRDHAND

ALL ANIMALS get their living at best at second hand, for as they cannot themselves directly use the earth, air, water, and sunlight to elaborate their food, they must eat plants that can; a number of animals, however (and some plants too), have gone further and get their livelihood at third hand, feeding on living animals which have already built up a supply of suitable carbohydrates and proteins. Such animals are the parasites and predators which were well represented in the house; all the animals there had parasites and most of them, except man, were the victims of predators from time to time as well. Although there were exceptions to this last in New England, at any rate in the early days. John Winthrop reported the sad case of a baby killed by a wild cat at Cambridge [63]. Rattlesnakes killed people, though strictly speaking they were not predators. Mountain lions and bears could kill; the first were seldom seen and the latter were nothing like so dangerous as imagined. John Josslyn said they were fierce only at rutting time, when they would walk about in groups of twenty to forty, "making a hideous noise [30]." This no doubt gave them their reputation. Wolves were also much feared, but far from being the fierce, slavering animals so dreaded by the settlers, they never deliberately attacked men. The plants that live on other living plants are mostly the parasitic, or disease-producing fungi.

At Bartons, fleas and lice, bugs and certain worms were the earliest parasites of the birds and mammals, while other insects, mostly belonging to the Hymenoptera, were parasitic on the insects.

There are different degrees of parasitism and a great number of complexities in the life of parasites. Some—the roundworms, for instance—live entirely within and at the expense of their host; others spend part of their life in one animal and part in another, as for example the sheep liver fluke, which passes part of its life cycle in a snail. Some parasites are external and can live on several different kinds of animals; others live within the host and specialize in one kind of animal and one situation in it. The effect on the host can vary from no particular harm to actual death; some are only dangerous to the host for a disease they can introduce with their bites, as for instance human lice carrying typhus, or the *Anopheles* mosquitoes, malaria. Others may confer benefits on the host, in which case the animal is really no longer a parasite, and we give its condition another name—symbiosis. The divergencies and variations in the parasitic pattern are so immense that though we know what we mean by parasitism, we find it a difficult word to define with exactitude.

The life of these animals living in intimate association with other animals falls into three classes of behavior—symbiosis, commensalism, and true parasitism, though the border lines between them are not clearly defined.

The lichen growing on the wall is an example of symbiosis, as it is an association between an alga and a fungus; both are intimately combined and one cannot thrive without the other.

Commensalism is a term that originally meant the state of two animals sharing the same food ("eating at the same table") and without doing each other any harm. However, if animals actually eat just the same food, they *do* do each other harm, for as their numbers increase they must come to compete for it sooner or later. Commensalism is better described as the state where two animals live in an association, neither harming the other directly; consequently both can live apart if necessary. The mouse is a commensal with man, eating at the same table as he, but in most cases man gets the bigger share of the supplies, so that from the mouse's point of view man is acquiring the status of a dangerous rival. When the situation is reversed and the mouse starts to dominate the position, then man gets worried and uses his ingenuity to restore his dominance. Another example, where the partners are more beneficial to one another, is that between starlings and sheep, where the birds sitting on the backs of the animals kill the lice and ticks living on the wool and, in the wild state, warn them of the approach of such enemies as wolves or foxes by flying away, usually giving the alarm cry. The sheep benefit from having their parasites destroyed and the birds from a supply of high-protein food, but both sheep and birds can live one without the other.

A parasitic state exists when one member of an animal association definitely harms the other; the parasite may suck in blood or other juices, or if it is an insect, it may live within the animal and allow the host to develop for some time before killing it and emerging as an adult to continue the cycle. Parasitism is a highly specialized state, in which successive adaptations of the parasite and host usually strike a balance. The parasite does not kill the host, or does not kill it quickly, for should it do so it would jeopardize its own future. It is an indication of a recent parasitic adaptation when a host is rapidly killed. The cabbage-white caterpillar is frequently parasitized by a hymenopterous fly, *Apanteles*. The young caterpillar is stung by an adult fly; a number of grubs develop and feed within the caterpillar; these grubs allow the host to grow normally but use the feed reserves meant for the caterpillar's metamorphosis to a butterfly for their own development. In fact, the parasitized caterpillar eats more food than an unattacked one. When the insect seeks a shelter for pupation—and many crept into Bartons for the purpose—the parasites kill it, consume the reserves, come out from the skin, and themselves spin their yellow-white cocoons, from which they shortly emerge as adult flies to continue the life cycle.

The *Apanteles* allows the caterpillar to live for as long as it can be useful to it, taking in this case as full advantage of the situation as is possible, and is thus an example of a successful adaptation. This must be the unconscious aim of all parasites, but the matter may became complicated by the fact that the parasite can be the carrier of other organisms, such as microbes or protozoa which cause disease in the host. It is of no advantage to the louse that its human host should die of a typhus infection, a disease which may also be killing the lice, for to continue its existence, the louse must find its way to a new host, frequently a matter of some difficulty. Nor is it any advantage to the mosquito that the malaria-causing protozoa weaken or kill men; the malaria organism does not harm the mosquito, but by killing men it does reduce its food supply. These particular insects would both be more successful without the secondary infections they carry.

The field of parasitism is another example of the expansion of life into all those spaces where it can obtain a foothold, even to those corners created by the very expansion itself. To us as humans, the word "parasite" has a base and pejorative meaning, but scientifically, parasitism is just another way of life, a way which is at one more remove from the main elements of life: air, earth, water, and the sun.

Many kinds of commensals and parasites came to the house from the beginning and quite a number have been extinguished there. When John Barton married Susannah Palmer in 1633 they were both free of lice and fleas, but they soon became infected with both of these pests, picking them up from the Indians, who suffered severely from lice, and from settlers and children less careful than they.

One of the constant tasks of the housewife in those times was to prepare ointments, powders, and herb extracts to use against these creatures. It can be seen from its very name that fleabane was thought to be a remedy. A close relative to the English species—which in the old country was a weed growing to six inches or a foot high, with purple flowers—was found growing wild in New England. It was larger, as most things in America turned out to be, though the flowers were smaller, more numerous, and white, sometimes tinged with red, but it was sufficiently like the plant known in Europe to be worth a trial. It seemed to have some slight insecticidal activity, but as in many things even today, there was rather more in the name than in the performance. The plant is now known as horseweed (*Erigeron canadensis*). Pennyroyal (*Mentha pulegium*) was also used for the same purpose.

It was far easier to keep down the lice than the fleas, for the hair would be constantly combed, clothes washed, and ointment applied, lice spending most of their lives on the body (though a fever will drive them off), whereas fleas only attack from time to time, and while tending to live on the body when adult, they can hide in bedclothes and cracks and, in any case, lay their eggs and conduct their larval existence quite elsewhere. Flea eggs are laid in crevices in floors and the larvae develop there in dirt and dust. They take but little food, but may eat any blood they can find in the excreta of adult fleas or other animals; in due course they pupate and emerge as adults to start the attack again. Fleas have amazing powers of resistance to the absence of food and are extremely sensitive to its arrival. Many people have had the experience of entering a long-empty room or cabin and soon being set upon by fleas; they have been waiting for a host. The adult fleas are able to remain at rest in their cocoons for a long time, and it is the stimulus of the vibration of an animal returning to its burrow, or of a man walking over a floor, that leads them to hatch and, using their powerful legs, hop onto their host, seeking ravenously to feed.

The settlers soon learned to be very wary of entering apparently deserted Indian huts, not for fear of an ambush but because of the fleas which, very hungry, would spring on any intruders by the hundred, within seconds of their entering. The insects thus made good guards for the Indians. Would, today, a fine collection of hungry flea pupae be a better protection for a bank vault than steel doors? Alas, no! The legitimate customer would be attacked as much as the bank robber. More so, in fact, as the robber no doubt would be wearing a protective suit. But then, entering a bank in a flea-proof outfit would look a little suspicious!

Over the years there were human, cat, dog, rabbit, bird, raccoon, squirrel, and rat fleas in the house, and each one preferred to feed on the blood of its own particular host, though a flea would turn to other animals if its own food could not be found; all were nuisances to their hosts. The rat fleas were potentially the most dangerous because they could transmit the bacteria of bubonic plague. Fortunately the plague never reached the Bartons, but for a long time there was a risk that it might. A curious feature of some species, such as the rabbit flea, is that the females lay eggs only on pregnant female rabbits. Presumably the young rabbits are an easier source of food than adults, and the fleas can sense the best host animals for that purpose.

Fleas

Two things in the new house had an influence on the life of the fleas. One helped them and the other did not. The advantageous factor was that the house was made from substantial and unseasoned beams and boarding. The timbers shrank, leaving cracks between them—very good hiding and rearing places for flea larvae. The floor of the combined kitchen and living room was just dirt, because John Barton could not waste time cutting timber for such a luxury as a wooden floor. The dirt floor was also a good refuge for fleas, and the larvae started to grow there, but a custom of that time operated against them. The settlers were mostly educated people and wanted their children to be so too. On Sundays, and when guests were expected, the floor would be raked smooth and a text or message of welcome written onto it, the children being encouraged to show their skill in inscribing "God is love," "Fear the Lord," or "Welcome Godfather Experience." It was a great moment in a child's life when the youngster had learned enough to be able to write the Sunday message. The constant raking killed the flea larvae and other insects in the dust. Moreover, the board floor of the bedroom, which was over the cellar, was scrubbed and then sanded (sand from the seashore was plentiful), a pattern of arcs being put into the sand for Sundays. The water from the scrubbing would have helped the larvae in the cracks, but the salt sand made things difficult for them, so that with one thing and another the fleas were not very numerous in the old house.

As time went on and the house expanded, sanding was given up and a wooden floor provided in the kitchen. Abigail Barton was proud of her floors and had her maids polish them with beeswax—despite her mother-in-law's insistence that elbow grease was a much more satisfactory substance—so that there were few refuges for fleas on the first floor, though they still could be found at times in the bedrooms.

Dogs and cats chase fleas in their fur and sometimes catch and swallow them, which is one of the ways they can acquire tapeworms; the flea larvae become infected with the bladder-worm stage of the tapeworm as they feed on the dirt in the floor cracks, so that cleanliness is a method of avoiding both disease and worm infections. Rats and mice can also acquire worms in the same way, as could humans, though they are unlikely to swallows fleas. The few humans at Bartons who became infected with tapeworms did so by eating raw or insufficiently cooked beef or pork, as these products are among the intermediate hosts of the two common human tapeworms.

At one time tapeworms were fairly usual among the laborers, who would often eat raw pork or beef when preparing slaughtered beasts for the house. They did not do the humans any great damage; it is an extremely ancient parasite in man and has so adapted itself over the centuries as to be singularly harmless. The greatest evil it does, more particularly today, is the shock and horror the individual may suffer on finding he is carrying such a creature. Some few people may be more sensitive to the worm and experience discomfort, and if the intestinal wall is penetrated, undesirable bacteria may at times be allowed to enter the blood, in which case the results could be serious. There have been no human tapeworms in the house now for more than a hundred and fifty years, due to the decline of home slaughtering and greater care in cooking.

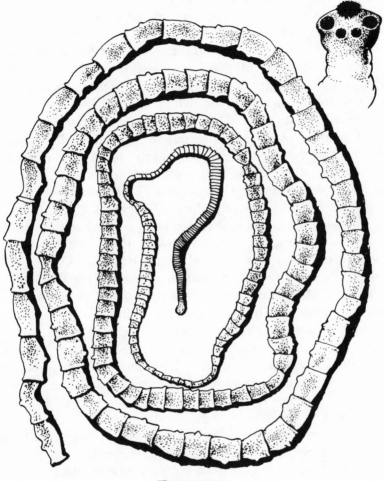

TAPEWORM

Such worms are still occasionally found in cats and dogs, when remedial measures are at once put in hand.

To return to the fleas, the biggest population of human fleas built up during the regime of the rather shiftless Elkanah Hoag, when the house was far from clean. It ended abruptly when the place was empty because they were starved out. They were found from time to time during the Civil War when Bartons was crowded with refugees, many having had long and difficult journeys. But they were fought energetically:

Floors were waxed, clothes and bed linen washed and hung in the sun, and much pyrethrum powder used, so that fleas were soon contained.

Strangely enough it was the movies that led to the introduction of the flea to the house again. In the 1920s John Barton VII and his sister, Janet, and brother, James, often went to the movies together, where they picked up a flea or two from time to time. This they took in their stride; it was quite a usual event and the punctures were called "movie bites." They hardly reported the event to their mother, but set about destroying the creatures. A damp cake of soap was an effective instrument; the covers on a bed would quickly be drawn back, and if the offending insect was spotted, it would be dabbed with the soap, from which it could not free itself.

The next generation of Bartons had no such knowledge. Soon after the second World War, Edward, Desirée, and Phoebe Barton were taken by their parents to see the wonders of the old Maya civilization in Mexico and Central America. One morning Edward came to his father in great distress, thinking he had caught some horrible tropical disease. He had a dozen ghastly red, irritating spots on his body and was most worried. They were flea bites. John Barton VII calmed his son's fears, refrained from laughing, and showed him the soap technique. "It makes me feel young again," he said. At the local drug store, where they went for insecticide powder, the pharmacist was most shocked that such a thing could happen in his country and refused to charge for the powder. "Now if it had been in South America—*esos tipos* . . ." he said. But that did not explain why he kept a stock of flea powder. . . .

Fleas have been virtually extinct in the house since 1922, as far as breeding is concerned, though they have been occasional visitors. The main reason for their nonestablishment has been the installation of the vacuum cleaner, which clears so much dust and dirt from floors and carpets—as well as any eggs, larvae, and adults—as to leave no breeding place for the creatures.

Dog and cat fleas were occasionally found but the Deanes eliminated them rapidly. Up to 1962 dogs were treated with

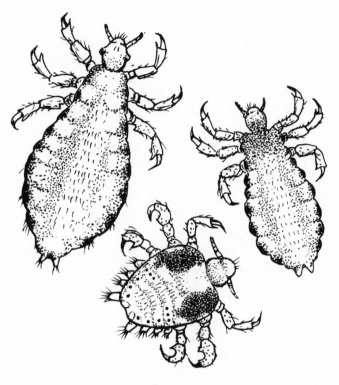

LICE

DDT powder but cats were not, for DDT was very bad for them. Derris dust was used for the felines. Derris is now used on both dogs and cats.

The three forms of human lice were soon introduced to the house by the Bartons' Indian friends: They were the body louse, head louse, and pubic louse, or crab. Human lice adapted themselves to living the whole of their lives on or near the body and so enjoy a standardized environment as regards temperature, humidity, and food. The body louse consequently cannot thrive on a naked man; the creature is an adaptation of the head louse, one which came about when man started to wear clothes—an example of the expansion of life into a new field.

Other organisms have taken advantage of lice to introduce

to man their forms of life, such as typhus and relapsing fever, and still others get into him when the host scratches because of the irritation of louse bites.

All the humans disliked the presence of lice, though the earlier ones did not regard them with the same disgust as would the present inhabitants; in the early days they were considered to be unpleasant but more or less inevitable, and against them one took what steps one could. Pepys in England recalls that when he, his wife, and Deb. Willet visited a town near Salisbury they found the beds at the inn "good but lousey, which made us merry." One combed one's hair, washed one's clothes and even one's body from time to time, and squashed the insects and the "nits," that is, the gray-white eggs which stuck to hairs or clothing. The body louse lives mostly in a person's clothes, only visiting the skin to feed when the individual is quiet and at rest. Unlike the head louse, it can survive a few hours away from the body—for instance when the clothes are taken off at night—but otherwise lice soon succumb to the loss of their chosen environment. Very elementary hygiene serves to keep down body lice, and as a consequence the head louse was the commonest of these animals, particularly in children. Head lice are now beginning to be found again in children in the big cities, but they have not been in Bartons for more than a century.

Strangely enough, the wearing of wigs did not increase the infestation of humans with lice and fleas. The Bartons did not affect wigs, but Stephen Deane I, the prosperous Boston merchant, did, especially on important occasions, though he gave up the practice in his later years. Their ladies tended to follow the fashions of Europe and wore wigs on special occasions and a sort of cap on ordinary days, but they never wore the complex and enormous structures of the European courts, where wigs were so elaborate and so entwined with the ladies' own hair that they would not be undone for weeks, greatly encouraging lice and fleas. Many ladies had on their dressing tables elegant ivory sticks with small hands or claws at the ends which they could push under the wig to scratch the scalp and relieve the irritation.

The ordinary well-to-do citizens' wigs were not only carefully tended, but were worn only on special occasions, which meant that any head lice they picked up would either be killed or would die of exposure and starvation before the wig was worn again. Moreover, in the case of men, the wearers' own hair was kept short, which in itself discouraged lice and fleas by enabling them to be seen and killed by the servant who dressed the master's hair before he retired.

The cats, dogs, mice, and birds in Bartons were also infected with various forms of lice from time to time; today the domestic animals are treated with piperonyl butoxide or derris powder when occasion arises, and so the population is kept down.

The next bloodsucker to discuss is the bedbug, which was a comparatively late arrival, for though it was well known in London and the seaports, it did not become general in New England until the middle of the seventeenth century, being carried by the extensive shipping. There were so many bedbugs in the sailors' lodging houses and quay-side inns that it was no wonder they got into the ships. At Bartons they arrived for the first time in some furniture Mrs. Palmer gave her daughter; it had come from an old ship broken up at Plymouth Plantation. In 1654 the furniture was put into the lean-to extension. Steps were taken against the bugs when they got into John and Susannah's bed. They were soon eliminated by persistently catching them and painting the bed framework, particularly the joints, with a mixture of oil and candleberry wax.

Bedbugs were generally such a problem in those days that they gave rise to professional exterminators, and it is interesting to note that one such (T. H. Tiffin) started his business in London in 1695. He would guarantee to keep a bed free of bugs for the sum of "3 shillings [60 cents] per year, ready money." The firm is still in existence—not killing bedbugs but preserving timber.

The next bedbug invasion at Bartons was in 1745 in the west wing and that was eliminated in much the same way. In the mid-nineteenth century they were noted for their persistence and tenacity of life. Stephen Deane II said that he almost believed the Yankee tall story reported in an account of a symposium on "Bed-bugs and their Remarkable Tenacity of Life." Old Hanks, it seems, took one of the creatures to an iron foundry and dropped it into a ladle of molten iron, which was then run into a mold for a skillet. The instrument, when completed, was used for six years by the Hankses and, being dropped one day, broke into pieces. The bedbug walked out "and made tracks for his old roost upstairs, but," Hanks added by way of parenthesis, "he looked mighty pale."

Belief in their tenacity of life arose from three things: first, their flat, thin shape that allowed the insects to hide deep in the cracks and joints of beds and there lay their eggs; second, their ability to suck blood from humans without first injecting an irritant to make the blood flow more readily, and thus awakening them. And third, it was difficult to treat thoroughly all the hiding places in beds, furniture, and walls; usually a few eggs or adults escaped destruction and reinfestation quickly developed.

There were a few found in the early twentieth century, but by the 1920s they were rare insects. However, a bug produced a dramatic crisis in 1956 (see p. 258).

Bedbugs are Mediterranean insects that have extended their zone by adapting themselves to the ways of man and birds. They seem originally to have been parasites of bats, and no doubt first adapted themselves to man when both were living together in caves. Bedbugs need warmth and darkness in which to thrive and, of course, a suitable food supply, which may come from many warm-blooded animals. Like many creatures that use man, they are much flattened and can creep into cracks, joints, nail holes, and suchlike corners in furniture, floors, and walls. Often they cluster around the buttons of mattresses; as they find their food in man's beds, they tend to lurk in the framework of bedsteads or in walls nearby, and come out to feed on man when he is there, lying quiet, since on the whole they prefer to feed just before dawn, rather than as soon as it is dark. Perhaps the bug has learned that its host is sleeping more soundly then, and it can feed for longer undisturbed, for it needs some five or ten minutes to get a complete meal. The eggs are laid in the same cracks in which the adults pass the day and are so securely cemented down that the shell remains stuck to its support even after the egg has hatched.

Bug bites cause more irritation and discomfort than those of fleas and lice, but bugs do not seem to transmit any dangerous diseases, as fleas and lice do. Either the opportunity has not yet arisen for some organism to use the bug for this purpose, or if it has, resistant strains of bugs have triumphed over an attempt by an outsider to reduce the food supply. Charles Munroyd made a determined and successful effort to get rid of them in 1750 by using a supply of Mr. James Southall's "Non pareil Liquor" which was advertised as drawing out and killing bugs from their hiding places. Said to have come from Jamaica (perhaps it was an extract of quassia, an insecticide), it not only made its exploiter prosperous but also secured him membership of the Royal Society in 1730. In fact, carefully painting all cracks and surfaces of a bed with a feather dipped in turpentine or some oily substance would destroy most of the bugs present. It is merely a question of doing the job thoroughly.

During the Victorian era, the bedbug was reintroduced and was continually being fought, for conditions were advantageous to it. Heavy furniture had plenty of cracks, papered walls provided cover when parts of it came loose, plentiful coal meant the house was much warmer, and large families assured a good supply of food. During this time the presence of bugs carried a certain social stigma; barroom and vaudeville jokes were made about them and a number of euphemisms were invented, such as "b. flats" or "mahogany flats," which are descriptive. An English epuhemism was "Norfolk Howards," the origin of which is either the 11th Duke (of Norfolk), "distinguished by his habitual slovenliness," or a Mr. Joshua Bug, who advertised he was changing his name to Norfolk Howard.

The bedbug did not have it all its own way, for it was bitterly attacked not only by man but also by another bug, sometimes called the "assassin bug" from the savageness of its assaults on a large variety of insects and mites. It was also called the "fly-bug," because it tended to fly into lighted rooms during summer nights. In fact, it still does come into Bartons in this way, and there are some in the loft preying on insects, mites, and spiders. The adult is black with a yellowish tint, and in the larval state the insect covers itself with dust, refuse, and cast skins as a disguise, hence its specific name of *personatus*, or "disguised." Although it attacks and kills bedbugs, it is not above biting man at times and can give a sharp and painful bite which is really worse than that of the bedbug, but it does not often do so. Assassin bugs are more numerous in the country than in towns, and as they attack bedbugs so readily, they helped to ensure that there were fewer bugs in the country than in the own. One cannot help feeling that the part of the Ichneumon fly in Capek's *The Insect Play* should really have been one of these assassin bugs. Though in this country mostly beneficial to man, similar species in South America not only can cause painful bites but may transmit serious malaria-like diseases such as Chagas' disease.

Very soon after the house fell empty in 1784 it became free of bedbugs, for besides being attacked by the assassin, they were unable to last out an even averagely cold winter. They have not entered it again, although there was one unfortunate incident recently.

In the spring of 1976 John and Caroline Barton acquired an *au pair* girl from France just at the time the house was being painted. Two days after the arrival of Louise Essonne the Bartons were horrified to find bedbugs in their bedroom and could only conclude that Louise had brought them with her. A series of misunderstandings conducted in halting French and English reduced Louise to tears and filled the Bartons with despair, until at last they consulted the distinguished entomologist of the local research station as to the course of action they should take in face of the threat. Somewhat sardonically he said that all they could do was apologize and perhaps improve their French, for the bugs were not bedbugs but the swallow bug from the house nests, which had taken refuge in the house as the painters were knocking down the nests. The two insects are very similar and there is yet a third kind—the pigeon bug. The presence of these bugs in swallows' nests is one of the reasons why it is no unkindness to the birds to destroy the nests at the end of the season, though perhaps it would be better still to sprinkle them with insecticide powder and thus leave the returning birds the same, but pest-free, home. However, this course of action might only have the effect of encouraging the English sparrows, who so frequently take possession of the nests in winter and who would thrive just that little bit more were they free from parasites.

Fleas, lice, and mites are also found in the nests, the fleas being comparatively recent transfers from mammalian hosts and the lice feeding mostly on the feathers. Birds can harbor such a big community of life that A. E. Shipley said, "Birds are not only birds but aviating zoological gardens [50]." The larvae of bird fleas need comparatively humid conditions; consequently they are not much found in high, airy, dry nests but in those made of mud, or near the ground, and the swallows' nests provide splendid opportunities for them. The adult fleas spend most of their time in the nest itself and only go on the bird to feed, though they may take immense quantities of blood when they do so, most of which is excreted unchanged into the nest and serves as food for the larvae.

Fleas are not as closely bound to a host as lice and, though free, have few powers of searching for a bird, but find a new host more by luck than judgment; however, they are assisted in this by being able to do without food for a very long time.

They are attracted by warmth and are sensitive to smell and the closely related sense of taste; each particular flea species shows a marked preference for one host, though they may be able to feed on several. Horses have been able to develop a smell which repels fleas (or perhaps it is a chance adaptation), and are not attacked by them; nor are grooms, provided they do not wash too much—one of the few advantages of uncleanliness. The enormously strong legs of fleas serve, in place of the wings they have lost, to enable them to hop away from enemies and find new hosts.

Swallows, swifts, and martins, because they continually return to the same nests, suffer very much from fleas, for hundreds may be found at a single site. If by chance a nest is abandoned, the fleas migrate and some find their way into the house, where they will slowly perish as they vainly search for more nests; frequently they may alarm the humans there in the process.

The fleas have their enemies; man, of course, is one of them. He attempts to destroy his fleas as best he can and has done so from early times; one recalls De la Tour's marvelous picture, painted in the first half of the seventeenth century, of the woman lit by a solitary bright candle, squashing a flea between her thumbnails. Similarly, birds, in preening themselves, destroy large numbers of fleas. and desiccate many more by taking dust baths. It is doubtful if splashing in water rids the animal of fleas; it may even help the insects, as they like a humid atmosphere.

The rat flea can get the plague and die of it, the gut being blocked by the growth of the bacilli and the flea starving to death. The insect infects man with the disease because it cannot pass the blood through its system as is normal, but has to regurgitate it through the mouth, mixed with the bacteria, which then gain access to the man through a fleabite and set up the disease. Bird fleas can be attacked by protozoa, and at times half or more of a flea population may be infested. They are also attacked by roundworms which, feeding on the generative organs, have the effect of sterilizing them. Other worms use fleas as the intermediate host. Certain beetles devour fleas in large numbers, as do also ants if they can get access to the birds' nests.

The most serious enemies of the nest-inhabiting fleas are the mites, several species of which live in the nests and destroy larvae and pupae, making one wonder whether Dean Swift's famous stanza arose from observing fleas with a magnifying glass, or poets with his yellow eye—in the latter case, working his simile backward, leaving an observation that was triumphantly verified when the microscope showed him to be right.*

These flea-destroying mites, when in the resting stage, attach themselves to fleas (nearly always choosing the females, as only they will have larvae) and are transported to new nests.

When a bird dies the fleas leave it and seek a new host, which of course they may be unable to find, and when a flea dies the mites, both in the resting stage and otherwise, leave it to do likewise. Birds frequently preen themselves, so the fleas have to live in the nest most of the time to escape these attentions. However, they are not safe there, for all these other dangers await them.

* So naturalists observe, a flea
  Hath smaller fleas that on him prey;
  And these have smaller fleas to bite 'em,
  And so proceed *ad infinitum.*
  Thus every poet, in his kind
  Is bit by him that comes behind.
           —*Pastoral Dialogues*

Bird lice have chewing mouthparts and so bite and masticate their food, which is mostly feathers, in contrast to the fleas, which suck blood from their hosts. Lice are far more successful on birds than on mammals; there are hundreds of species that attack birds, and relatively few that live on mammals. These Mallophaga (or "wool-eaters") must first have been scavengers that adapted themselves to feeding on the reptiles which were the predecessors of birds, and are consequently a very ancient order of insects, being but little changed over the evolutionary centuries. On the other hand, birds have greatly changed, and it is sometimes possible for scientists to discover to which families birds belong by making a study of their feather lice, for it is most likely that birds were parasitized at an early stage in their evolution. All the game birds have the same kinds of lice, all the ducks, and so on, and while the birds have changed, the lice have not.

The feather louse lives most of its life on the bird, in contrast to the flea, which only visits the bird to feed. The eggs are cemented to the feathers, usually along the barbs against the stem or rachis of the flight feathers, or on those of the head and neck. They soon hatch, but in a curious manner: The young louse within its shell sucks in air, which is blown out behind itself and then bursts the eggshell open. The lice have no metamorphosis, as do butterflies and so forth, but grow and molt, grow and molt, three times before becoming adult. They live by cutting off pieces of feather and chewing them, though some species take blood as well as skin, scales, and serum, and have thus adapted themselves to a difficult diet.

Unless their population is very high, the lice do little harm to the birds. On the small passerine birds, such as sparrows, the numbers of lice are few—from none to ten in number is common, but two thousand can often be found on large birds. Heavy populations prove excessively irritating to birds; even Pliny remarked that lice can kill pheasants unless they rid themselves of the parasites by means of dust baths.

As the lice spend their whole time on the bird, they are living almost under incubator conditions and in these circumstances no very large number of eggs is needed to secure the survival of the race. They are very sensitive to temperature, and if a bird dies, soon leave the body to seek a new host, a matter in which they cannot very often be successful; it is the great problem these animals have to face—the death of the host and the subsequent question of race survival—and one can imagine it as the penalty of their comparatively easy parasitic life. It is the same problem that faces the human parasite, the great man's hanger-on. What does he do when his patron dies, or falls from power? Usually he must, like the louse, fall from power, too.

The race does survive and so the individual lice must pass from one bird to another, for which purpose a number of different methods are used: There is contact between birds during copulation, brooding of the young, and roosting. Lice adhere to bird flies and so are transported, and even to other insects such as fleas, mosquitoes, dragonflies, bees, and butterflies; as flies tend to visit a bird soon after it is dead, they very often pick up lice, who will drop from the fly when they find a warm atmosphere prevailing, that is, when the fly is on a warm-blooded animal. However, any particular feather louse is usually adapted to feeding on only one kind of bird, or just a few kinds, so that it will not be successful unless the fly transports it fairly rapidly to a similar kind of bird, an event which cannot be common. While on the fly or other insect, the louse rapidly cools and becomes torpid, a condition in which it will not long survive. In view of all these difficulties, it is surprising that there are so many species of bird lice; one would imagine it would be so much easier for the chimney-swift louse to be able to live on various other kinds of birds rather than only on chimney swifts, but the fact is that isolation tends to breed species, and the lice on their specific bird are rather like the animals and plants on an isolated island, where all sorts of strange, uncommon varieties can arise.

Apart from the birds themselves, the lice do not have many enemies, but nevertheless they do have their difficulties, as do all varieties of life in their struggle for existence.

In preening themselves, the birds not only pick off fleas but also clean up the lice where they can, to which action lice have responded by acquiring protective coloration, or siting themselves where the beak cannot reach them, on the head and neck. In some other cases lice in such sites do not need camouflage, but in yet others, as birds help each other by cleaning their mates' head and neck feathers, some protective coloring is of use. The birds shake off lice in dust and water baths, though they may also pick them up in a dust bath if another and lousy bird has just used it. Finally, birds may have another strange anti-louse measure in "anting." This is when they allow a swarm of ants to run through their feathers and over their skins. Or sometimes a bird will pick up an ant and rapidly dab the insect under first one wing, then the other, then drop it, usually with the abdomen broken, and repeat the process several times; it is more than likely that the formic acid from the ants either repels or kills the lice. Birds will "ant" with other substances as well, such as hot charcoal from bonfires and even burning matches. Maurice Burton thinks that this may be the origin of the story of the phoenix rising from the ashes, for a bird rising from a bonfire site might well be thought to have been born in it.

A great variety of other creatures is found in the chimney swifts' and house sparrows' nests on the walls, eaves, and roof of the house. In fact, the nest fauna is almost as great and as varied as that of Bartons itself, so that we can consider only some of the animals. There is a big range of parasitic worms, with their complicated life histories. In vertebrates, particularly warm-blooded ones, worms find the best conditions: The medium is larger, standardized, and usually warmer than that of an insect, and the vertebrates moreover wander over a bigger area of ground, allowing the eggs to scatter more widely and with a better chance of finding the primary host. Were man an insect-eating creature, his worm population would be as high as that of the insect-eating birds and the bats.

Louse flies and black flies are important inhabitants of the nests; the adult louse flies live permanently on the bodies of the swallows and other birds and run in and out of the feathers in the same way as does the bat fly described in Chapter 5, to which they are related. The insects suck the blood of birds and will also bite man and other mammals. As with all parasites living permanently on a host, large numbers of eggs or larvae are not needed to secure the future of the species. The larvae of the bird louse-flies are, in fact, raised one at a time from an egg retained in the body of the female and incubated there, the larva being deposited fully grown in the bottom of a nest, where it immediately pupates, in which state it passes the winter, hatching in the subsequent spring. The adults in their protected environment live quite a long while; they have almost lost their wings, and about half the population of birds can be carrying these insects. It is suspected that the louse flies carry the avian malaria parasite—the creature with which Sir Ronald Ross conducted his epochmaking experiments in India in 1897 and thus solved the human malaria transmission problem.

Mosquitoes and gnats feed on birds and are dealt with in the next chapter, as only part of their life is spent in the house, the larval stage taking place in water. Black flies are mostly pests of mammals. They greatly troubled the settlers and still trouble vacationers in the open in some rural parts of New England, but now they are excluded from the house by flyscreens. In the past, would-be settlers in New England were told that unless they could put up with mosquitoes and black flies they should not come. Josslyn, in describing the creature, calls it ". . . a small black fly no bigger than a flea," thus indicating how common the latter creature then was [30]. Some black flies attack birds; here again, the larvae are aquatic and are found in swiftly running streams clinging to rocks, stones, and submerged branches. The adults have a curious way of emerging from the cocoon: By accumulating a pressure of air within the pupal case the adults burst it open, rise to the surface with the emerging bubble of air and immediately fly away. It is a matter of some difficulty to transfer from one medium to another because of the small size of the creatures involved; few insects can drink from the surface of water because the surface tension and capillary action of the water can grasp them and hold them there. If the black fly does not at once fly away as its bubble bursts, it will be caught by the tension of the surface skin of the water and be most unlikely ever to escape from it. Moreover, living in running water, unusual for insects, means the flow could easily wash them away as they emerge from their pupal cases. But this risk is balanced by the advantage of having a medium (running water) not so heavily exploited by rival life-forms as still water.

The horse-biting stable flies sometimes attack birds, and

bluebottles and greenbottles breed in the birds' dead bodies. The special birdbottle fly lives on the nectar of flowers as an adult but the larvae live in the nest and at intervals suck blood from the nestlings. There are a number of other flies, as well as those mentioned, and all help spread the diseases to which birds are heir.

A large number of different kinds of mite are found on birds and in their nests. The red mites suck blood, others eat feathers; some are scavengers, and yet others feed on the parasitic mites themselves.

Ticks can be very dangerous to a bird. They tend to attack it in the region of the eye, and as they gorge themselves on blood, they inject saliva into it which may blind the unfortunate creature. Among these animals living on the birds are others which live on the parasites, such as the predatory mites and histerid beetles already mentioned, fierce anthocorid bugs who are greedy for mites, and many others involving a whole complex pattern of life cycles dependent at third and fourth hand on the food arising originally in the green plant.

Among the large number of animals found in the swallows' and swifts' nests, fleas predominated; next came flies, then moths, among these last being the common clothes moth and related insects. It is indeed strange that these birds can apparently be so cheerful and energetic when they have this big colony of parasitic life dependent on them; one can only suppose that they get their food comparatively easily and that the parasites somehow regulate their appetites so as not to kill the goose that lays the golden eggs.

We must now return to some of the other thirdhanders found on the premises, and will start with that complex subject, the parasitic worms of the mammals.

The parasitic mode of life of these worms has no doubt arisen in the course of evolution from a free-living life, and it is tempting to imagine that the creature has given up its freedom for a life of ease—no question here of "give me liberty or give me death," a choice that does not arise in nature. Actually it is merely life once again filling up a gap—taking advantage of space and opportunities that are not being used. In many cases the life pattern of parasitic worms is so complex that one is tempted to imagine that it cannot have arisen by means of natural selection, though one would be wrong. As an example, the eggs of the fish tapeworm are laid in the small intestine of man, passing out in excreta, after which they must find their way to fresh water to hatch and swim. Many die, but some will be eaten by a small crustacean, which in turn must be consumed by a trout, salmon, perch, or eel and then eaten raw or undercooked by man in order to complete its life cycle, which can be completed in no other way. Similarly, a cat liver fluke uses a snail and a fish as intermediate hosts.

Have these complex patterns arisen by evolution, by chance, or by Divine intervention? Strange as these life histories are, evolution—the survival of the fittest to survive—can explain them. Our surprise at the existence of successive hosts arises from considering ourselves the center of things, and working outward from that point. How surprising a story it seems that man should pass the eggs first to the crustacean cyclops, then to the fish, before they get back to man, whereas the reverse process could be the evolutionary pattern. The addition of successive animals to a simple parasitic relationship gives the parasite a bigger field and a wider range. Some of the worms in the cyclops hatched when their host was eaten by fish and found they could live there with advantage, so they throve at the expense of those that did not hatch inside fish; again, some of those in the fish when eaten by man found this advantageous to the race as a whole, for birds and mammals are able to scatter the eggs over a far wider field than fishes and crustaceans, and soon this pattern was obligatory for the species. Such a design is not, of course, fixed forever. Evolution is not something that has happened in the past and has then stopped, but is going on all around us all the time. Parasitic worms are now rare in man and are being rapidly reduced in our domestic animals, because man cooks most of his food and takes measures against the worms in his animals, destroying the intermediate hosts, using drugs to kill the worms, and maintaining a high standard of general cleanliness. This has left an empty field and we may well ask, "Can nature fill it?"

The most dangerous worm found in man at Bartons was the trichina. The life cycle here can be carried out wholly in one animal, and pigs, humans, and rats are commonly infected. No eggs are excreted, but the worm forms cysts in the muscle flesh of its host which hatch when this flesh is eaten by any other suitable mammal. The worms can set up a painful condition known as trichinosis, when severe rheumatic pains arise wherever the larvae are turning to cysts in the muscles. Pigs usually become infected by eating rats, and man by eating raw or insufficiently cooked pork. Infected pork or ham is excessively dangerous; the tiny cysts have a hard shell and can be felt against the knife edge as it cuts a slice. The worm is rare in man today because of meat inspection and careful cooking, but there is still a danger, for inspection may miss an infection and cooking must be long and thorough to kill deep-seated cysts; for instance, all parts of the joint must be raised to a temperature of 137°F.

The dogs in the house were attacked from time to time by a number of worms, of which the dog roundworms and three tapeworms were the most usual. Many dogs, if not most of them, are born infected with roundworms. Eggs are passed out with excreta and do not become infective for several days; when eggs in the right stage are swallowed, the embryo worm hatches in the intestine, bores through its wall, and gets into the bloodstream and from there to the lungs, where it can cause a type of pneumonia; from here it passes to the small intestine, where it becomes mature and produces eggs again. Provided they are not too numerous, the worms do little or no harm to the dog in this position, though they can inhibit growth and harm puppies.

The secondary hosts of the two dog tapeworms are fleas and rabbits, dogs becoming infected either by eating fleas or raw rabbit containing the appropriate stages of the worms. Sheep can also form a source of infection for other worms. Effective modern drugs are now available for round- and tapeworm control. The droppings from infected dogs contain millions of eggs and should be collected and burned.

The small hydatid tapeworm can attack dogs, cats, and man, the last-named being infected from the handling of dogs, from being licked by them, or eating raw vegetables fouled by dogs; it will not reach sexual maturity in the cat.

Cats may also be attacked by roundworms and tapeworms, the dog-flea tapeworm being very common in cats as well.

I have mentioned mites attacking birds or their parasites, and living on debris or food in the house; they can also live on the mammals there, and the results are known as mange and scabies.

Mange in the dogs was usually caused by the sarcoptic mites which live among the hair and on the surface of the skin. The young mites burrow into the upper layer of the skin, over which point a scab forms from the yellowish fluid seeping from the entry hole. The scab protects the mites, who then lay eggs and extend the scabby condition of the animal, while the hair falls away. Scabies in man is caused by a variety of the same mite and is a very ancient trouble to him. The itch was well known in the early days of the farm. The female mite burrows into the surface of the skin, is fertilized by the male, and then continues her burrow, laying eggs as she goes. The mite carries a number of backward-pointing spines, so she is never able to retreat and after something like eight weeks she

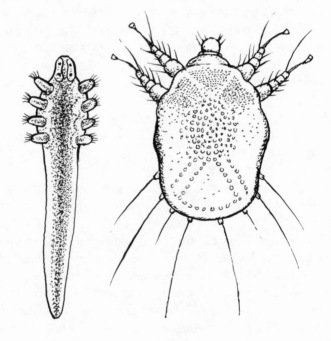

MANGE

dies at the end of her burrow, having laid some two eggs daily during the period.

These activities produce scabs on the skin which are very irritating, causing the patient to scratch himself violently and open the skin to secondary infections. The curious thing is that the irritation does not necessarily occur where the mites are working; the attacked individual becomes very sensitive to the mite, for whereas the first time a person harbors these creatures the itch will not start for three or four weeks, after he has become sensitized by one attack he will find himself wanting to scratch within a day or two of a new one's starting. The hands and wrists are the areas most frequently attacked, and the head but rarely. The young stages of the mite have a high mortality rate and the parasite is transmitted from person to person by contact of hands or bodies, facilitating the passage of the adult female mite.

Another form of mange was also found at times on the dogs and was a much more serious condition for them; this was the follicular or demodectic mange, which like the sarcoptic is also caused by a mite. This time it is a long worm-shaped creature, only one eightieth of an inch in length, unlike the sarcoptic mange mite, which is round. The mites penetrate the tubes from which the hairs spring—the famous follicles of the barber's sales talk on hair restorer. These mites can also attack man but do him no particular harm, although on dogs they can cause a severe and unpleasant mange.

Similar mites cause the mange of sheep which has been overcome now for more than a hundred years by the invention of sheep dips based on sulphur or arsenic. Today better and less toxic chemicals are used.

Bartons is to some extent a microcosm of the world in general and all the animals it has sheltered have reacted one on the other all the time, but it is these parasitic thirdhanders that have been most influenced by the development of the house, for nearly all of them have been extinguished from the premises and from much of the world outside as well. While there are places, particularly in the tropics, where fleas, lice, and worms make man miserable, there are many cities where it is almost impossible to find these creatures. They have been abolished and have left an unfilled space; or is it unfilled? We might well say that it is man himself who has filled the gap. He can do with less food because he does not have to feed his parasites as well as himself, and doing with less food, creates a balance enabling his own numbers to increase. Has man in destroying his parasite lost anything of advantage? One would think not, but parasitism is a strange relationship and can border on symbiosis, so that one can ask questions that cannot really be answered. Did the tapeworms supply a vitamin or a protective antibody which helped man to survive? Did fleas and lice form pets or companions for oppressed peasants or laborers? The Eskimos tell fairy stories in which lice are the hero and heroine, and with regard to dogs, David Harum thought ". . . a reasonable amount of fleas is good for a dog —keeps him from broodin' over being a dog, mebbe!" Were these parasites advantageous in that the misery they caused led man to seek to make a better world?

The tolerance some animals show for their parasites suggests that there is something about their activities that the host enjoys, even though it is being harmed. The bat, an excessively clean animal, takes no notice of the large bat flies in its fur, and may get some pleasure from their movements; it is possibly analogous to the pleasure man gets from tobacco, which he continues to use though he knows it disposes him to lung cancer. It may well happen that an animal will not always do what is the absolute best for itself, but can be influenced by the activity of some other form of life to adopt a slightly lower standard and thus permit this other form of life to expand too. Certainly if the tobacco plant had not developed its particular alkaloid—nicotine—so attractive to man, it would be an insignificant American weed instead of, as it is, a major crop plant covering thousands of acres throughout the world.

Something of the same thing may happen with the cuckoo, which parasitizes many kinds of birds, some of whom realize the cuckoo is an enemy and attempt to drive off the invader. The cuckoo never fights back, for she would not want to injure her offspring's foster parents, so she retires and waits for another opportunity to lay her egg. Other birds seem to welcome the cuckoo and almost invite her to lay in the nest, though as a result their own chicks will be destroyed. Moreover, small foster parents have to work tremendously hard to satisfy the enormous cuckoo in the nest; is it possible that they, too, get some psychological satisfaction from these activities?

11

~

VISITORS

U NTIL NOW we have mainly been dealing with animals
that live, or have lived, permanently at Bartons, making
the place their home. Some of them, such as the swallows, or
the tapeworms in the restaurant trout and ornamental tropical
fish, might at times range far from it. Even the bats moved
away in winter. There was a wide range of more or less permanent residents, running from mite to mammal, over the
house's history. A similar range of animals visited the house
from time to time, and we will now deal with the more important of these visitors.

Most of them had definite visiting periods, often in spring
or summer—the houseflies for instance. Others might call in at
any time—for example, rats and humans, though even these
last usually came more during the summer. On the other hand,
the house was selected as winter quarters by a few other animals, including queen yellow jackets and other insects.

In the old days the housefly was among the commonest
summer visitors, but it is still by no means unknown. A house
might seem to be an unexpected environment for a fly, since
its larvae live in excreta and decaying organic matter, on which
the adults feed as well. But some flies have adapted themselves
to living on man's food as well as on his body fluids and excreta. Others seek his blood.

Very many kinds of flies flew in and out of Bartons. The
commonest were the two species of houseflies, the stable fly,
the fruit or vinegar fly, and the black flies of various kinds.

The two houseflies bred in the dung in the farmyard, pre-

FLY

ferring horse, human, and pig dung in that order. They do not
like cow dung. Such dung heaps, due to bacterial action, are
usually hot, which makes them attractive to flies. Decaying
and heating piles of organic refuse, such as compost heaps,
were also used for egg laying. The females laid the eggs in
cracks in the dung heaps, and the blind, headless, and rather
revolting maggots hatching from them bored their way into
the interior of the heap, seeking a zone with a comparatively
high temperature; they liked one of about 115°F. After three
molts the larvae sought a place to pupate, usually digging well
into the soil for this purpose and choosing a far cooler situation. They would even leave the heap if it was too hot for them
and travel some yards over the ground.

The complicated transformation from a legless, blind maggot to an elaborate, winged, keen-sighted fly takes place inside
the pupal case, the end of which is burst open, when the time
comes, by the adult alternately blowing up and deflating a
special bag known as the ptilinum, carried between the eyes;
it is the only time this organ is used. When the adult emerges
it has to pause for some while to pump its wings full of blood
and dry and harden them before it is ready to fly away, feed,
and renew the cycle.

The common housefly was the variety most seen, but during the cooler weather the lesser housefly also occurred; the stable fly was a frequent summer visitor, giving rise to the belief that houseflies could sting, for the stable fly sucks blood and is not unlike a housefly in appearance. The two houseflies, feeding indiscriminately on excreta and human food, can transmit diseases which occur on the former material, and they were in the past one of the causes of the high infant death rate, for they were the usual agents in the transmission of enteric fever and diarrhea, which helped kill so many babies. Today there are not only fewer flies but children, and their food is better protected from these insects.

The fly's role was defended through the medium of Don Marquis's cockroach, Archy. Archy reported a conversation between a spider and a fly, caught in the web. The fly put forth reasons why he should not be eaten by his captor, indicating that he scurried around gutters, sewers, and garbage cans and then carried disease germs into men's houses, when:

> "all the people who
> have lived the right
> sort of life recover
> and the old soaks who
> have weakened their system
> with liquor and iniquity
> succumb. . . . [36]"

The spider admitted the fly's utility and agreed that he was "a vessel of righteousness," but ate him just the same.

The humans always found the flies annoying, but in trying to get rid of them usually attempted the impossible by attacking the flies themselves rather than the larvae. The chief characteristic of flies is that they fly; another is their rate of rapid breeding, so that killing a roomful of these strong-flying, fertile creatures does not do much to lower the number of flies coming forward to continue invading the room, attracted to the house by the smell of humans, food, and a lower light intensity.

A succession of measures was used against flies, few with much success until quite recently. In the early days, even in summer, the help was up before sunrise. Before they retired at night the curtains would be drawn back and the shutters opened on an eastern window, which led the flies to accumulate there; the first task of the girls was to get rid of these by killing them with a flyswatter or by shooing them out of the window. Another method of keeping a room free of flies—as effective today as then—was to kill all the flies in it and then to keep the doors and windows shut. That was all right for the parlor, but not of much use in the kitchen, where the nuisance was greatest.

In the eighteenth century, fly baits were used consisting of decoctions of fleabane, wormwood, and other plants, with a little sugar or honey as an attractant, but they were not very effective, nor, had they been, would it have made much difference to the general fly population.

Theophilus Chilton brought back certain anti-fly measures from his journeys to the tropics, where flies were a greater pest than at home. One was the sealed and darkened room, which was much cooler in the heat of summer than one with the windows open, and another was the bead and bamboo curtain over the doors, for though flies could easily pass between the hanging strings of beads, they very much hesitated to do so. The device enabled the gallant sea captain to take his *siesta* undisturbed through many a hot afternoon when he was at home on leave.

The Deanes in the mid-nineteenth century devoted a lot of thought and energy to the suppression of houseflies, mosquitoes, stable flies, no-see-ums, gnats, and midges. Alice Baker, who married Stephen Deane II in 1838, detested all the creatures and seemed to inspire her four children with the same sentiments. They were always trying the latest thing in fly control. Theophilus, when fourteen years old in 1854, invented a primitive flyswatter, a piece of leather attached to a stick. He would kill all the creatures in the parlor, closing the windows and locking the door, only admitting people one at a time and watching for flies entering, which, with his swatter at the ready, he would kill. His younger sister Jane maintained that a rolled-up newspaper was just as effective and scorned his great invention, much to his annoyance. But their parents said they were being stifled and a window must be opened, which naturally let in more flies.

The next item to be tried was poisoned flypapers. They

were of absorbent paper containing arsenic and sugar which was dampened and left exposed for flies. They were effective but dangerous, as the arsenic was poisonous to all animals. Children might well lick the sweet papers, or the arsenic could be soaked out of them and used for the purpose of murder. The arsenic papers were abandoned.

Muslin screens on the windows were the next device used by Alice and young Theophilus. They kept out the flies but had various disadvantages. For one thing, you could not see out of the windows. The screens got wet and rotted and they tore easily and the flies came through open doors. The next thing they used was "Fowler's Patent Fly Fan." This was a large propeller on a vertical post. It had a solid base containing a clockwork motor. The apparatus was put on the dinner table and the spring wound up. The fan then gave a downdraft of air, driving off the flies. The only drawbacks were that it needed a lot of winding up and could give everyone a stiff neck.

About the same time, sticky flypapers were used, Tangle-foot being a well-known brand. They were hung from the lamps in the middle of the rooms. Such a paper was apt to clear off the lesser housefly more rapidly than the common fly, as the lesser tends to circle high in the center of the room; and, of course, the supply of flies from outside, coming mostly from the farmyard dung heaps, was almost infinite.

Keeping the flies out of the house was made easier by the invention of the metal fly-screen and the spring door. The first metal screens arose from the desire of secrecy in the frequenting of bars. A fine mesh screen allowed the customers to look out of the barroom but did not permit the passersby to look in. By 1860 the Deanes had obtained a quantity of fine copper mesh, enough to cover their windows, from Lee and Co., New York. In 1867 "Magoun's Patent Adjustable Window Screens" were put on in the early summer and taken off in the fall. It was a major operation, but still left the problem of the doors. Easy. A wire mesh door was placed in front of or behind each entry door. Not at all easy was to get people to close the extra door on coming in or going out. The "Excelsior Door Spring" solved this problem for them. But the screens were expensive, they corroded and tore, they and the frames did not always fit, or they warped, allowing mosquitoes and black flies to get in, if not ordinary flies. Moreover, flies came in as people opened the door, but on the whole the screens were the answer to the problem of the winged Diptera nuisance, and still are.

The promotion of fly-screens was an early example of the advertising jingle. For instance, in 1880:

> We use the Porter Screen
> That keeps our house so neat and clean.
> Sold by C. J. Blackstone, Springfield, Mass., and Boston.

Pictures showed two families, one sitting at peace and in contentment and the other plagued and bad-tempered because of the flies. Guess which was which! Not a difficult question, reminding one of today's TV commercials and the dreadful suspense of watching the test between Wash-It-Clean and Brand X. Will Wash-It-Clean turn out to wash whiter than Brand X?

In the 1920s a general understanding of the nature of the problem arose and it was at once seen that the real solution of the fly menace was to stop the larvae developing. The houseflies do not breed much in loose droppings but mostly in dung and compost heaps.

One method of control was to keep these fermenting so fast that they were too hot for the flies; another was to put the horse, pig, and human dung beneath the cow dung and thus out of reach of the houseflies; and a third method was to apply insecticide to the heap.

The next anti-fly measure was the introduction, between the wars in this century, of the "Flit" type of spray. These sprays started as white oil solutions of pyrethrum to which were added other insecticides, with DDT and Allethrin finally being used after the second World War, to make a rapid and effective product. They were good, but the basic objection remained that they killed only the flies present in the house. The spray had much the same effect in reality as killing the flies one by one with a swatter, except that it was easier and quicker. Sprays were developed which left a toxic residue of DDT on walls, ceilings, and paintwork, killing all flies (as well as most other insects and spiders) alighting on them. DDT may no longer be used for this purpose, but in any case it was losing its utility, for the flies had developed a countermeasure. They produced races resistant to the insecticide and were thus able to keep up their numbers.

Today flies in and around the house are nothing like as numerous as they were a century ago. That is due mainly to the virtual disappearance of the horse, depriving the insects of their favorite breeding medium. No horses, or very few of them, combined with better handling of refuse at dumps and their treatment with insecticides, the use of screens, and a certain amount of spraying and swatting in the home has reduced the nuisance at Bartons House Restaurant to very small proportions, in spite of the attractiveness of the kitchens to those insects.

In addition, the few farms around Bartons now have top-class dairy herds and must keep down flies. The manure is stacked on concrete middens having larvae traps around them in the form of shallow channels always full of liquid. The gutters not only drown the larvae as they leave the stack to pupate, but also allow the valuable liquid manure to be collected and used on the land. Safe insecticidal sprays are used in the milking sheds. Flies are not extinct, but their numbers are a tenth of what they were when first seen on the premises.

Man has now become the fly's worst enemy, but such was not always the case, nor today is he its only opponent. Spiders and a fungus still attack flies and take a considerable toll. A spore of certain fungi can germinate on a fly and the mycelium enter the body, grow, and block vital channels, killing the creature within a few days. The insect becomes attached to the surface on which it last rested by a white fungus growth. The fungus puts out darkish fruiting bodies from the insect segments, giving it a striped, yellow-jacket appearance. Masses of spores are then produced, ready to infect more flies. Such fungus-killed flies are often seen on windows, and Victoria Deane, when a child, used to say the flies were trying to turn into tigers, being much mocked by her elder brother, Edward, for supposing such an unlikely transformation to be possible.

"Where do flies go in the wintertime?" was a cry (from a song) that rang around the world in the 1920s, the author speculating that perhaps they migrated to "some distant foreign clime" or even to "Gay Paree." In point of fact, most flies pass the winter as pupae. As the temperature drops in the fall, their rate of development slackens. In winter, growth stops unless the medium in which they are sheltering is warm. By the end of winter only the most favorably situated pupae will still be living, but their powers of reproduction are so great that a few survivors can quickly breed and reoccupy all suitable sites. In Chapter 1, mention was made of the rapid buildup of elephant populations if all offspring should survive, although the elephant is a slow breeder. Biologists are much given to exercises of this kind when wishing to impress their readers with the powers of the life-force; some pretty impressive calculations along these lines have been made for the fast-breeding housefly. For instance, a pair, should all the offspring of each subsequent generation survive, could increase to some 200 million billion in a season. That quantity would be enough to cover the entire earth to a depth of forty-seven feet with houseflies! It can thus be seen that a shortage of food is a more important factor in keeping down fly populations than the activities of parasites and predators.

Black flies were another nuisance in the house from the earliest days. Being so small, they can get through cracks or tears in screens, dash in as doors are opened, and be transported on clothing. Two unusual features of black flies are that, if examined with a lens they will be seen to have a large hump on the back, and secondly, they live in running water. Thus measures taken to reduce mosquitoes by drainage of ponds and stagnant pools into little fresh-running streams encourages an equal nuisance, the black fly. In some tropical areas they are dangerous to man, as they carry a worm leading to infections of onchocerciasis, or river blindness, fortunately not known in North America.

Blowflies of different kinds, such as the bluebottles, greenbottles, and flesh flies, visited the house from time to time. They are scavengers and carrion feeders and were attracted to the house by the smell of the meat in the larder, kitchen, and storerooms. From the earliest times, measures were taken to preserve steaks, roasts, and poultry from the attacks of these flies, for the Bartons soon realized that maggots were not spontaneously produced in old meat but came from the eggs laid by these flies. In this sort of thing farmers and housewives were often ahead of the scientists in their knowledge. Meat exposed for a very short time can get these scavenger flies' eggs laid on it, even when lying in the dog's dinner-bowl. However, when eaten, such eggs either do not hatch, or if they do, the stomach juices quickly kill the maggots.

One anti-blowfly device much used in the mid-nineteenth century was a bell-shaped wire-gauze meat cover, but even these seemed to fail at times and maggots developed in the meat. What had usually happened in such cases was that, in spite of the cover fitting tight to the plate, if the mesh was big enough or was broken, the female fly would position herself over the hole and drop eggs through it onto the meat beneath. There they soon hatched to larvae and infested the whole piece. The voracity and numbers of fly maggots that can arise in meat led Linnaeus to state that a fly can eat an ox as quickly as a lion.

Ripe fruit also attracted its own particular kind of fly—the pomace flies or Drosophilidae—already mentioned in connection with vinegar and its eelworms. This family of fruit flies has achieved a certain fame, as it has been much used in genetical research. Swallow flies, as the name suggests, lived in the nests of those birds. Once when the Reverend R. Standish, godfather of Janet Barton (born 1915), was staying at Bartons some of those flies migrated from the nests into the reverend gentleman's bedroom. He was severely bitten and thought his room was infested with fleas, creatures which were not expected to be in a gentleman's house in those days. His caustic comments as to whether a Boston businessman could be considered to be a gentleman led Victoria Deane to defend her home and husband and to make a full investigation of the reverend gentleman's bedroom. Not a flea could be found; a few "stable flies," well known as biters, were noted on the windows (really they were the swallow flies) and peace was restored in the family. What had happened was that a swallow in one of the roof nests had died and the flies left the body as it cooled, to search for a new host. Although their natural hosts are hirundine birds, they will experiment with other animals, hence their assault on the worthy cleric.

Mosquitoes and gnats are both summer and winter visitors at Bartons. They too are Diptera—the large family of two-winged insects—and feed on a wide variety of animals. They were particularly fond of man and birds in the early history of the house, certain of the mosquitoes being dangerous because they could transmit diseases such as malaria, yellow fever, dengue, and encephalitis. These troubles are found more in the tropics, but nevertheless some were not unknown in New England. The larval stages of mosquitoes and gnats are passed in water, the larvae feeding on particles of organic matter found there, such as protozoa, bacteria, algae, fungal spores, pollen, and so forth. By means of small brushlike appendages to the mouthparts, these materials are worked into a ball and swallowed. However, there are a few mosquitoes which are predacious on other species.

Few of the common gnats bite man, but the Ceratopogonidae—the punkies or biting midges—do and can be very annoying to man and birds. The spotted Anopheline mosquitoes are the ones transmitting malaria, and their larvae lie flat to the surface of the water, whereas other species (such as *Culex*)

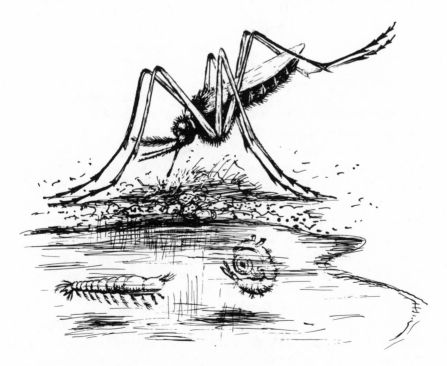

MOSQUITO

hang head downward from this layer. Both breathe through spiracles in contact with the air when the creatures are on the surface, having valves to close them when they dive—very like a submarine in fact. The anophelines swim tail-first just under the surface in a series of random jerks, whereas the culicines wriggle about under the surface skin of the water. Both kinds of larvae plunge down deep (if they can) when frightened, but they must eventually come to the surface again and project their breathing tubes in order to get air. They breed mostly in rainwater barrels, but some come from puddles, ponds, water pockets in hollow trees, and so forth. The pupal stage is in the water, and the pupa emerges by bursting the dorsal side with air pressure. The adult then rests on the old skin or on nearby plants in order that its wings may fill and harden.

The dangerous anophelines and the harmless culicines are most readily distinguished by the position assumed by the adults when at rest, the former pointing its head down and tail up and the latter having its body parallel to the surface on which it is standing. It is only the female mosquitoes that take blood from man and animals; the males live on juices sucked from fruit and flowers, as the females also do at times. In the old days the house gnats would haunt the dairy and suck the milk from the cream-setting pans; having to push the proboscis through a layer of cream to get at the milk beneath was to the gnat the same as pushing it through the skin of a vertebrate animal in order to get at the blood.

Apart from infecting one with malaria, mosquitoes can be very disturbing at night and there are many people who lie in bed in the dark listening to the whine of the creature and waiting for the abrupt cutoff that means the insect has settled and may be about to strike—a silence reminiscent of the ominous cutout of the flying bomb's roar. The musical may obtain some relief from this tension by knowing that the males (which will not feed on blood) have far higher-pitched notes than the females and that the note of the hungry female drops from the normal of F to that of D when she is fully fed.

Stephen Deane started to take a greater interest in insects after he found the moth larvae attacking the corks of his port-wine bottles. He used to aver that his mosquitoes were particularly virile and voracious and that they enjoyed nothing more than a sup at his glass of port, provided that the glass was filled to the brim so that the creature could get at it. Beulah maintained that this was done not so much in the interest of natural history, or to follow in the footsteps of the great Buffon, but as an excuse for Stephen and his friends always to have their glasses full.

It is unfortunate that in his diary Stephen records only the bare fact—which is quite possible, since port is only a sort of fruit juice—and not the subsequent behavior of his toping insects; one would like to know if the clarity, pitch, and steadiness of their flight notes were in any way affected. Stephen's contention that Bartons had giant and very voracious mosquitoes was not just a Yankee tall story. Crane flies—the daddy longlegs—look very like giant mosquitoes and any sufferer from the ordinary painful bites might well imagine the crane fly to be a special New England horror. But such is not the case. The crane flies are vegetable feeders and merely look like mosquitoes.

The females of mosquitoes and the common gnat used to winter in the house, mostly in the cellar, but they were also found in dark cupboards and the loft. They are not now so numerous as formerly because of the various insecticidal treatments given to the house, its drier condition, and the fact that the rainwater barrels are treated to keep down the larvae. During the summer, whenever the Deanes were spraying the roses against greenfly or giving any such insecticidal treatment in the garden, they always squirted a little of it into the rain barrels as they went by, which is quite enough to keep down gnats and mosquito larvae there. A few drops of oil can be poured on the top of the water, but that is soon lost when it rains, if the barrels overflow from the top, as most of them do. Some of the wintering females may feed from time to time during the cold season; they convert this food to fat reserves, not to eggs, and come out in the spring to find suitable water sites on which to lay their eggs. Some mosquitoes do not lay in water but in depressions in the ground, hollow trees, and so forth, which will eventually fill with water and allow the eggs and larvae to develop.

The dangers of malarial infection in New England are now almost extinct. To transmit the causal organism, the Anopheline mosquito must bite an infected human, wait the necessary time for the parasites' life processes to develop within it, and then bite another human. Though the causal mosquitoes are still common, they are not so numerous as they once were. Wild and domestic warm-blooded animals (except birds) are now fewer, and as the insects prefer to feed on those rather than humans, that means less of their favorite food is available. Moreover, as rooms in houses are now kept cleaner, more over-wintering female mosquitoes are destroyed. And finally, malaria-carrying humans are now comparatively rare, as those infected soldiers and planters returning from the tropics are usually cured with powerful antimalarial drugs soon after arrival, so that we are fortunate in there being but little residue of the disease in the country. This is another example of an organism (the malaria parasite) facing extinction because its numbers are falling below a certain critical level. When the house was first built "the ague" was a common complaint and often a wretched laborer or servant, reprimanded and abused for being shiftless and idle, was merely suffering from malaria or the enlarged spleen that goes with it.

Bites from mosquitoes (*Anopheles, Aedes,* and similar genera) are often blamed on the harmless house gnats, but as the gnats are excessively irritating and harmful to birds, these last live an easier life if the gnats are sprayed and killed; it is indeed no kindness to a cage bird to leave it uncovered at night, as it exposes the bird to the vicious attack of gnats. There are, of course, a large number of small, biting midges to be found around the farm, but these rarely enter the house. There is also a parasitic mosquito which will not attack animals itself, but draws its meal of blood from other already gorged mosquitoes. The fall and winter deaths among mosquitoes and gnats are very high, but their powers of reproduction are enormous and the vacant spaces for mosquitoes are quickly recolonized by the few survivors of the winter weather.

There were many occasional visitors to the house; there is not space to deal with them all. Among the more numerous and important were: ants, wasps, bees, greenfly, earwigs, butterflies and moths, sow bugs, snakes, lizards, raccoons, squirrels, and chipmunks. The carpenter ant was the most usual invader of the house, particularly of the kitchens and larder. At

CARPENTER ANT

one time the tiny Pharoah's ant was present and the small Argentine ant made an attempt to establish itself but without success. Two of these belong to the most advanced ant family, the *Formicidae*, leading the usual complex social life of these creatures with a caste system of specialists—workers, queens, drones, and so forth, while the Pharoah's ant is a myrmicine with an omnivorous diet. Maeterlinck has pointed out that the social development in the ant realm is not unlike that of the human world. The two most primitive families of ants (Ponerinae and Dorylinae) have but little caste distinction and are carnivorous; their life is thus comparable to the hunting stage of primitive man. The Dorylinae are not found in North America but are the wandering ant hordes of the tropics, ceaselessly searching for animal food and making no permanent homes—which again bears a resemblance to our own nomadic ancestors. Among the remaining three families (Myrmicinae, Dolichoderinae, and Formicidae) may be found the parallels to the herdsman, farmer, and city dweller. Some ants carefully tend aphids (or greenfly), stroking them for the sugary secretion they give off, carrying them to new favorable sites to start a new colony, and driving off the herd's enemies; such ants may be seen on almost any rosebush in summer.

The true farmer ants, which are not found in the north, cut leaves from plants, chew them up, and then plant a special fungus on the resulting hotbed, keeping it well weeded and trained so as to kill all alien fungi and to produce a good crop of the special *bromatia* on which they feed. The omnivorous ants may be compared to the city dweller, who will now eat almost anything. "Go to the ant, thou sluggard," says Solomon. "Consider her ways and be wise." Perhaps it is only from the point of view of the energy and determination they show that we should admire them, for their social organization has led them into as many undesirable activities from the moral point of view as has that of humans: to wit, wars, slavery, child labor, parasitism, and overeating, all admirably expressed by W. W. Watt in his verses entitled "Had enough? Vote Ant."[*]

As noted above, the carpenter ant was, and occasionally still is, a visitor. The early Bartons used to sprinkle antwort around, but even if it killed a few ants it had no real effect on the colony as a whole. The breeder in the nest—the queen—must be killed or restrained if ants are to be controlled. The carpenter ant does not usually nest in the house, but in an old tree or nearby building. Nevertheless it did secure a foothold at Bartons from time to time. This black ant is so common it hardly needs any description; the workers, shiny black, 6 to 18 mm long, are scavengers in many houses. The carpenter ant has the usual ant life-style. The workers are incomplete females; the queen and princesses are winged, fully sexed females; the winged males only occur in spring and early summer, when they take part in the mating flight and fertilize the virgin females.

A newly mated female selects a site; it may be an old tree, a cupboard in a kitchen, or a partition wall, and excavates a cavity. There she lays fifteen to twenty eggs and seals the entrance. She stays in the chamber she has made and feeds the resulting larvae with fluid from her mouth. This food comes very largely from the dissolving of her powerful wing muscles, which she will no longer require when in the nest. The larvae pupate, become small incomplete females (workers) and open the sealed chamber. They collect food and regurgitate it for the queen and larvae. They also set about enlarging the nest and excavate long galleries in wood (hence the name "carpenter"), a feature of the galleries being that they are free of

[*] *New Yorker*, November 1946.

frass and quite smooth and polished. The frass is carried away, not eaten. The galleries are made only as nests and usually run along the grain of the wood. Frequently they are not seen, as the ants may hollow out a post or establish themselves in a hollow tree. They usually start the nest in a soft portion of the wood and subsequently extend it to the hard area. The queen then settles down in the nest to become an egg-laying machine, controlling the nest by means of chemical substances she puts out, and is herself controlled by the secretions of the workers. In winter they hibernate deep in the nest.

The workers, who are sterile females, forage for a wide range of foods: They kill small insects, take nectar from flowers, carry back small seeds, and collect the sugary fluid exuded by their carefully tended greenfly. They send out scouts to look for food, and when an ant finds a good source she is able to indicate the fact to certain of her fellows, regurgitating a drop of the material in question and signaling with the antennae. These leader ants organize the work so that soon a long trail of the insects is winding to and from the new supply. It is these scouts that find their way to food in houses, and soon the line forms to the pile of spilt sugar on the larder shelf or, if they need protein, to the cold Sunday roast. The trails, once established, persist for some time, as the ants recognize them by the smell left on the track. They now find leftover pet food very useful.

During the long history of the house a number of strange, usually faint, and not immediately explicable sounds were heard in it; they were usually more apparent at night, when all else was quiet. "Things that go bump in the night" can seem most eerie, leading the lone watcher or insomniac to suspect the supernatural. But as far as can be ascertained, they all had factual explanations. There were groans from the shrinking of the timbers, tapping of the various insects known as the death-watch beetle, fanning of bees, the faint sounds of psocids in books, the call of owls, twittering of young swallows and sparrows in the nests, rustlings of the swifts in a disused chimney, and also a raccoon and chipmunks, the scurrying of mice, the high-pitched calls of the bats, and the shuffling of pigeons and crows as they alighted on the roof, but the most curious was the noise made by a nest of carpenter ants.

In 1968 ant infestation was so bad at Bartons that the exterminators were called in, and a handsome young man showed Phoebe Deane where the nest was, in a paneled wall in the east wing. By putting an ear against the wall, tapping it, and then listening, one could hear a distinct dry, rustling sound. It was not the ants extending the nest by mining wood but a recognition signal put out by those ingenious insects. Another sign of the nest was the frass carried away and dropped out of "windows" (holes to the exterior), such debris looking like pencil-sharpening trash. The paneling had been installed after the DDT treatment of the house; otherwise the ants could not have used it.

The odorous house ant has been in Bartons on a few occasions but usually was cleared pretty quickly, because it advertises its presence by giving off a musty smell (hence its name) of rotten coconuts. It is after sugary foods, and so penetrates the kitchens and storage cupboards. It nested outside, but did open up cavities in the foundations on two or three occasions.

At Bartons House Restaurant the ants still persist in visiting. None are nesting there and every effort is made to follow up the ant trails at night, when they are most active, discover the nests and destroy them, which perhaps is a pity, as they are interesting and ingenious creatures and might well be our successors on earth if we insist on destroying ourselves with plutonium in its various activities.

The installation of central heating gave the tropical Pharaoh's ants an opportunity to install themselves in the house. They like warmth and can follow the pipe runs to hide their nests under floors or in the walls. They are not much seen, though sometimes they cause trouble to humans by getting into their beds and feeding on a wound, or taking eye or nose fluids for the food and water they contain. This makes them very objectionable in hospitals, a splendid environment for them because of the steady heating and supply of food there. The tiny, palish ants emerge and form their trails to and from food of all sorts: meat, cheese (protein), fats such as butter, lard, and margarine, sugar, jam, honey, and so on. The tracks will also lead to water sources, such as taps and drains; for finding water is one of their main problems. They are able to discover food in the most unlikely places; that piece of chocolate forgotten in a drawer will be found by these ants. Their method of forming new colonies is very different from that of the carpenter ant. Although the winged sexual forms arise, they never fly and a new colony is made by a mass migration of several mated queens with a staff of workers, eggs, grubs, and cocoons.

Once they are established in a well-warmed building, they are difficult to eliminate, as they are so small and persistent, squeezing through the smallest cracks to establish colonies in quite inaccessible places. It is no good spraying the ant trails to kill the insects found there, as such small numbers will be eliminated that the operation is hardly worthwhile. The ants can be offered poison bait, but it must not be strongly poisoned or the wily creatures will soon leave it alone, either because those that take it die before they get the bait back to the nest, or because they discover it is not a good food for the grubs.

A lightly poisoned slow-acting bait is the ideal material against these house ants, because the workers will then take it back and feed it to the queen. Once the queen is poisoned, the colony fades away. The baits are put into waxed pillboxes or little tins with holes in them and have to be renewed frequently.

Of course the fundamental method of ant control is to find and destroy the nests. Those of the Pharaoh's ant are so hidden and so inaccessible that it is almost impossible to find all of them; it means tearing down walls and taking up floors to find even some of them. It is, however, easy to find the nests of the black ant simply by following back the long trail of workers which must eventually lead there. If the nuisance warrants it, for otherwise it seems a pity to destroy such diligence, nests can be eliminated by finding them and sprinkling in a moderately volatile insecticide powder.

Another visitor was the earwig, a plague of which was found in the house the summer after it was built and arose from the disturbance to the local population on the site. Because plants such as wisteria and ivy were trained up the sunny walls, access was made easier for earwigs, and to this day they are frequent summer and fall visitors. Earwigs do not breed indoors but in soil under stones, posts, in wall footings, and in the damper parts of the creeper on the walls. The female insects are remarkable in the care they take of the eggs and the newly hatched young, fussing over them somewhat as a hen will over her chicks. It is remarkable that the eggs become moldy and do not hatch if the female neglects them. They feed on both animal and vegetable food and can be particularly objectionable to the gardener, especially if he grows chrysanthemums, dahlias, and peaches, as they can destroy many choice blooms and ripe fruits. They dislike the light and so feed at night. They have one generation a year and are mature from August. The large wings are seldom seen; they are very delicate and have to be carefully folded up with the help of the familiar tweezers on the insect's final segment.

Indigenous earwigs were common around Bartons when the first building was undertaken. Much seen then was the wingless seaside earwig, as the house was near the shore, and the striped earwig. The settlers brought many animals with them, and another introduction of theirs to America was the European earwig, now very common in New England; they also brought in the little earwig, another species that competed with the native insects.

A curious feature of earwigs is their name. While it is true that they creep into small cracks and crevices to hide, they are by no means especially addicted to entering the ears of man or animals and are but rarely, if ever, found there.

Ticks are far commoner in the human ear than earwigs. "Earwig" is an old word and its use can be traced back to ninth-century Europe. In all probability the word is a corruption of "earwing." The wings of earwigs (not all species are winged) are very delicate and their shape is like an ear. Even the alate ones are seldom seen flying.

Other visitors who constantly came and went were the humans. They had much effect on the life of the place because their presence required certain patterns of behavior, cleanliness, furnishings, special food, and so forth, all having an influence on the life there.

Visitors who were found, like the humans, in both summer and winter were the wasps, for during the summer the premises, particularly the kitchen, would be invaded by the worker wasps, while during the winter, first in the thatch and then under the shingles, numerous queen wasps would be found in hibernation.

The wasps coming into the house at first were mostly the yellow jackets and black hornets. In the eighteenth century the European or golden hornet found its way to Bartons; while it destroyed a lot of ripening fruit, it also devoured many insects, such as flies, bees, butterflies, and moths. It did not attack them with its sting but used its powerful jaws to tear its prey to bits. One reason for this hornet's success was the fact that it was a hard worker, as were many immigrants at that time. The European hornet gained an advantage over its indigenous cousins by working day and night.

Queen yellow jackets and hornets feed heavily before their nuptial flight. Like bees, they mate while in the air and a queen may mate with more than one male. After pairing the queen seeks a dryish, safe, reasonably warm spot for hibernation, which is why they so often come into houses, frequently being found clinging to curtains and under roofing shingles. However, the position must not be too warm or dry, for if it is, the insect will either not be able to go into hibernation, or will come out of it in, say, January, and find neither food outside nor a suitable place for its nest. Or she will become dehydrated. The modern house really only suits the dry-litter habitat insects, and not always them. Yellow-jacket nests may be found in the ground or above it on trees and buildings, according to species. The queen, having found a suitable site, terrestial or aerial, proceeds to make a cell out of "wasp paper," which she prepares by rasping off weather-worn but sound wood and chewing it up with saliva. It is first spread under the roof of the cavity, and from the center of this disc, or inverted saucer, a stalk is dropped which opens out to form another disc, or lower story. On the lower side of this the queen makes the cells, hexagonal like a honeycomb (in fact, bees are really only wasps that have lost the carnivorous habit) and open at the bottom end. In these she lays and cements down the eggs, some thirty in number, feeding the young larvae until they are ready to pupate—which they do hanging in the cell—and closing the bottom with silk.

Up to this point the queen has been doing all the work herself—and an immense task it is to find and prepare the site and the paper, then feed herself and the grubs. All the grubs emerge as workers (that is, immature females), who immediately set about extending the nest and caring for the young, the queen subsequently devoting herself solely to egg-laying, fertilizing them from the stored sperm she obtained when mated on the nuptial flight. Successive lower stories are added to the nest as its strength of workers grows, and the whole is protected by the formation of a "paper" envelope around it. The cells are used again at least once, and some of the older ones carry a third brood as well, so that though a nest may contain some eleven thousand cells, it may well have produced twenty-five thousand wasps during the season and have a strength of some five or six thousand at the end of it. Toward the end of summer bigger cells are constructed and the grubs in them are better fed, becoming the mature females, or queens, of the next generation. At the same time numerous males are produced from unfertilized eggs, and some mate with the queens on the nuptial flight, the cycle then being repeated.

It is a curious fact that all this tremendous activity during the summer is directed solely to the production of a few large and favored females—queens. In the early fall all the workers and males die, due to cold and starvation, though after the queens have flown, the others do spend their last few days in a final reckless orgy, feeding on fruits and any human food found available—"the last of the summer wine."

The food of wasps is both animal and vegetable. They take flies, butterflies, and other insects, and meat and fish from the kitchen, which they partially masticate before feeding it to the young. As is only too well known, they also like sugary fluids, ripe fruit, honeydew from aphids, and the nectar of flowers, but they are not as successful as bees in obtaining this last, as their mouthparts are not long enough.

Wasps were attracted to the house for the same reason that so many other animals were: Man made it much easier for them to get their food. Rich proteins and splendid carbohydrates would be left lying around in large quantities for the taking, in addition to which, large numbers of insects would also be drawn to the premises by man's activities and would be of use to the wasps. No wonder that the presence of man in a neighborhood always leads to an increase of the social wasps. Had they only learned not to sting their benefactor they would have been yet more successful, for though killing workers one by one on windowpanes makes very little difference to their numbers, the unpleasantness of the sting leads man to seek out and destroy the nests. At first he would burn sulphur in the mouth of the nest; today he puts in a spoonful of insecticide powder which is carried into the cavities by the successive entries of the workers.

Edward Hopkins had noted the yellow jacket queens entering his hideout; when he became Stephen Deane I's gardener he spent quite a bit of his spare time studying the creatures, being somewhat saddened by the fall holocaust of males and workers. He noted one thing that enabled him to astonish his friends and the Deane children. It was that male yellow jackets do not sting and can be distinguished from workers by having longer antennae and an extra abdominal segment. He also found out that the males preferred certain flowers much more than did the workers. For instance, the now thick ivy on the east wall bore numerous fall flowers and fruits, on which the male yellow jackets assembled. "I can charm these critturs," he would say to the children, running his fingers among them as they clustered over the ivy heads. Or he would carefully pick a sprig covered with the insects and put it in his buttonhole, actions which never failed to give rise to cries of astonishment. "But don't you go trying it, Miss Mary," he would say. "It's only us Springfield folk as can do that." However, even Edward Hopkins got too confident, for on one occasion at least, there were some workers present and one of them stung him, an event he attempted to conceal with the fortitude of a Spartan.

Another of his inventions was to tie a piece of white thread to a yellow jacket or hornet in order to slow down its flight and thus get an idea of the whereabouts of the nest—an operation akin to the advice given by the mouse in the matter of the cat problem—to put a bell on the cat. However, if done, the thread is very effective in finding nests.

Other summer visitors in New England were the numerous butterflies and moths. One of the cheering sights for the settlers in the early days was the occurrence of beautiful butterflies

BLACK SWALLOWTAIL

AMERICAN COPPER

MOURNING CLOAK

Cabbage white

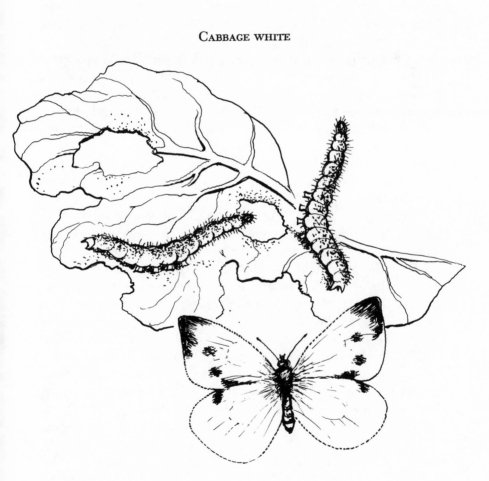

in the spring; they were far more spectacular than anything they had seen in the Netherlands or old England. Among the creatures blundering into the house from time to time were two swallowtails, one dark (the spicebush swallowtail) and the other yellow and deep brown. The caterpillars of the spicebush butterfly fed on that bush, and those of the other swallowtail (the "common eastern" insect) on umbelliferous plants such as parsley and parsnips. It was soon observed which butterflies came from which caterpillars and then the problem arose, even in early times, of whether the damage done by the "worms" was compensated by the beauty of the adult butterflies. In 1649 there was such "a strange multitude of caterpillars" that the selectmen said this sentimental attitude must stop and all worms be collected and destroyed, whatever they might turn into. It seldom happens that a second big plague of insects follows a severe attack, because the creatures' enemies increase at a yet greater rate and reduce the subsequent population to normal. Such proved to be the case in 1650. Experience, Susannah, and John IV continued to collect big caterpillars, feed them in cages, and hatch out the big and attractive adults. Susannah would not allow them to be killed but released them into the fields.

There were many others besides the swallowtails that came into the house in the early days when there were no fly-screens on it. No soul-stirring butterflies coming into a house is one of the penalties of having this amenity, not that a house is of much use to a butterfly except as hibernation quarters. Among these creatures were the strange monarchs which assembled in great flocks in the fall, often coming into or perching on the house. They had two unusual characteristics: The caterpillars lived on the poisonous milkweed, making themselves unpalatable to birds in the process, and in the fall, having turned to adults, they migrated south, most of them going to Mexico, and started back north again in the spring [41].

That worldwide butterfly, the admiral, was also a visitor. It is a striking insect when adult and is not so named because it has crossed so many seas but in error for "admirable." The scientific name of the genus (*Vanessa*) is also of interest. It is not descriptive or derived from the classics, as are so many such names, but is the name given by Dean Swift to one of his attractive correspondents, Esther Vanhomrigh. Fabricius (died 1808) named this beautiful butterfly after that beautiful woman.

The common sulphur, or puddle, butterfly was sometimes in the house, being attracted by spilt water or the wet soil around houseplants after they had been overwatered.

Finally there was the great spangled fritillary, another visitor in the pre-fly screen age, but one which might have a future at Bartons. Recently a salesman approached Mr. La Flèche with the suggestion that he, La Flèche, release tropical butterflies in his restaurant from time to time. "Think how cute it would be," he said, "for your lady customers to have a fine live *Morpho* perched on her drink." Mr. La Flèche thought not. *Morpho becula* was far too big, out of place, might scare the lady and even excrete into her drink. But it gave him an idea. He would raise some New England butterflies for his restaurant and have a bar in the "butterfly vivarium." To start with he would have the great spangled fritillary, manageable in size and very attractive. And the caterpillars fed on violets; that was a nice touch. "Violet-fed butterflies" to

GREAT SPANGLED FRITILLARY

put alongside the peach-fed hams. Imagine a lot of Brazilian *Morphos* fluttering around, getting torn and tired and dropping dead into the dishes. No. He would try the fritillaries. So there is going to be a run on violets in this part of New England.

Next we must consider the moths—insects much attracted to lights in the house. It would take too much space to give an account of them all. Two of the large ones were the handsome brick-red, yellow-spotted regal moth and the large *Cecropia* with its feathery antennae and strikingly patterned dark wings. The regal catepillars fed on hickory and walnut and the *Cecropia* on a wide variety of trees and shrubs.

A frequent visitor, one introduced from abroad, was the gypsy moth. A mistaken French naturalist brought it to the United States in 1866, thinking it might be the basis of a silk industry. He was greatly mistaken and it became a severe pest of shade trees.

Another moth found battering away at the fly-screens and glass windows at the end of the nineteenth century was the brown-tail moth. It too had reached the Boston area from Europe, but its introduction was accidental, not deliberate. It became a tremendous pest of shade trees, quite defoliating them, and the catepillars shed stinging hairs onto anyone who handled them and even raised painful rashes on people who came near them. In 1902 the moths were so numerous that the caterpillars invaded the house, their hairs causing much damage to the humans. As they were so many that summer, they got everywhere, and an unusual and unwelcome feature was that they swarmed over the washing on the line. Their toxin was so powerful that when the clothes were worn they too produced the rash.

It is a commonplace that moths are attracted to light, and one might well ask why, if this is the case, they do not eagerly fly out into daylight? At least part of the answer is the nature and distance of the light in question. Up to a certain point, light attracts; beyond that amount, it restrains.

The reactions of insects to light vary according to species. For instance, fly larvae always avoid it. Other insects like it at one stage of their lives and avoid it at another. An example is the red admiral butterfly, one of the *Vanessas*; the adults

FIG. IV. (i) (ii).   INSECT ORIENTING ON A LIGHT.

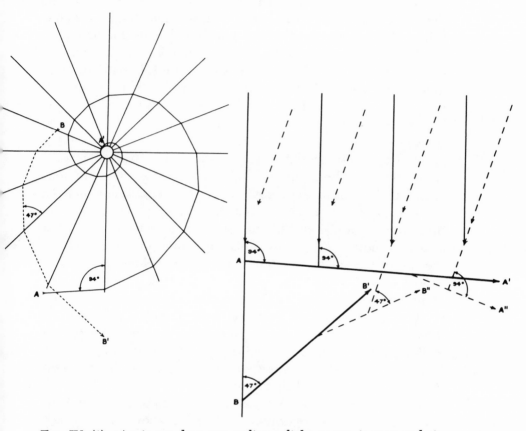

FIG. IV (i)   An insect does not realize a light source is near and, in orienting itself on one, acts as if it were distant. Consequently, the insect maintains a constant angle of light on its compound eyes, spiraling inevitably toward the source (A–A′) or away from it (B–B′), according to its starting angle.

FIG. IV (ii)   The rays of a distant source of light, such as the sun or moon, are parallel, and an insect starting at A and keeping a constant angle with this source of light (in the above case 94°) will move in a straight line from A to B—that is, over a short period of time.

In practice, the sun appears to move 15° in an hour—represented by the successive dotted lines from left to right above, which are at an angle of 3° to each other and represent intervals of 12½ minutes of time. This means the insect changes course every 12½ minutes and would proceed from A′ to B′ keeping the same angle (94°) all the time. Actual journeys of an hour's duration in what the insect thinks is a straight line are very rare. Bees orient on the sun and compensate for its movement.

seek the light and the caterpillars avoid it. In passing it may be noted that the larvae feed on the common stinging nettle and that they are protected from the stinging hairs by having their bodies covered with spines a little longer than the hairs. When Edward Hopkins was reprimanded once for letting a patch of this alien weed flourish, he defended himself on the grounds that it was the food of that beautiful butterfly, and in any case the nettle was much less harmful than the poison ivy, so a patch of stinging nettles was always allowed to flourish at Bartons.

More insects are attracted to a lighted window on a dark night than on a moonlit one, because light-attracted insects are drawn more by a point of light than by sheet illumination. It is for this reason that moths come to a candle and not to the sun. The sun is so distant that its rays are parallel, whereas those from a candle spread from a point. Insects (for instance ants and moths) often use a distant source of light, such as the sun or moon, as a reference point in traveling. By moving so as to keep roughly the same retinas of the compound eye illuminated by the distant source, the insect moves forward in a straight line, at any rate over a short period of time. The insect is, in effect, keeping the angle the sun or moon makes to its direction constant. A child is often struck with the fact that, in walking along a street at night, he can catch up with a streetlight but never with the moon.

But if, in error, the insect is orienting on a near source of light, such as the streetlight mentioned above, it will not know this and may well act as if it were using a distant, natural source. That is, it will keep the light angle on its retinas the same, leading it constantly to turn toward the source and make a spiral approach to it, eventually hitting the light and being killed or injured. Such a path is demonstrated in Figure IV: It is a logarithmic function of the path the insect was pursuing when first it started to orient on the light. Such a lamp may be considered to be emitting rays of light from a center, rather like the points on the card of a mariner's compass or the spokes of a wheel. If the insect is pursuing a course other than a chord of the circle and if the insect every time it crosses a ray, or spoke, keeps this angle constant, then it must spiral toward the center if this angle is greater than the chord

Potato moth

angle, and away from it if it is less. Some insects are repelled by lights, perhaps for this reason, as we can easily see in summer, and indeed we speak of them as fluttering around a lamp.

As children, Victoria Deane and her younger sisters used to collect caterpillars from the potato patches in the neighborhood, then put the insects into homemade cages and there raise pupae and adults. The "worms" grew to big, green to darkish-red caterpillars with conspicuous greenish-white diagonal marks on them, and prominent anal horns. Victoria's uncle, Theophilus Deane, used to travel on business to England from time to time and, knowing his niece's suspicion (quite unjustified) of the American entomologist Thaddeus Harris, brought her back on one occasion W. F. Kirby's *European Butterflies and Moths* [33]. The girls prized this handsome book and, after examining it, expected their potato worms to turn into the fabulous "death's-head moth" of Europe, which not only had a skull firmly imprinted on its large thorax but squeaked like a mouse, too. Surely that would be enough to frighten any benevolent uncle into fits? Alas! The American potato worm, though still an impressive member of the same family (the Sphinxes), was of a different species, but the childen did their best with it.

Showing her uncle the three stages of the insect—moth, caterpillar, and pupa—Victoria said, "It looks a *little* like a death's-head, doesn't it, Uncle Theo?" He agreed it did. "And," put in Constance, "you mustn't touch the horn. It's very poisonous and will make you very ill." Uncle Theophilus agreed he would not dream of doing so after such a warning, though, he reflected, the caterpillars did not seem to be doing his nieces any harm. "And look at this pupa," said Victoria. "It has this strange handle to it. It's a special case for the moth's long mouth."

"It looks like the handle of a pitcher," said Uncle Theo, suppressing the fact that he had obtained this information from reading the despised Thaddeus Harris's book, which he had consulted shortly after his sister-in-law had told him of the girls' new craze. It was hairy caterpillars that caused irritation, not strange-looking ones. Theophilus was a much-loved bachelor uncle.

Other summer visitors attracted to lights were assassin bugs (already mentioned), male fireflies (jealous, perhaps!), and numerous species of beetles and Diptera.

Another winter visitor in considerable numbers was the ladybug, whose very name suggests that its beneficial qualities for man, in eating many kinds of insects, have been known for a long time. In French (*bête à bon Dieu*), German (*Marienkäfer*), and Spanish (*vaca de San Antón*) it is similarly recognized. These insects lay batches of yellow eggs on a number of plants which soon hatch into hungry gray-black larvae, feeding voraciously on plant lice, or greenfly they find living on the plant. The larvae pupate in due course and emerge as adult ladybugs, who are equally hungry for greenfly. In the fall the adults frequently move into houses and flock together, sometimes causing alarm. They are, however, doing no harm and should be encouraged to depart when the warm weather arrives, though it is unnecessarily cruel to speed them on their way by suggestion that disaster has overtaken their homes and families.

LADYBUG

Some visitors to the cellar may now be considered. These premises have already been mentioned a few times, together with the animals found there—the firebrats, silverfish, cockroaches, house moths, spiders, beetles, and so forth. There were two different cellar communities. When it was first built it mostly housed beer and wine barrels and was very damp. This attracted aquatic creatures: mosquitoes, slugs, snails, and toads. Later on, the central heating boiler was installed and dried up the place so that a quite different fauna became established, those liking warmth and able to stand some degree of dryness in the surroundings.

In the first community two kinds of toads established themselves: the comparatively large hoptoad and the somewhat similar Fowler's toad. The hoptoad rather took to the settlers and frequented their yards and cellars, particularly if there was some loose earth in which to burrow, water, and plenty of live insects. Tryphena Barton, who was always collecting strange animals as pets, kept some hoptoads in the cellar and yard, causing a certain amount of opposition from her parents and the help. Try attempted to overcome that by pointing out that according to Shakespeare, the toad carried a jewel in its head,

TOAD

but she would never allow anyone to kill one of her toads to see if that were the case.* In point of fact, the toads earned their keep. The adults fed on many noxious insects, slugs and worms (though they also took spiders), and other night-roaming creatures, catching them as they moved by darting out their long tongues. On that diet they lived to a great age. A strange feature of that insect food was that the toads often took fireflies and swallowed them whole. In the stomach, more or less undamaged, the male fireflies continued to flash for a while, thus making the toad's abdomen luminous. Even Tryphena was slightly worried the first time she saw this strange sight.

The eggs of toads are laid in water, in much the same way as those of frogs, and the creatures pass through the same tadpole stage; the eggs, however, are laid in long strings rather than in gelatinous masses. Both toads and frogs have a great sense of direction and locality; they find their way to water by smelling it, the males moving off first and then calling the females to it. After breeding they frequently come back to their original locality.

* "Sweet are the uses of adversity,
  Which like the toad, ugly and venomous,
  Wears yet a precious jewel in his head."
  (*As You Like It,* ii. 1. 12.)

One cannot think that the Bartons and their contemporaries really believed that the toad carried a precious jewel in its head, for had they done so, the animal would have been extinct by now, as it would have been so widely slaughtered. It was a poetic symbol, the jewel being its intelligence, which even an ugly being such as a toad could house. However, one must not dogmatize too much; perhaps humans did at one time kill a lot of toads looking for the jewel and gave it up after a series of disappointments, so that the species survived. One could even postulate the possibility that some toads at one time *did* carry a jewel in the head and that the species was consequently hunted to extinction, like the goose that laid the golden egg.

Here I must leave the animals in the house with just a brief mention of a few more, though not much account of their activities. They were nearly all visitors. Aphids grew on the potted plants and often formed the first meal of the ladybugs moving out of hibernation. Soft scale was also found on them and tarsonemid mites attacked the crowns of cyclamens. Lacewing flies sometimes attacked these greenfly, the delicate creatures laying a number of white eggs on thin stalks among the leaves; the larvae on hatching set to work to eat the aphids. Earthworms were sometimes present in these pots. Blossom beetles came into the house with cut flowers, as did swarms of small elm beetles, doing no harm but causing disquiet to the humans.

Centipedes, or the hundred-footers, were found in the damp Bartons cellars from time to time; it is not a well-named animal, as the common hundred-footer found at Bartons usually had only thirty legs. (In the Caribbean the large tropical

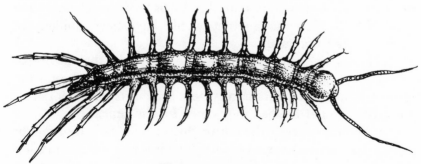

HUNDRED-FOOTER

centipedes are called "eighty legs," a rather more accurate designation. However, in other tropical areas they can have as many as 200 feet.) The house centipedes disliked light and moved very quickly if suddenly exposed to it, so they *looked* as if they had a hundred legs. They fed on insects, worms, spiders, slugs, mites, and the injured of their own species, and sometimes they left faintly phosphorescent trails behind them. Like spiders they had hollow fangs for injecting poison, but rarely were people bitten, nor, if they were, was any serious harm caused.

A whole zoological garden of animals came into the house with the kindling wood and logs—slugs, snails, springtails, beetles, pupae of all sorts, pseudoscorpions, and even a few termites—but the house was lucky in that this last pest never established itself in the building. The eastern termite has found man very useful and over the last hundred years has used his buildings to spread its range ever northeastward into the New England states.

A few garden snails found the cellars useful as winter quarters. Here the snail closed the entrance to its shell with a winter door (the *epiphragma*) made of mucus and lime. The Deane children found the silvery snail trails very fascinating.

Moles also made use of the cellar and these in their turn, together with the slugs, spiders, and insects, attracted the eastern garter snake, harmless to man except for the unpleasant musky-smelling liquid it can discharge from certain glands at the base of its tail. Black rat snakes were sometimes in the attics and helped in rodent control, though they also took bats when these were present. Lizards and skinks were occasional visitors. Dog ticks in vast numbers would be found climbing up walls in dark patches in the 1920s and were feverishly sprayed with Flit, though they would have been unlikely to have attacked humans.

Live fish are now present in the house, in the inevitable aquarium of decorative tropical fish in the bar as well as in the tank of trout in the restaurant where the customers themselves are invited to net the fish they fancy for their meal.

In the mid-years of the house, doctors occasionally brought in leeches to bleed their patients, many a sick man being finished by the process.

The most remarkable creature to visit the house was one, apparently abundant, of a metaphysical nature. When John Barton VII became prosperous he acquired a valuable Welsh housekeeper who kept the place as bright as a new pin and charmed his wealthy friends. The war against insects preyed on the poor woman's mind until she nearly became distracted by the attacks of small invisible insects "living under the skin." Needless to say, they were entirely imaginary—such illusions are quite common still—and fortunately Caroline was able to convince her "treasure" that painting herself all over with a solution of methylene blue, supplied by the local doctor, so that she looked like one of her savage ancestors, was an effective and permanent cure, though they had some anxious moment with her during insect incidents with the refugees in the second World War.

12

PAST, PRESENT, AND FUTURE

"What is a man,
If his chief good and market of his time
Be but to sleep and feed? A beast, no more.
Sure, He that made us with such large discourse,
Looking before and after, gave us not
That capability and god-like reason
To fust in us unus'd."

Hamlet, iv. 4. 33.

W HEN BARTONS WAS BUILT a revolutionary disturbance of the life in the neighborhood took place. For example, the spider community living on the insects and mites on the site was destroyed, as were also those animals living on the trees used to make the house and in the forest environment that they formed. Clay was dug for the bricks and shells burned for the mortar, both actions involving disturbance to the surface life of clay pits and quarries. In exchange the house rapidly filled with a life of its own, which was possibly as great as the life destroyed in building it, but was very different in nature.

We have followed the development of some of these creatures and it is possible roughly to measure these changes, for as Lord Kelvin said, one can only understand a thing when one can measure it. There are, however, a number of different ways of measuring life—for instance, we can count the numbers of individuals of the different species existing at different points in the history of the house, or we can calculate their weight, or the weight of the vital animal protein they contain. The rate at which they live—their oxygen consumption, or metabolism—can be measured and some consideration could be given also to the numbers of generations they have gone through in the course of the house's history. Finally, we can attempt to assess the quality of the life in the house from the points of view of dominance and moral values, or the relative happiness of the animals there. Each of these methods will show up some differences and similarities between all the diverse creatures. Their relative numbers are best shown in the table below, which has been done for the principal animals. Some crea-

TABLE I

Approximate numbers of principal animals living at Bartons in certain years. Census day June 1.

	1635	1685	1735	1785	1835	1875	1935	1980
Humans	5	9	15	0	14	27	12	2
Dogs	1	2	2	0	1	1	1	4
Cats	1	4	3	0	2	2	1	2
Mice	5	30	20	0	10	20	0	0
Bats	0	0	0	50	10	0	0	0
Birds	10	10	20	15	40	50	30	15
Spiders	††	†††	†††	†††	††	††	†	†
Wood-boring beetles	60	100	200	300	500	500	500	50
Fleas, lice *	200	150	150	100	250	200	50	20
Bedbugs	0	20	30	0	30	10	0	0
Clothes moths	50	100	150	40	100	150	40	20
Crickets	0	†	††	†	†††	††	†	0
Cockroaches	†	†	†††	††	††	†††	†	0
Flies	500	600	800	1,000	1,000	100	50	20
Springtails, silverfish, etc.	†	††	†††	††	††	††	††	†
Mites	††	†††	†††	††	†††	†††	††	†

* of humans, dogs, cats, bats, mice, and birds
† some   †† fairly abundant   ††† many

tures, such as springtails, mites, crickets, and cockroaches, are too small and too numerous to count and are shown in the table by a series of † signs, a greater number of signs indicating a bigger number of animals. The figures are also set out in graphic form for humans and wood borers in Figure II and for spiders in Figure III, pages 70 and 132.

The insects, mites, and spiders were obviously the biggest group of creatures living in the house, while the vertebrates recorded run from a commencement of twenty-two to a peak of one hundred in 1875 and back to the starting figure at the present time. These figures, however, do exclude the toads. The humans obviously dominated the life of the house. Though not the least numerous creature, as one might expect them to be, they were nearly always the heaviest accumulation of living matter (biomass) except, of course, when the house was empty of them and that distinction passed to the bats—ten or twelve pounds of them.

The rate at which the animals used oxygen is an interesting facet of the life because this varies enormously between different animals, when we consider it on an equal weight basis. Animals obtain their energy by oxidizing food within their bodies, virtually burning it there, and warm-blooded ones also maintain their temperature in the same way. As he breathes in and out, man draws cold air in and exhales warm air, and about one fifth of the heat he loses is due to that process, most of the rest being radiated away from the skin. In a well-covered dog, nearly all heat is lost through the mouth, which is why a dog pants so in hot weather: It is his only method of getting rid of heat and keeping cool. The heat and energy requirements of an animal are measured in calories, a calorie being the amount of heat needed to raise a liter of water from $0°$ to $1°$ centigrade. A man asleep uses them at the rate of 1,500 a day; doing heavy work he needs 3,500, while sedentary work uses 2,500. If we take a figure of 3,000 calories a day for a 70-kilo (157-pound) man, he is using 41 calories a day per kilo of body weight, thus providing for all his movements and the keeping up of the body temperature. The calories are obtained from his food, a gram of carbohydrate or of protein giving him 4.1 calories and a gram of fat 9.1. One might imagine that a cold-blooded animal, such as an insect, would need far fewer calories to keep it active, but strangely enough the reverse is the case. It is not difficult to measure the oxygen consumption of insects and from this to calculate their calorie needs. Naturally there are very big differences according to the insect's state and its activities. The table on page 291 gives some of these figures.

TABLE II

Metabolism of different animals at Bartons

Animal	Air temperature during estimation °C	Weight in grams	Calories per kilo per day	Notes
Bee, in flight		0.09	10,500	W
at rest			218	W
Fly, adult	20	0.021	357	K
"	30		705	W
larva	20		150	K
"	30		240	W
pupa	20		30	K
"	30		58	W
House gnat (*Culex*)		0.008	65	E
Cockchafer	20	1	82	R & R
	20		108	B & S
Cockroach	20	0.7	31	V
Mouse	7	13	639	T
Rat	16	117	227	T
Bat, active			700	V-F
torpid			58	V-F
Sparrow		22	755	T
Dog		18,200	46	L
Cat		2,500	80	L
Horse		450,000	27	L
Man,		70,000	41	
basic			24	

W: Wigglesworth. K: Krogh. E: Ellinger. R & R: Regnault & Reiset.
B & S: Batelli & Stern. V: Vernon. L: Loewy. V-F: Vesey-Fitzgerald.
T: Tigstedt.

5.047 calories per liter of oxygen

A bee at rest uses about fifty times more energy for its weight than a man and, when flying, some two hundred and fifty times more. An active bat uses fourteen times more. The sparrow, mouse, and bat are much the same size and have similar energy requirements. In general, the larger the animal, the less food per kilo of its weight does it need; for instance, the horse, much bigger than a man, needs only about two thirds of the food per kilo that a man does, while flies to the equivalent weight of a man would need about nine times his ration. It may well be that man's comparatively economical use of oxygen is one of the reasons for his success in life. On the other hand, man has been more successful than the horse, which uses its food to better advantage. With all these animals, if one works out the calorie intake per unit area (per square meter for example) of body surface, it will be found that the figures are very similar for all of them, as one might expect.

The numbers of generations of the different animals in the house also showed wide variations. There were, in effect, sixteen generations of humans, for this is the number of different owners or tenants, though they were not all lineal descendants from previous occupiers. At the other end of the scale there were some four thousand generations of some of the mites. Intermediate numbers are seen in the 140 generations of furniture beetles and the 50 generations of dogs, where again in this last case they were not by any means direct descendants but represented a number of different varieties, purchased and introduced one way and the other at different times. If ownership of the house may be said to belong to the direct descendants of original occupiers, then the wood beetles have the best claim to it, for they were in the original timbers of the house and were the first inhabitants. A few of the direct line are still there after the many generations that have passed since the place was built. If we take a human generation as twenty years, the wood beetles' descent is equivalent to 2,800 years of human succession, which would date Bartons to about 800 B.C.—a period when the site was covered with forest and the life was very different.

We have taken four thousand generations for the mites; a similar number of generations for man would put us back in the second Ice Age, well before modern man, about 80,000 B.C. This was the time of the Acheulean man, the being who had started to improve the almost natural flint tools (the eoliths) of his forebears by making the more massive, shaped, unshafted hand axes sometimes called "fist-flints."

Evolutionary forces were at work at Bartons, as elsewhere, and four thousand generations—or very considerably less—are quite enough to produce well-marked effects, as may be seen in man himself, for the Acheulean man was an apelike creature very different from ourselves. It is difficult to assess the evolutionary changes that took place around Bartons in its 350 years of existence, as some of these may be truly genetical and others a reversible response to changed conditions. Man became taller, healthier, longer-lived, and more and more dependent on his increasingly complicated artifacts. Some birds adapted themselves more closely to man's dwellings for nest sites and to his neighborhood for food, as man tended to breed insects on his farms. The sparrows likewise followed suit, but became more closely attached to man, frequenting him more in the town than in the country. They may well have to desert him or decline, as man has almost given up the horse. Woodborers were continually experimenting with new imported timbers. Spiders have adapted themselves to the house and are now seeing if they can live in the new, warm, dry conditions. Most of the dry-litter community have developed an affinity for man's goods so great that today they can scarcely do without them. Only the cats, except those deliberately bred by man, have hardly changed at all, retaining the attributes of the animal first brought into the house by John Barton.

The food of all these animals was, and is, basically the same, but the area from which this food was drawn showed great diversity. At first the swallows drew nourishment from the most scattered area, for they traveled twice a year right across the world, whereas the Bartons fed entirely from their own farm. The wood borers were perforce confined to the house as larvae, though some adults ventured afield to feed on flower pollen. The spiders fed only in the house, for the young that migrated were unlikely to return. Lice and internal parasites ventured abroad with their hosts and some of the fleas did so, though the majority stayed in the bedclothes or other nesting material. As time went on, the actual area from which the humans drew their food at first decreased as farming became more efficient, and then increased again as more and more meat was eaten (plants consumed as cereals, beans, and so forth give more food per acre than when converted into meat and then eaten), and as the weight of the crops harvested per acre increased, so in general did the farmers become more prosperous, though at times a big crop meant less money for the farmer, as the price was so much lower per ton of produce reaped. From the last half of the nineteenth century the districts from which the food was drawn were much extended.

As the frontier was pushed west, grain for bread and stock feed came from the prairies and was eventually carried by the railroad. The steamship made tropical fruits, such as bananas, a commonplace.

The approximate daily calorie intake of the house at three different periods is given in the table below, using the same calorie rates as given in the table on page 291 and averaging the spiders and mites at 1,000 calories per kilo per day.

TABLE III

Total calories (approximate) used per day (June 1)

	1635	1835	1980
Man	9,810	29,215	5,500 *
Dogs	500	650	1,700
Cats	400	880	1,000
Birds	160	640	140
Insects, spiders, mites	30	300	12
	10,900	31,685	8,352

* The two residents only: restaurant customers and staff not included.

The calorie requirements of the house are now a quarter of the 1835 figure because there is so much less weight of resident life in it. The protein requirements have not dropped in the same proportion for two reasons: More animal protein is now eaten, and nearly a quarter of the present protein need is for Dal (the Afghan bitch whose real name is "Dalkiesh III of Bartons") and her three puppies; much of that is supplied by high-protein meat.

Some 6 percent of the weight of the life was composed of nitrogen combined with carbon and hydrogen to form this protein. The nitrogen cycle is the key to the life of the house and to the improvement of the living conditions of the animals. Let me recapitulate the story: Nitrogen is absorbed from the soil as nitrate and is formed into protein in the sunlit green leaf. The soluble nitrogen, under natural conditions, reaches the soil in three ways: from the decay of vegetable or animal matter, from thunderstorms combining the nitrogen of the air with its oxygen, or from the action of certain bacteria found in the root nodules of leguminous plants. The farmers at Bartons started to get bigger crops when they managed their land well, which was in effect either when they added more nitrogen, phosphate, and potash to the land, or when they conserved what they already had or used it with greater skill. Until about 1835, in common with the rest of the world as a whole, they could not increase their total store of nitrogen in the soil, for that obtained from thunderstorms and clovers only made up their losses; all they could do was move it around, transferring the fertility of one piece of ground to another piece, as compost and farmyard manure were moved.

Chile nitrate, about 1835, and synthetic nitrates (obtained by taming the thunderstorm in a factory) around the turn of the present century greatly increased the district's prosperity.

To a considerable extent Bartons is a model of the world outside. Over the course of evolution, the only characteristic of the progressive change that is common to all of life is its constant tendency to expand—its effect of filling up all vacant spaces, even those formed by the very expansion of life itself. Life expanded when plants started colonizing the seashore and then the land, after which vertebrate amphibians started to fill up this new expansion by climbing out of the sea and eating the plants. In the same way, the house was an expansion of opportunity for life: Built for man, it filled with many other creatures who found they could use the vacant spaces not used by man, or not sufficiently well protected by him. The number of individuals now living there and their weight is less than when it was built; the dominant creature is less annoyed by parasites and there is now a vacant space in the house which was at one time filled with life. At present, the amount of life—that is, its weight and the number of individuals, human and animal—in Bartons depends very much on the day of the week and the time. On a busy Saturday night the restaurant can have a hundred customers, twenty staff, a stock of fresh clams and oysters, trout in the fish tank, and ripe cheeses (the mites there making very little addition to the weight but a vast increase in the number of individuals) in addition to the cats, dogs, insects, and birds already mentioned; the life then present weighs more than eight tons. But by breakfast time on Sunday morning, with most of the shellfish and half the trout eaten and only Mr. La Flèche and his assistant there, plus a few extra birds on the roof, the life in or on Bartons weighs about 350 pounds. Whether such drastic changes strain the structure or the psyche of the old house has never been considered.

As to the future of Bartons, Edward Barton (born 1938) is still interested in the place, both financially and aesthetically. The restaurant is doing well at present, but should it begin to fail Edward has, under the conditions of his sale, a right to re-purchase the property on favorable terms. If that happened he would convert it to two or three "country cottages" for himself, Desirée, and Phoebe (his sisters), and the life in the place would once more increase. But in, say, twenty years time, whether or not there is going to be fuel for such amenities as country cottages is a moot point. If there is not, Bartons could again become a farm, using horses and mules if atoms are too dangerous and nobody has the will to develop alternative power sources. How the flies would like that!

We have now discussed the more tangible aspects of the matter—the numbers of individuals, their weight, descent, and food requirements. Is there any way of measuring the quality of the life there? It is a difficult, if not impossible, thing to do.

The thought processes of animals are much less complex than those of man, the need for them being replaced in most cases by the existence of instincts. We could attempt to measure the quality of the animal life in Bartons, finding possibly that the furniture beetle obtained more satisfaction from its life than did the springtail from its precarious existence and so forth, but to do so we have to set a human standard and postulate that the various animals react to circumstances and obtain satisfaction, if not in the same way that we do, at least in similar ways—which is not the case. We must admit then that we cannot measure the quality of life in the house with any objectivity; we can only make personal subjective judgments of it and admire the earwig for her mother love, the spangled fritillary for its beauty, the dog for its devotion, and the swallow for its flight thus committing the greatest crime in the modern biologist's calendar—anthropomorphism —or else assess the quality of their life in terms of its bearing on the future of the species—the adaptation of the animal toward its survival as a species, a subject already adequately covered in other books.

The existence of these instincts in animals may well have a bearing on contentment, because the more a being is controlled by instinct, the more it will always know what to do. It may not do the best thing for itself under the circumstances but it will be in no doubt as to what should be done. The less instinctively controlled animal, on the other hand, may frequently not know what to do, as witness the admittedly somewhat extreme case of Aesop's donkey who, unable to reach a decision, went hungry when placed equidistant between two equally delicious bundles of hay. The higher animals have to think things out, and it is not finding answers to certain problems that leads to unhappiness, particularly in man.

We have thus another dilemma: Is it best to react to a problem instinctively and be happy, but probably wrong (and one can pay for an error with one's life), or to worry over the problem and be unhappy if one does not solve it?

Human emotions and feelings are undoubtedly descended from those of animals. The human has gone so far ahead because of his one great, early discovery—the passage of time; the appreciation that there is a past, a present, and a future. Animals live mostly for the present; their appreciation of other time states is very little, for though the swallow and the wasp may learn a route, they indulge in few modifications of behavior because of some past experience. Such changes as they do make because of these are relatively simple and require but little thought. Birds build nests as a provision for future young; mice store food against winter scarcity, but that is an instinctive pattern, not a thought-out activity. Man made his first step on the road to success when he used his leisure (in contrast to the animal who just played or slept) to think of the past, the present, and to devise improvements for the future, developing not only tangible assets from the flint axe onward, but a number of very difficult intellectual concepts as well—language, the zero, writing, money, to give some examples—all things which were difficult to invent and are of immense value, but which, like so many things, can be used by anyone once they have been invented. The artifacts helped him to live; the concepts enabled him to pass the information on, both to his fellows and to unborn generations, and to become aware of yet more, wider, and higher concepts: the arts, morality, science, ethics, and religion.

The moral qualities have a biological value for us and though they are rare in the animal world, yet they are not unknown. Mother love, for instance, has immense survival value among a large number of animals. In the case of insects (the earwig and some hymenoptera being notable exceptions) the female lays many eggs in a suitable spot near food and then abandons them; usually enough survive to continue the race. Other animals find fewer offspring with more parental care a better way of ensuring their posterity; hence, if the parents, particularly the mothers, do not love and care for their children, these last are not likely to live, with the result that the fine moral quality of mother love is strengthened in the race by its very survival value. The males of a race may dominate and exploit the females, making them do all the work, but the process cannot be carried too far—at any rate with the young females—for if they are overburdened, they will not be able to raise the next generation; hence the moral qualities of chivalry, politeness, and consideration for women have considerable survival value.

Similarly, in conducting his daily life a man can lie, cheat, and swindle, which may make him prosperous; on the other hand, a reputation for virtue and honesty in dealing is more likely to do so, as is borne out by the success of the large Quaker business houses, whose fortunes were founded by honest dealing in the eighteenth century, when business morality was not high. Peace of mind and happiness are more likely to arise from fair dealing than from foul, and it is at least likely that the contented in mind have more children and raise them more successfully than do the discontented; this has a biological effect and is perhaps the reason why there are more relatively honest people in the world than dishonest ones. But man, as Hamlet implies, is not a beast, and apart from any worldly success arising from the virtues, man appreciates the desirability of good behavior for its own sake and for the satisfaction of that inner compulsion, the soul, for the majority need to use "that capability and god-like reason" to advantage. Honest dealing had a direct survival value in the early days of

Bartons, for a man or woman could be hanged for the theft of goods valued at over five shillings. There may well have been no genetic difference involved, for we do not know if the admittedly fewer descendants of the hanged really would be more likely to steal than the unconvicted. The majority of the humans in the house were fundamentally kind, and indeed mutual trust between master and man helped establish the farm; hence this moral quality certainly had biological effects, the honest dealing and inward satisfaction leading to contentment and a measure of prosperity, by the standards of the age, for the farm and its dependents.

The secondary differences between the sexes in animals have arisen mostly through sexual selection, the males or females respectively desiring some one particular characteristic in the opposite sex more than another; for instance, female crickets would respond to the loudest-singing male crickets and had no need to make any noise themselves. Differing secondary sexual characteristics with little or no survival value may thus develop in a species, as for instance the smooth cheek of a woman and the hairy one of a man. But even here the difference may have had a biological significance. It could be that man used part of the scarce protein food to grow a beard protecting him from the cold, whereas the woman, foregoing facial protection, used the protein to better biological advantage—the nourishing of the unborn child. The human generations during the life of Bartons were too few for the race to be much affected genetically by these higher qualities. However, the men did select their wives, and the women accept their husbands, with some appreciation of beauty and manliness in mind, for even if Sophrinia Frost was "as beautiful as an heiress with steel shares," Susannah Palmer and her granddaughter-in-law, Abigail Gifford, were both beautiful, intelligent, and well-educated women. An appreciation of the beauty of the house and of its historical associations in fact saved it from decay, because though Stephen Deane originally purchased it in 1788 as a property speculation, he was soon so struck with its qualities that he restored it, married, and lived there with his family.

Intellectual ability and mechanical skill have immense survival value for the race, enabling man to fill empty continents with his species and feed millions where only thousands were fed before, but the balance between success and failure is precarious; it is quite possible that some small change will extinguish man at Bartons, or even as a species on the earth itself.

The Bartons now have small families due to two causes: deliberate birth control and the existence of low-fertility genes in their makeup. Of course, the desire for few children, for whatever reason (social, economic, etc.), is really the same thing as the possession of low-fertility genes, since small families are what they both produce. In short, this desire is a low-fertility gene. Nevertheless, it has a survival value, because offspring receive more and better attention if they are few rather than many. The successes of low-fertility species, such as bats, elephants, and humans, prove that much. The three species persist with steady or slightly increasing populations (except possibly elephants, the ivory being so much coveted) whereas high-fertility mammals, such as mice, suffer violent fluctuations of numbers. High fertility is no guarantee of success; in past ages many such species have become extinct.

Naturally, low fertility must not be pushed too far. For instance, should a large number of women have children by means of surgical intervention or fertility drugs, the low-fertility genes in the population would increase. Should radiation escapes from power plants, or atomic warfare, spread low-fertility and sterility incidence, the critical point could be reached where there were not enough meetings between fertile males and females for the race to be continued.

One imagines that man would again intervene before this situation arose and save himself once more by the skin of his teeth, for as Thornton Wilder shows, he has survived many catastrophes—floods, ice ages, pestilence, massacre, war, and famine—so he should be able to survive this, too. This intervention might merely be the recolonizing of the United States by a more fertile race of men from overseas, for in all the time there are men on earth, none of the space habitable by them is likely to be surrendered to any other creature. Man, however, does now possess the power of destroying himself entirely by means of a major hydrogen-bomb war. While he and many of the higher animals could be wiped out by such a disaster, life itself is unlikely to be entirely destroyed, and as the killing radiation died away, the evolutionary process would take up its task again from whatever remnants of life were left, and once more at least the site at Bartons would fill with life. But that does not necessarily mean that man would arise again —Dr. G. G. Simpson thinks it unlikely, for man's ancient ancestral forms have vanished, together with the sequence of biological and physical conditions that gave this pattern to our evolution [51]. Man obtained his dominant position because of his intelligence, the adaptation of his forefeet to holding things, and to a close cooperation of hand and eye. Many other mammals outside the apes and monkeys have these last two qualities, for instance squirrels, rats, and mice—even some birds can use a foot as a hand—so that a life of this nature might well fill the space should man vacate it.

There is very little space that life could not fill, and the only future development, unlikely though not impossible, that Simpson foresees is the colonization of the air: ". . . a truly aerial flora and fauna of organisms living and reproducing in air as a medium, as seaweeds and fishes do in water. . . ." Charming as it sounds, it might turn out to be most inconvenient to us. The swifts, perhaps, have taken a step in this direction. At times they mate while in the air.

There has been much "throwing about of brains" in this book. Bartons now stands in its quiet, well-tended garden, a source of profit to its owners and pleasure to the customers visiting it. It is a monument to man's efforts. Its present life is not so varied as it was, but the supplies it draws in now affect the lives of other men in far wider fields than when it was new. Now, as then, the house gives out as well, for the restaurant is more like a club than just an eating house. Ideas and businesses are discussed, meetings arranged, proposals for marriages (and divorces) put, introductions made, and political opinions canvassed. Bartons does much to stimulate the minds as well as the stomachs of its frequenters, for it is such an attractive place.

"What a piece of work is a man! how noble in reason! how infinite in faculties! in form and moving how express and admirable! in action how like an angel! in apprehension how like a god! the beauty of the world! the paragon of animals. . . ."   *Hamlet*, ii. 2. 315.

This, written thirty-one years before Bartons was built, had an ironic tone then, is not quite true today, but can become true if man will only use his gifts with sense and goodwill.

APPENDIX

~❧~

LIST OF ANIMALS AND
THEIR SCIENTIFIC NAMES

ENGLISH NAME	SCIENTIFIC NAME	MEANING OF SCIENTIFIC NAME
	Chapter 1	
Man	*Homo sapiens*	Wise man
Bee	*Apis mellifera*	Honey carrier bee
	Chapter 2	
Pinhole borers	*Ernobius* spp.	Bud-borer
	Hydrobreginus spp.	Water-cheek
Lyctus borers	*Lyctus linearis*	Linear Lyctus (a town in Crete)
	L. bruneus	Brown Lyctus
Horntail	*Tremex colomba*	Colombian trembler
Oak bark beetles	*Scolytus intricata*	Shortened on the inside
	S. multistriatus	Shortened and many-streaked
Furniture beetle	*Anobium punctatum*	Pitted dead-shammer
Oak borer	*Scobicia declivis*	Sawdust sloping down
	Chapter 4	
Ivory-marked long-horn beetle	*Eburia quadrigeminata*	Ivory four-jeweled creature
Hickory longhorn	*Buprestis lurida*	Sallow burncow
Spider beetle	*Mezium americana*	American Mezium (Tyrant of Caere)
Old house borer	*Hylotrupes bajulus*	Wood and rock carrier
European deathwatch beetle	*Xestobium rufovillosum*	Red-headed polished life creature

ENGLISH NAME	SCIENTIFIC NAME	MEANING OF SCIENTIFIC NAME
Carpenter ants	*Camponatus herculaneus*	Herculean born in the fields
	C. pennsylvanicus	Born in the fields of Pennsylvania
Carpenter bees	*Xylocopa virginica*	Virginian wood borer
	Ceratina duplex	Double wax creature

Chapter 5

Cat	*Felis maniculata*	Small-handed cat
Deer mice	*Peromyscus polionotus*	Gray, mouselike from the South creature
	P. leucopus	Brown mouselike creature
House mouse	*Mus musculus domesticus*	Domestic little-mouse mouse
Dog	*Canis familiaris*	Domestic dog
Big brown bats	*Eptesicus fuscus*	Dark house flier
	Myotis lucifugans	Light-fleeing mouse-ear
Raccoon	*Procyon lotor*	Washer of Procyon (the star)
Eastern chipmunk	*Tamais striatus*	Striped storer
Gray squirrel	*Sciurus carolinensis*	Carolina squirrel

Chapter 6

Daddy longlegs spider	*Pholcus phalangiodes*	Long-legged squint-eyed
House spider	*Argyrodes tepidariorum*	Silver creature of warm places
Funnel spider	*Tegenaria* spp.	Roof creature
Hunting spider	*Oonops pulcher*	Beautiful egg-face
Fierce spider	*Ciniflo ferox*	Fierce hair-curler
Mouse-gray spider	*Herpyllus blackwelli*	Blackwell's creeper

Chapter 7

Robin	*Turdus migratorius*	Migratory thrush
Crow	*Corvus brachyrhynchus*	Short-beaked crow
Starling	*Sternus vulgaris*	Common starling
Jay	*Cyanocitta cristala*	Blue, swift, crested creature

ENGLISH NAME	SCIENTIFIC NAME	MEANING OF SCIENTIFIC NAME
Swallows	*Hirundo rustica*	Country swallow
	H. americana	American swallow
Chimney swift	*Chelura pelagica*	Sea Chele
Purple martin	*Progne subis*	Progne (who was turned into a swallow) from under
Canary bird (Serin)	*Serinus hortulanus*	Garden serin
Northern flicker	*Colapes auralis lutens*	Golden yellow banger
Redheaded woodpecker	*Melanerpes erythrocephalus*	Redheaded, black-spotted
Wren	*Troglodytes aedon*	Cave wren
English sparrow	*Passer domesticus domesticus*	Domestic sparrow
Turkey	*Meleagris galloparvo*	Meleager's little hen
Heath hen	*Tympanuchus cupido cupido*	Eager drummer
Passenger pigeon	*Ectopistes migratorius*	Migrating outside creature
Rock dove	*Colomba livia*	Livia's dove
Cardinal bird	*Richmondena cardinalis cardinalis*	Richmond's red red creature
Snowshoe hare ticks	*Dermanyssus gallinae*	Skin-pricker of poultry
	D. avium	Skin-pricker of birds

Chapter 8

Common or webbing clothes moth	*Tineola biselliella*	Double-seated little moth
Casebearer clothes moth	*T. pellionella*	Little fur moth
Carpet moth	*Trichophaga tapetzella*	Hair-eating carpet creature
Spider beetle or bookworm	*Ptinus tectus*	Thieving feathered animal
Carpet beetle	*Anthrenus scropulariae*	Scrofulous wasp
Larder beetles	*Dermestes lardarius*	Bacon- or leather-eater
	D. maculata	Spotted leather-eater
Flour beetle	*Tribolium confusum*	Disorderly three-pointed creature

ENGLISH NAME	SCIENTIFIC NAME	MEANING OF SCIENTIFIC NAME
Black flour beetle	*T. audax*	Bold three-pointed creature
Drugstore beetle	*Stegobium panicea*	Covered bread creature
Pea bug	*Mylabris obtectus*	Covered grinder
Furniture mite	*Glycophagus domesticus*	Domestic sugar-eater
Grain weevil	*Calandria granaria*	Grain weevil
Cellar beetles	*Tenebrio molitor*	Contriving darkness-lover
	T. obscurus	Dark darkness
Brown house moth	*Hofmannophila pseudospretella*	Hoffmann's false disdainer
Indian meal moth	*Plodia interpunctella*	Little pitted Plodia
Lesser mealworm	*Alphitobius diaperinus*	Barley meal perforator
Mediterranean flour moth	*Ephestia kuhniella*	Kuhn's fireside creature
Angoumois grain moth	*Sitotroga cerealella*	Thirst creature of cereals
Book louse	*Lepinotus inquilinus*	Lodging Lepidus
Springtail	*Sminthurides aquaticus levanderi*	Light weight water cord
Sow bug	*Isopoda*	Equal feet

Chapter 9

Grain and flour mite	*Tyroglyphus farinae*	Flour cheese borer
Cheese mite	*T. casei*	Cheese feeder
Predacious mite	*Cheyletus eruditus*	Learned hider
Clover mite	*Bryobia praetiosa*	Full of value sprouting-up creature
Bristletail	*Thysanura* spp	A little stalk
Firebrat	*Thermobia domestica*	Domestic hot-liver
Silverfish	*Lepisma saccharina*	Sugar scale
Book louse	*Trogium pulsatorium*	Ticking hole-gnawer
False scorpions	*Chelifer cancroides*	Crablike claw-bearer
	C. museorum	Museum claw-bearer
House cricket	*Gryllus domesticus*	Domestic grasshopper
Black cricket	*G. assimilis luctuosus*	Similar sorrow-causing cricket
Snowy tree cricket	*Oecanthus fultoni*	Fulton's house beetle

ENGLISH NAME	SCIENTIFIC NAME	MEANING OF SCIENTIFIC NAME
"German" cockroach	*Blatella germanica*	German little cockroach
"American" cockroach	*Periplanata americana*	American flattened on the edges
"Oriental" cockroach	*Blatta orientalis*	Eastern cockroach
Brown-banded cockroach	*Supella supellectilium*	Pig bed creature
Vinegar eelworm	*Anguillula aceti*	Vinegar little eel

Chapter 10

Human flea	*Pulex irritans*	Irritating flea
Cat flea	*Ctenocephalides felis*	Cat comb-headed creature
Dog flea	*C. canis*	Dog comb-headed creature
Rat flea	*Xenopsylla cheopsis*	Cheops's foreign flea
Mouse flea	*Leptopsylla segnis*	Slow thin flea
Sparrow flea	*Ceratophyllus fringellae*	Fringella horn-leafed flea
Beetle flea-predator	*Microglotta* spp.	Small-tongued
Human tapeworm	*Taenia segnata*	Flattened tapeworm
Pork tapeworm	*T. solium*	Usual tapeworm
Dog tapeworm	*Echinococcus granulosus*	Small-grained spiked animal
Cat liver-fluke	*Opisthorcis tenuicollis*	Thin-limbed testicles at the back creature
Human body louse	*Pediculus humanus corporis*	Human body louse
Human head louse	*P. h. capitis*	Human head louse
Pubic louse or crab	*Phthirus pubis*	Pubic louse
Dog louse, biting	*Trichodectis canis*	Dog hair creature
Dog louse, sucking	*Linognathus setosus*	Hairy linen-jawed
Bird lice	*Colpocephalum* spp.	Bosom-headed
	Myrsidae	Myrtle
Feather lice	*Menacanthus, Ricunis, Bruelia*	Moon-horn, Castor oil, Bruel's
	Sturnidoecus, Penenirmus	Starling stealing, Dweller
	Philopterus, Dennyus Eureum	Wing-lover, Dennis's Fair-flowering
Bedbug	*Cimex lectularius*	Bed bug
Swallow bug	*Oeciacus* spp	House pointed

ENGLISH NAME	SCIENTIFIC NAME	MEANING OF SCIENTIFIC NAME
Assassin bug	*Reduvius personatus*	Masked hangnail
Black flies	*Simulum* spp	Imitators
Dog roundworm	*Toxacata canis*	Dog arrow-poison
Dog tapeworm	*Taenia pisiformis*	Pea-shaped tapeworm
Trichinosis worm	*Trichinella spiralis*	Curled little hair
Dog mange mite, follicular	*Demodex folliculorum*	Follicular body-worm
Dog mange mite, common	*Sarcoptes scabies,* var. *canis*	Rough flesh cutter, dog
Scabies or itch of man	*S. s.* var. *humanis*	Rough flesh cutter, man

Chapter 11

Stable fly	*Chrysops vittatus*	Golden banded
Common housefly	*Musca domestica*	Domestic fly
Lesser housefly	*Fannia canicularis*	Straight-channeled Fannia
Bluebottle	*Calliphora* spp	Beauty bearer
Mosquito (malaria bearer)	*Anopheles maculipennis*	Spotted winged harmful animal
Gnats	*Culex* spp	Gnat
	C. pipiens	Whispering gnat
Biting midge	*Culicoides variipennis*	Variable winged gnat
Dog tick	*Dermacentor variabilis*	Variable skin
Brown dog tick	*Rhipicephalus sanguinis*	Bloody headed creature
Common toad	*Bufo terrestris*	Earth toad
Fowler's toad	*B. woodhouseii fowleri*	Woodhouse and Fowler's toad
Black rat snake	*Elaphe obsoleta obsoleta*	Common serpent
Common garter snake	*Thamophis sirtalis*	Bush snake
Ladybugs	*Adalia bipunctata*	Two-spotted unhurt creature
	Coleomegilla fusiclabris	Large-sheathed broad creature
Potato worm	*Macrosila quinquemaculata*	Big five-spotted snub-nosed creature
Monarch butterfly	*Danaus plexippus*	Danaus's braided creature
Hundred-footer	*Scutigera forceps*	Whip pincers

ENGLISH NAME	SCIENTIFIC NAME	MEANING OF SCIENTIFIC NAME
Great spangled fritillery	*Speyeria cybele*	Speyer's Cybele
Red admiral butterfly	*Vanessa atalanta*	Vanessa's Atalanta
Mourning cloak butterfly	*V. antiopa*	Antiopa's Vanessa
Spicebush swallowtail	*Papilio troilus*	Troilus's butterfly
Common eastern swallowtail	*P. polyxenes*	Polyxena's (daughter of Priam) butterfly
Brown-tail moth	*Euproctis chrysorrhoea*	Golden tail
Regal moth	*Citherona regalis*	The regal Citheron
Cecropia moth	*Hyalophora cecropia*	Glass-carrying King Cecrops
Gypsy moth	*Porthetria dispar*	Unequal destroyer
Odorous house ant	*Tapinoma sessile*	Stalked carpet creature
Pharaoh's ant	*Monomorium pharonis*	Pharoah's single part
European earwig	*Forficula auricularia*	Earwig of the ear
Seaside earwig	*Anisolabris maritima*	Seaside anis-lip
Yellow jacket	*Vespa arenia*	Dry wasp
Bald-faced hornet	*Vespula maculifrons*	Spotted-forehead wasp
European hornet	*Vespa crabro*	Hornet wasp
Polistes wasp	*Polistes annularis*	Ringed city
Rose greenfly	*Macrosiphum rosae*	Big rose sucker
Purple scale	*Lepidosaphes beckii*	Beck's scale
Oystershell scale	*L. ulmi*	Elm scale
The alternate Patula snail	*Patula alternata*	Wide opening alternate creature (because the shell can turn to the left or right)
White-lipped snail	*Polygyra albolabris*	White-lipped many turns creature
Five-lined skink	*Eumaces facialis*	Thin-faced
Firefly	*Photurus pennsylvanica*	Pennsylvania's light
Leech	*Hoemopis medicinalis*	Like a physician
Lake trout	*Salmo ferox*	Fierce salmon

BIBLIOGRAPHY

1   Bible. Saint Luke's Gospel. 19, 1–10.
2   ————. Saint Matthew's Gospel. 6, 19.
3   Bonfanti, L. *The Witchcraft Hysteria of 1692*, Vol. II. Wakefield, Mass.: Pride Publications, 1977.
4   Briese, Linda A., and M. H. Smith. "Competition between *Mus musculus* and *Peromyscus polionotus.*" *Jnl. Mammalogy*, Vol. 54 (1973), pp. 968–69.
5   Bradford, Wm. *Of Plymouth Plantation*, ed. Harvey Wish. New York: Capricorn, 1962.
6   Brookes, Charles. *History of the Town of Medford*. Boston: Rand Avery, 1886 (pp. 35, 95).
7   Browne, P. *Jamaica*. London: 1754 (p. 174).
8   Bulwer-Lytton, E. G. *The Last Days of Pompeii*. London: Richard Bentley, 1834.
9   Caffrey, Kate. *The Mayflower*. London: Deutsch, 1975 (p. 72).
10   Caius, J. *De Canibus Britanicus*. London: Cambridge University, 1570.
11   Calef, Robert. *More Wonders of the Invisible World*. London: Nathaniel Hiller and Joseph Collyer), 1700.
12   Darwin, Charles. *The Origin of Species*. London: Murray, 1859, (p. 80).
13   Dawkins, R. *The Selfish Gene*. Oxford: Oxford University Press, 1976 (p. ix).
14   Deane, S. *The Boston Cultivator*, July 1, 1848.
15   Earle, Alice M. *Colonial Days in Old New York*. New York: Scribner's, 1896 (p. 144).
16   ————. *Home Life in Colonial Days*. New York: Macmillan, 1898 (pp. 143, 253).
17   Fenwick, George. *A General History of Connecticut*. London, 1781 (p. 325).
18   Fernald, Charles H., and Archie H. Kirkland. *The Brown-tail Moth*. Boston: State Board of Agriculture, 1903 (p. 31).
19   Fletcher, R. *Instinct in Man*. London: Allen and Unwin, 1957.

20 Harris, Thaddeus W. *A Report on the Insects of Massachusetts.* Cambridge, Mass.: State Zoological Survey, 1841.

21 ———. *A Treatise on some of the Insects Injurious to Vegetation.* Boston, 1862.

22 Herebach, C. *The Whole Art and Trade of Husbandry . . .* Enlarged by Barnaby Googe Esquire. London: Richard More, 1614.

23 Herrick, G. W. "The snow-white linden moth." *Cornell Agric. Exp. Sta. Bull. 286,* 1910.

24 Higginson, Francis. *A True Relation of the Last Voyage to New England.* London: M. Sparke, 1629.

25 Hodgson, Ralph. "Stupidity Street," *The Atlantic Book of British and American Poetry,* ed. Edith Sitwell. London: Gollancz, 1959.

26 Irving, Washington. *A History of New York,* 4th ed. New York: C. S. Van Winkle, 1824 (p. 211).

27 Janvier, Thomas, A. "Mexican Superstitions and Folk-lore." *Scribner's Magazine* Vol. V (1889), p. 33.

28 Jefferson, T. *Writings,* Vol. 3, ed. P. L. Ford. New York: Putnam's, 1894 (p. 115).

29 Johnson, E. *Wonder Working Providence of Sion's Saviour in New England.* London, 1654.

30 Josslyn, John. *An Account of Two Voyages to New-England.* London: G. Widdowes, 1774 (pp. 116, 117, 121, 167).

31 Kalmbach, E. R. "Economic status of the English sparrow in the United States." *U.S. Dept. of Agr. Bull. No. 711,* 1940.

32 Kempt, R. *The American Joe Miller,* 2nd ed. London: Adams and Francis, 1865.

33 Kirby, W. F. *European Butterflies and Moths.* London and New York: Cassell, 1889.

34 Lowell, J. R. *Among my Books.* New York: Everyman, 1912 (p. 181).

35 Markham, Gervase. *The English Husbandman.* London: John Browne, 1614.

36 Marquis, Don. *Archy and Mehitabel.* New York: Doubleday, 1927.

37 Miller, P. *The Gardener's Dictionary,* 4th ed. London: J. Rivington, 1743.

38 Monceau, Duhamel du, and M. Tillet. *Histoire d'un Insecte quie dévore les grains dans l'Angoumois.* Paris: Imprimerie Royale, 1762.

39 Morton, Thomas. *The New English Canaan,* ed. Charles F. Adams. London: Prince Soc., 1883 (p. 166). (Original ed. London, 1632.)

40 Ordish, G. *The Living House.* New York: Lippincott, 1959.

41 ———. *The Year of the Butterfly.* New York: Scribner's, 1975.

42 ———. *The Constant Pest.* London: Peter Davies, 1976 (pp. 152, 193).

43 ———. *The Year of the Ant.* New York: Scribner's, 1978 (p. 3).

44 *Oxford English Dictionary,* Compact Ed. Oxford: Clarendon, 1971 (p. 402).

45 Pearson, T. G., ed. *Birds of America*. New York: Garden City Books, 1917 (p. 40).

46 Pope, Alexander. "Essay on Man," *The Poetical Works*, Vol. II. Glasgow: A. Foulis, 1785 (p. 171).

47 Raleigh, Sir Walter. *The History of the World*. London: W. Burre, 1614.

48 Regnier, F. E., and E. O. Wilson. "The alarm-defence system of the ant *Acanthomyops claviger*." *Jnl. Insect Physiology*, Vol. 14 (1968), pp. 955–70.

49 Riley, C. V., ed. "The toad versus cockroaches." Washington, D.C.: *Insect Life*, Vol. I (1888), p. 341.

50 Shipley, A. E. *Pearls and Parasites*. London: Murray, 1908.

51 Simpson, G. G. *The Meaning of Evolution*. New Haven, Conn.: Yale University Press, 1949.

52 Sloane, E. *The Diary of an Early American Boy, Noah Blake 1805*. New York: Funk and Wagnalls, 1962 (p. 5).

53 ———. *A Reverence for Wood*. New York: Funk and Wagnalls, 1965 (p. 17).

54 Summers-Smith. *The House-sparrow*. London: Collins, 1963 (pp. 112, 219).

55 Swan, L. A., and C. S. Papp. *The Common Insects of North America*. New York: Harper and Row, 1972 (p. 199).

56 Thoreau, Henry D. *Walden or Life in the Woods*. New York: Everyman, Dutton, 1962.

57 Thurber, James. "The Glass in the Field," *The Thurber Carnival*. New York: Grosset and Dunlap, 1945.

58 ———. "Interview with a Lemming," *My World and Welcome to It*. London: Hamish Hamilton, 1943 (p. 82).

59 Trollope, Frances (Mrs.). *Domestic Manners of the Americans*, 2nd ed., 2 vols. New York: Whitaker, Trencher and Co., 1832.

60 Wilson, A., and C. L. Bonaparte. *American Ornithology, or the Natural History of the Birds of the United States*. New York: Samuels, 1832.

61 Wing, C. P. *A Historical and Genealogical Register of John Wing, of Sandwich, Mass and his Descendants, 1632–1888*, 2nd ed. New York: Devine Press, 1888.

62 Wing, L. "The Spread of the Starling and the English Sparrow." Minneapolis: University of Minnesota Press, *Auk*, Vol. 60 (1943), pp. 74–78.

63 *Winthrop's Journal 1630–1649*, ed. James K. Hosmer. New York: Barnes and Noble, 1946.

64 Witt, P. N. *A Spider's Web*. Berlin and New York: Springer, 1968.

65 Wood, Wm. *New England Prospects*. London: John Bellamie, 1634 (pp. 32, 97).

66 Wright, Louis B. *The Atlantic Frontier*. Ithaca, N.Y.: Cornell University Press, 1966 (pp. 107, 119).

INDEX